DON'T PLAY DEAD WITH VULTURES

DON'T PLAY DEAD WITH VULTURES

JACK LEAVERS

The Book Guild Ltd

First published in Great Britain in 2022 by
The Book Guild Ltd
Unit E2 Airfield Business Park,
Harrison Road, Market Harborough,
Leicestershire. LE16 7UL
Tel: 0116 279 2299
www.bookguild.co.uk
Email: info@bookguild.co.uk
Twitter: @bookguild

Typeset in 11pt Minion Pro

Printed on FSC accredited paper
Printed and bound in Great Britain by 4edge Limited

ISBN 978 1914471 568

British Library Cataloguing in Publication Data.
A catalogue record for this book is available from the British Library.

Dedicated to all those, past and present, who've been out in the obvious doing the necessary.

PART I
CONVOY

CHAPTER 1

JUNE 2008

CAMP TAJI, 15 KM NORTH OF BAGHDAD

'But Mister John, don't you have children?'

Kemal's passionate outburst brought my briefing to a grinding halt. He remained seated, but a series of deep new furrows crisscrossed the veteran fighter's leathery features. Safe to assume he wasn't a fan of the proposed convoy route. Across the room, my guys barely stifled their amusement. Ignoring them, I returned to the floor-to-ceiling map of Iraq on the operations room wall.

The 350-kilometre mission trace, marked in red like an angry scar, ran north from the outskirts of Baghdad to US Forward Operating Base Q-West, 70 klicks south of Mosul. Then it branched east and west with arrows and timings showing three separate deliveries.

'Yes, I do have children. But that doesn't alter the fact we'll be driving up Route Tampa to Q-West.' I tapped the small hand of my wooden backscratcher on the map and swung it north along the thick red line. Some bastard had recently swiped my extendable pointer, so I'd decorated the unusual replacement in a camouflage pattern and embraced it as a nod to good old-fashioned British eccentricity. 'It's the approved route for the mission and it would take twenty-four hours to alter it, even if we could go up Highway 2, which we can't.'

Kemal launched out of his seat and his cracked fingers jabbed at the trace. 'This way is too dangerous. Through Tuz we have others that can help. Friends. Your way is big trouble.'

To emphasise the point, his fingers caressed the laminated map along his preferred route, a few inches to the right of 'my way'. His lived-in face and dark, penetrating eyes showed no sign of the smile he'd worn since earlier in the evening.

I shook my head. 'Highway 2 is out of bounds, so it's not an option. As I said in the briefing, once we reach Q-West we'll park the convoy, escort eight of the trucks to unload in Erbil, then recombine and move to the drop off in Mosul. After that it's on to the RV with your crane in Tal Afar. Okay?'

Kemal matched my head shaking and raised me an emotive appeal to the crowded room. 'It's crazy. The other way is much safer.' He swivelled left and right with widespread arms and an agonised expression.

The ops room fell silent apart from a rattling AC unit struggling to cope with the fug from the pensive, disparate onlookers. I shrugged my shoulders to indicate *tough shit, that's the way things are* before placing the decorated backscratcher on the desk to signal the end of the discussion.

When the silence lingered, I tried a more encouraging approach. 'Listen Kemal, we run convoys up and down Tampa all the time. Yes, it can be dicey, but let's close this up and get some rest, then punch out on time and get ourselves to Q-West.'

Any hope that would bring him round was misplaced. Kemal glared at me and flounced into a furtive huddle with his men.

Ryan, a resourceful ex-para, ex-Foreign Legionnaire, and the security team leader for the mission, closed in and murmured, 'It's designated black, so if you're thinking of going that way, remember it would mean no medevac, no support, and we'd have to turn off the transponders to stop Baghdad seeing our location.'

'Mate, that's not even an option,' I replied, keeping my eyes on our guests. 'We're going up Tampa as per the plan, and Kemal's gang are just going to have to get on board with it or Foxtrot Oscar back to where they came from.'

As Kemal's team broke from their scrummage, eight pairs of narrowed eyes shot daggers in my direction. Their folded arms and stern faces had all the hallmarks of a union strike.

Turning to the operations manager, Graham 'Hutch' Hutchison, I tried to control my growing frustration and keep my voice down. 'Sod this, I'm going to make a call and get it sorted. We're up at three a.m. and that's only...shit, five hours away.'

I pushed past Kemal's Turkmen security team and left the containerised unit housing the operations room and the country manager's office – my office. I wanted privacy while ringing the contact who had arranged local support, but the eight Turkmen trooped out into the dark behind me. I barked, 'Wait there,' and stalked off under the camouflage netting strung above the two parallel forty-foot office units comprising the HQ.

Weak light shone from both offices a few metres away across the gravel. I tried the left-hand door, which opened to reveal the quarter master scratching his head in front of a computer monitor and piles of paperwork.

'Hello boss,' he said with a West Country burr, putting his pen down. 'I'm almost finished here, ready for tomorrow. Fancy a brew?'

'Yes mate, thanks. A strong coffee would do the job, although it won't help me get my head down when I've finished dealing with this mob from up north.'

He flicked the kettle on and checked his watch.

I gave a rueful smile. 'Yeah, I know it's getting on. Just as we've got all the assets here ready to go, their team leader has taken a dislike to our route. Says it's too dangerous. It's a twenty-odd truck convoy in Iraq – of course it's fucking dangerous.'

With that release of frustration, a moment of clarity let me zero in on the way forward. 'Much as it would be very handy to have them along, if I can't reach my guy in London and get this squared away then we'll go without them. We need their crane in Tal Afar though, so I'm trying to make it work. Give me a second, mate, I need to make that call now.'

I stepped back outside into the embrace of the warm night and checked the Turkmen were still around. A lightshow of glowing cigarettes and a soundtrack of angry muttering provided the answer.

A distorted UK double ringtone buzzed twice before the call was answered by Cal Simmons, my indirect link to the truculent locals. 'Evening John, everything okay?'

'In short, no. Your guys aren't happy with the route and seem to be refusing to carry on unless it's changed to go through Tuz. Tuz is on Highway 2 which is designated black, out of bounds, so we can't go that way. I need these guys to either get on board with the plan or piss off out of my hair so I can launch this convoy on time in a few hours. Of course, that would mean no payment to you and M apart from the crane in Tal Afar, unless that would be screwed as well?'

A hiss-filled delay preceded his reply. 'Oh for crying out loud. Let me make a call to M. Stay off the phone and wait for him to ring you. Those arseholes are just trying it on. He'll get them back on track.'

'Thanks mate. I'll send you a message after I get the call and let you know if we're going ahead as planned or doing it all ourselves. If I don't hear anything in the next thirty minutes, then we'll plan to go without them.'

More hissing. '…worry. I'll make sure this is sorted and you get a call asap.'

'Thanks Cal. I'll let you know.'

Less than five minutes later, my phone rang as I sipped a potent coffee while the QM shut down his computer and grumbled about finding a crane in Tal Afar if the plan fell through.

Our Scouse motor transport manager had appeared through the office partition door at the sound of a boiling kettle and produced a jar of Bovril he was now spooning into a mug. A hot beefy drink on a hot summer night. My wife Claire hated the stuff, and an image of her face ambushed my thoughts; her pretty nose screwed up in disgust on hearing I occasionally drank it during long nights. My brief smile faded as I slipped through the open doorway into the adjacent MT office to take the call.

'Mr Pierce? It's Mehmet in Ankara. Cal informs me there is some difficulties with Kemal. Can you tell me please?'

I explained the difference of opinion regarding the route and the realities of the situation i.e. we had no choice about it.

'Is Kemal with you?' asked the Turk.

'Hang on, I'll go get him now.'

I stepped outside and aimed a shout at the characters milling around by the ops room door. 'Kemal, over here a minute.'

A figure crunched across the gravel towards me.

'He's just coming.'

'Put him on the phone,' said Mehmet, his voice now gruff and authoritative. Cal claimed the guy had been a senior officer in the Turkish security services. It didn't sound like he'd be taking any prisoners on this call.

Even in the shadows I registered Kemal's standoffishness when passing him the phone. It was a shame because we'd been getting along so well earlier, until the mission briefing. Kemal's initial passionate Arabic soon lapsed into shorter and shorter answers as his demeanour and quiet replies took on a beaten air. Ninety seconds after taking the phone he was handing it back to me with a face like a scolded puppy.

'Everything is fixed,' said Mehmet in a genial tone. 'Kemal and his men will follow your orders and do everything to help your mission.'

'Thank you, Mehmet. I appreciate your help.'

'You're welcome. If you have any more issues then call me, immediately.'

'Sure, will do.'

Mehmet hadn't finished. 'Directly. Call to me directly. If any of these men disobey my instructions, then I can take steps to make them comply.'

Kemal's downcast expression indicated Mehmet's dark warning had real substance. I stowed the phone and set my mood to cheerful – as if his troubles weren't down to me. 'Everything okay?' Your team will be up at zero three hundred hours, ready to move at zero four-thirty?'

He hesitated as though trying to find the right words before replying with a flat, 'We'll be ready.'

While he slunk off to give his team the news, I returned to my coffee and sent an SMS update to Cal in London. Kemal had a reasonable point about driving north on Highway 2 via Tuz instead of our intended route. It would avoid some difficult places, although they'd only be swapped for some other badlands. It's not like there were any good choices when it came to running convoys here. But my hands were tied because Ryan was right: an out of bounds route meant no guarantee of medevac helicopters or military support if we ran into trouble. Plus, vehicle trackers beamed our position to the Reconstruction Operations Centre in Baghdad.

The ROC monitored, coordinated, and deconflicted private security movements with the military operations of the Multi-National Forces Iraq – the organisational name for the foreign military units engaged in the quagmire that was Operation Iraqi Freedom. Flouting the rules would result in a world of trouble from the US military contracting officers and a big black mark against the company.

It was already difficult enough to win the individual tenders for each mission against the other five companies on the US Department of Defense contract that provided the bulk of our earnings. Anything that made winning less likely threatened the survival of the company's operation in Iraq. And, as country manager for the small British security outfit, I knew full well how tight the margins had become.

★

Ryan was the team leader for the mission, but out of habit I gave the paperwork, route card, and timings a final check. Even though it was almost 11 p.m. and yet another mosquito had evaded my defences.

The cunning plan would see us take an over-sized convoy of twenty trucks and two spare tractor heads up to FOB Q-West. There, the team second-in-command would remain with his vehicle and the twelve loads bound for Mosul and Tal Afar, while me and the other eight were escorted to Erbil.

After the Erbil drop-off, the team would recombine at Q-West, escort the remaining trucks to their destinations, and then roll back home to Taji for tea and medals a couple of days after setting out. Meanwhile, I would remain in Erbil to attend a set of meetings and fly back afterwards.

An unexpected bonus had been the addition of a back-haul load down to the Iraqi Army National Depot, located on another part of our home base. With that added to the original three missions, we would be invoicing the DOD for nearly $300,000.

The company owner was pleased about the income and the plan was sound. Once we were on the road it was only the insurgents we'd have to worry about, which came down to training, preparation, and a healthy dose of luck. Right now though, I was still battling through the hardest part of any mission: getting all the right assets in the right place, fuelled up, loaded out, and ready to rock and roll.

Normally the problem was the local Iraqi truck drivers, but the boss had come up with an inspired idea and as a result we now had twelve Indian truck drivers, in shiny new trucks from Kuwait, shitting themselves as we careered around the less salubrious parts of Iraq. Usually they were all we needed – convoys of more than ten trucks were an unwanted exception – however, for this mission we required ten additional local trucks and drivers along for the ride. Arranging that had taken some doing. The reason the boss needed the Indians in the first place was because unpaid bills meant the company was blacklisted by the local truck mafia. It was from before my time, but I had to smile at those cut-throats and thieves being seen off by a British security company.

Heading for my cabin after locking up the office, I glanced towards the main gate 100 metres away. Our Gurkha guards looked alert under the powerful lights illuminating the red and white striped vehicle barrier at the camp entrance.

Whenever we had local drivers in our camp, we mounted additional patrols to keep an eye on things, especially once cargo had been loaded. I couldn't spot patrolling guards this side of the central accommodation block. They were probably by the trucks on the other side, drinking chai with the locals in the large temporary drivers' tent. The duty guard commander was a former Gurkha sergeant major and a reliable pair of hands. I trusted he'd be on the ball and keep things in check, so I called it a night.

Once inside, I turned on the air conditioning to frustrate the mosquitos and took off my desert boots. My laptop sat closed on the desk and I considered firing it up for a Skype call to Claire and my daughters in the UK. But given the late hour, I put it off until the following day – after the mission – and instead chose to recheck my laid-out kit before hitting the sack.

CHAPTER 2

0320 HOURS THE FOLLOWING MORNING

The camp bustled with activity as I made my way from the horseshoe of expat cabins to the HQ offices fifty metres away. Ryan had the team well drilled in their pre-mission preparations. The drivers were already running through first parade vehicle checks under the exterior accommodation lights, while other team members queued to receive their personal weapons and ammunition from the QM in the armoury.

For this mission, we'd assigned four B6-armoured Ford F350 'gunship' pickups with turret mounted PKM machine guns atop each rear compartment, together with one B6-armoured Toyota Land Cruiser to act as lead scout.

B6 armour provided good protection against non-armour-piercing small arms rounds and Improvised Explosive Devices but there were no guarantees. And the increasing prevalence of an IED type known as an Explosively Formed Penetrator was a concern to everyone in theatre. EFPs fired a copper slug that could defeat armour, and the insurgents conjured up ever more ingenious methods to covertly deploy them and defeat new countermeasures.

Because of the larger than usual convoy size, I'd used my personal contacts to secure the assistance of a Turkmen security team from our ultimate destination of Tal Afar – Kemal and his men – who operated two up-armoured Toyota Hilux pickups with floor mounted DShK 'Dushka' 12.7mm machine guns in each uncovered rear flatbed.

I headed towards the two battered pickups, shivering despite the lightweight fleece over my fire-retardant t-shirt and body armour. The

9

days were redders but this early in the morning the clear night skies had sown a chill into the air.

'Morning Kemal. You guys sleep alright?'

Kemal offered a strained smile. 'Yes, thank you. We eat before leaving?'

'We'll have breakfast once we're all set. Half an hour or so. I'll get someone to grab you when it's ready. Did you fuel up last night?'

Kemal confirmed the lads had taken them to suck on the US military's free fuel teat the previous evening, and I reminded him there would be a final brief at 04:15 in the HQ. Next, I moved on to do the rounds amongst our mixed Sri Lankan and Nepalese team. We also had a lone Fijian for good measure.

★

When I entered my office, Hutch called out from the adjacent ops room that we had a problem.

'Already? Do I need to sit down for this one?'

'Well...' Hutch knocked and appeared through the connecting door '...you might need to pull out that bootneck charm and use it on the local drivers.'

I dropped into my chair behind the desk. 'Why, what's happened now?'

'Rumour control says the drivers have found out we're going north. They're all Sh'ia and now shitting bricks. Message is they'll need some encouragement to join our jaunt up to the Sunni heartlands.'

'All of them? Do our spies suggest a ringleader?'

Hutch flashed an evil smile. 'You know the really tall, ugly one? With the face like a smashed crab and the breath of Shaitan?'

'I know the guy you mean. It would be him. I bet he's still got that bit of chicken skin hanging out of his teeth from yesterday.'

Both of us lifted our hands to our mouths and wiggled our fingers to signify the scrap of meat hanging out of his gob and burst out laughing. We came from different military backgrounds – him from a

Guards regiment and me from the Royal Marines – but we shared a similar sense of humour.

'Can you get Hamoodi so I can talk to this clown?'

Hutch stood up with a satisfied snap. 'Already on it. I've just sent one of the lads to give him another shake and drag him out of his pit if necessary, although God knows he needs his beauty sleep.'

We only had two Iraqis working for the company: a deaf mechanic with a dubious claim to have looked after Saddam's fleet of cars, and Hamoodi, our translator and liaison with the Iraqi security services.

Hamoodi was a Sunni Muslim from Tikrit and had a vast array of contacts everywhere. His fat fingers were firmly stuck into many different and dodgy pies, but he'd proved himself invaluable more than once in the three months he'd been with us. He wasn't a morning person though.

I followed Hutch into the ops room where he stood by the kettle. He waved a mug in my direction.

'Yes please, mate. Coffee no sugar. Are the guys okay this morning? Only I was chatting with a few of the team and they seem a bit subdued.'

As Hutch tried to disguise a snigger with a cough, the external door opened and Ryan walked in.

'The boss is asking if the lads are a bit subdued this morning,' Hutch said with an annoying smirk on his face.

'Aye, I wonder why that might be?' replied Ryan in an exaggerated Scottish brogue.

There was an expectant pause and I looked from one to the other. 'Well, is one of you comedians going to enlighten me then?'

'I dinnae want to hurt your feelings, boss,' was Ryan's cryptic reply.

'What the fuck are you talking about?'

When they both remained standing there with stupid grins, I about-turned and stomped back into my office calling out 'Twats' over my shoulder.

My computer was booting up as the brush of knuckles against the door signalled Hutch bringing my coffee through. 'Actually boss, this issue with the guys is something you should be aware of.'

The look on my face must have shown my scepticism.

'Honestly, it's not a bite,' continued Hutch. 'Ryan, you're closer to the lads. You explain.'

Ryan joined us with a twinkle still in his eye.

'Go on,' I said. Face set to neutral.

Ryan took a quick slug of his drink. 'Well, the thing they're concerned about, the Sri Lankans anyway – I don't know about the Gurkhas so much – is that you're coming along on the mission. Even if it is only the first part up to Q-West and Erbil.'

He wasn't laying on the thicker Scottish accent anymore. His five years in the Legion might have had an impact, but he claimed that everyone in his hometown near Inverness spoke posh English like the Queen.

'What, they're worried I'll be checking up on them?'

'No, no. Nothing like that. It's just they don't call you Mr John, they call you Mr Jonah, like with the whale.'

'Mr Jonah?'

'Aye. They think every time you come out something bad happens. That you bring bad luck. We've been whacked the last couple of missions you've been with us. And remember the other times before that. Like the breakdown in central Baghdad, the IED in Muqdadiyah, the attack near Besmaya...'

'Yeah, yeah, I get the picture. Thing is, I only normally come out if it's a tricky mission. And no one got hurt or killed in those incidents.'

'Apart from Ravi,' cut in Ryan.

I almost spat my coffee out. 'That was a scratch. And it'll teach him to get into cover next time he's in a contact instead of strutting around like a figure eleven.'

'Even so,' Hutch added, 'maybe it would be a good idea for you to give one of your rousing peptalks this morning before you set off. Make them think you're a good luck charm instead of a bad omen. And it wouldn't hurt to mention when we're getting paid.' His tone hardened. 'For all of us, that one.'

'Okay. For the pay, I have some good news from the boss and it'll all be sorted this week. But bad omen? Seriously? Judging by the incident reports, we must be the luckiest convoy operators in Iraq this year. Although you're right, a peptalk is a good idea. I'll sprinkle some of my natural charisma around. Let's just hope we don't run into trouble today. That reminds me, where's Hamoodi so I can sort this lanky troublemaker out. And has anyone got any mints I can force feed him?'

0430 HOURS

Normally the expats drove through the internal checkpoints to the US side of the huge camp to eat at one of the well-stocked Dining Facilities, or DFACs. But due to the early start, we'd eaten with our Sri Lankan and Nepalese guys in their kitchen. I didn't fancy what they were serving, so I threw a couple of egg banjos down my neck and felt much better for it. Fried egg sandwiches – the breakfast of champions.

Buttered up with a hot breakfast, the local drivers had been persuaded we were 'all in it together' and they had sufficient protection. I returned from that drama just as the convoy team filed out from Ryan's final mission brief and gathered by the vehicles for my rallying speech. We were on time and even Kemal's team cracked a few smiles.

I raised my voice while still trying to project a genial tone. 'Listen in, gents.'

The volume of chat lessened but a familiar Sri Lankan voice continued spinning a loud dit.

'That includes you, Ravi.'

Ravi stopped talking and turned towards me with a sheepish smile. 'Sorry, Mr John.'

'No problem. Right guys, this won't take long. I only have a couple of points for you.' I noticed Hutch and the other expats stood on the periphery of the convoy team. No doubt word had spread there was an update about pay.

'Firstly, you will all be pleased to hear that I spoke with the boss yesterday, and he told me that last month's pay will be transferred over the next couple of days.'

A brief eruption of ironic cheers and chatter quickly faded.

'Anyone who has changed bank accounts or had problems with failed payments, see the QM. It's in your own interest guys. The company can only pay to the account details you give us. Make sure they're correct. I don't want another phone call from an angry wife.'

Everyone turned and looked at Deepak as his name was blurted out by one of his mates and a ripple of laughter accompanied a playful punch on the arm and some piss-taking.

'Okay, settle down. The other point that's been brought to my attention is that I'm known by some of you as Mr Jonah – bringing bad luck whenever I come out on the ground.'

Looks bounced around the team while other heads turned away.

'Guys, you're all aware of the threat. Every mission out here has its dangers, but I only tend to come out on the tougher ones. I'd never ask anyone to do anything I wouldn't do myself, and I think it's important for the man in charge to lead by example. I know we've had issues when I've been out with you recently, but we all came home. No one has been seriously hurt and we've completed every mission successfully. If anything, that should make me a good luck charm.'

My last comment didn't raise the laughter I'd expected. Under the weak glow of the building lights, I couldn't tell if my words were having much impact. At least most of the faces were now raised in my direction rather than staring at the ground.

'Today we're driving some difficult routes. I know the convoy is bigger than we like, but we have some extra firepower and local knowledge from Kemal and his team from Tal Afar. I won't be with you all the way but if we have a contact, whether I'm there or not, you all know what to do. You know your SOPs, you've been trained by some of the most experienced convoy operators in Iraq, and you have command, control, and medical support from a great team of expats. Good luck today and I'll see you all back here by the weekend.'

I turned to head for the office to grab my gear and signalled towards the other expats now gathered behind me. 'Over to you, Ryan.'

An unhappy-looking Hamoodi loitered by my door as I unlocked it. As part of the deal with the drivers' hygiene-challenged ringleader, I'd agreed Hamoodi would travel on the convoy in his truck. Not only did it make the driver feel better supported, it meant we had eyes on this potential troublemaker.

When it had dawned on Hamoodi this meant no safety for him inside an armoured vehicle, he'd begun to pull on his collar and fidget. To his credit, he kept translating until the deal with the drivers was agreed.

Afterwards, he'd unsuccessfully begged me to allow him to carry an AK-47. I assumed he was here for another appeal, although the desolate look on his face gave away his estimation of changing my mind. He was in for a surprise though.

'Before you say anything, I've decided you can carry your Tariq for personal protection, but no AK. I'll speak to the QM and see if he can give you four mags. The TL has a radio for you, so come with me to the armoury now and then find Ryan before we mount up.'

He dropped his face into his hands. 'Shukran. Thank you, thank you.'

My earlier decision to leave him without a weapon had been bugging me. I liked the guy and knew I wouldn't fancy riding shotgun unarmed for hundreds of kilometres with the problem driver.

The Tariq was an Iraqi-manufactured version of a Beretta handgun, with a magazine that only held eight rounds. It might be insignificant in the context of the convoy operation but arming Hamoodi should give him status as 'one of us' as far as the drivers were concerned.

The QM dug out five magazines for Hamoodi's Tariq, which paled in comparison to the nine magazines and 270 rounds of ammunition I drew with my AKMS – a Kalashnikov with a folding metal stock designed for airborne forces – and the extra magazines I signed out for my Glock 19, which I held on permanent issue and wore in a belt holster.

Ryan's F350 was waiting outside when we left the armoury. As I clambered into the rear seat, Hamoodi took a radio and Ryan invited him to jog over to the trucks now lined up to leave the camp and form up on the roundabout.

The ageless call to prayer from a far-off mosque carried on the air as we drove to the gate and waited for Hamoodi and the last few stragglers to mount their vehicles. The big Iraqi was puffing when he reached his ride behind us. The usual smile was absent as he heaved his large frame into the cab of the truck, an action made tougher by his tight body armour topped off with a WWII-style US Army helmet – the only one in the store able to fit his big head. His appearance had prompted hoots of laughter from the rest of the convoy team, and I could hear catcalls from our gunners and the nearest vehicles as he flopped into his seat and gave a thumbs up.

Like several other contractors, we lived on the Iraqi side of Camp Taji. Our 9,000 square metre compound, ringed by a razor-wire topped fence, sat on the south-eastern corner of a large roundabout. On the opposite side squatted a prison rumoured to be full of captured extremists.

A pack of feral dogs lived in the scrub of the roundabout and provided an early warning system if anyone approached our camp. Probably because the guards and team members fed them scraps despite the standing orders not to. Somehow, they recognised our vehicles and never ran, growled, and barked at them like they did to everyone else.

Our setup was basic but clean and with all functioning utilities. The main downside came from the regular waft of human excrement from a leaking sewer down the road at an Iraqi Army barracks, which added unwelcome flavour to the cloying heat of the daytime.

The previous day, an intransigent Iraqi officer had refused to even consider allowing us to exit the main gate at o'crack sparrow's fart in the morning. No movement before the official gate opening time of 0800 hours ensured he and his colleagues got their beauty sleep.

A legacy from an incident the previous year also meant leaving via Gunner's Gate on the US side of the camp was out of the question. It was before my time, and I had tried and failed a number of times to get us off that shit-list.

Instead, we'd been forced to plan a less than ideal exit down the rough tank trail to the main road – Route Tampa. Provided none of the trucks got stuck or threw a load down the narrow, pitted track, we would emerge onto Tampa by 0530 hours.

CHAPTER 3

0500 HOURS

By 05:00 the sounds of blaring horns and frustrated shouts from the security team had ceased; the trucks now shepherded into the correct order of march in a long snake leading from our base, around the roundabout, and onto the southern exit road.

We took our position behind the scout vehicle and in front of the lead lorry, which was manned by one of the Indian drivers. Behind him, the ten local trucks alternated with our Indian-driven vehicles throughout the convoy. The two spare tractor heads bringing up the rear were also ours.

By keeping the local drivers separated, we hoped to avoid any disruptive action they might consider if grouped together. With Hamoodi sat next to their leader and all the drivers' phones confiscated, each man should stay concentrated on following the truck in front. And our security 'sweep' vehicles would be patrolling the line like tooled-up sheepdogs, encouraging them to keep their road position and spacing.

Ryan checked comms with Hutch in the ops room. 'Sierra-Zero, this is Sierra-One, radio check, over.'

'Sierra-Zero, I have you loud and clear, over.'

'Sierra-One, Lima Charlie, out.'

The other four vehicles of the convoy team now completed their own radio checks. Prompted by Sierra-Zero, Kemal then followed suit surprisingly well using the assigned call sign 'Kilo'. The final check involved Hamoodi. He'd been given the call sign 'Lone Wolf', and his plaintive voice during the radio check had both me and Ryan shaking our heads.

In the rear of the cab, I checked the grab bags and other equipment were firmly tied down. In the event of an IED attack, unsecured kit flying around the cabin was more likely to kill someone than the explosion itself.

As the vehicle commander and team leader, Ryan occupied the front passenger seat. His Sri Lankan driver was named Jeevan, who he'd christened 'Jeeves'. Completing our crew, we had two affable Sri Lankans manning the machine gun turret in the rear.

I flicked through the mission briefing and the schematic showing the convoy order of march.

Leading the line: Sierra-Two – the forward scout Land Cruiser commanded by Ashen, the most experienced of our Sri Lankan ex-soldiers.

Next up: Sierra-One – my ride. An F350 Gunship commanded by Ryan the TL.

Behind us: the twenty loaded trucks & two spare tractor heads, patrolled by two F350 sweep vehicles – Sierra-Three, a Gurkha and Fijian-manned vehicle commanded by our American medic, Jamie; and Sierra-Four commanded by Ravi.

Also acting in the sheepdog-style sweep role – and instructed to stay either side of the first two lorries – was Kemal's team: call sign Kilo. It comprised the two non-armoured Hilux trucks with their big machine guns scoping menacingly from each open rear flatbed.

Finally, the tail-end Charlie was Sierra-Five commanded by the team 2IC, Mike.

Mike was another rugged ex-para who'd been Ryan's section corporal back in the day, before passing selection and moving on to the SAS at Hereford. He was in his late-forties and the oldest expat in the camp. A safe pair of hands and almost horizontally laid back in every situation, it was rumoured he'd been a top SF operator and was still involved in SAS reserve training when back home on rotation.

He once told me he lived by the motto: 'If you've gotta go, go hard.' I hadn't needed to see that put into practice but everything about the way he carried himself inspired confidence.

The VHF radio crackled into life. *'Hello Sierra-One, this is Sierra-Zero. I confirm tracking operational for you and Sierra-Five and mission launch is authorised. Please acknowledge, over.'*

Hutch would have spoken to the duty operator at the ROC to confirm our trackers were live on their screens and we had permission to proceed.

'Sierra-One, mission authorisation acknowledged. All convoy call signs, this is Sierra-One, prepare to move. Respond in sequence, over.'

'Sierra-Two, roger prepare to move, over.'

'Sierra-Three, confirm prepared to move.'

There was a silence for five seconds and Ryan began to shake his head and muttered off air, 'Switch on, Ravi, for Christ's sake.'

Finally, *'Sierra-Four, say again…over.'*

Ryan didn't hide the annoyance in his voice and his Scottish accent became more pronounced. 'This is Sierra-One. Sierra-Four are you ready to move, over.'

'Yes, sorry. Roger, over. Sierra-Four.'

'Sierra-One, roger, out to you. Kilo and Sierra-Five are you good to go, over?'

'Kilo is ready.'

'Sierra-Five, roger, good to go, over.'

'Sierra-One, roger. Lone Wolf, this is Sierra-One. Are you all set, over?'

'Lone Wolf, good copy.'

Ryan shook his head and murmured 'Dickhead' at the American-style response, which caused a snort of laughter to escape from our driver, Jeeves.

'All call signs, this is Sierra-One, convoy set. Switch to normal convoy voice procedure, out.'

'This is Sierra-Two, moving, over.' That message from Ashen, in the forward scout vehicle, indicated the mission was underway.

'Sierra-Five, roger convoy moving, out.' If Mike at the rear had received Sierra-Two's message, then all other vehicles between them should have heard it. During the convoy, the primary use of the radio would

be messages bouncing between Sierra-Two 'calling the road' and Sierra-Five acknowledging receipt.

Other transmissions would be prompted by traffic, obstacles, incidents, and regulating the convoy speed and gaps between the trucks. On the main roads we'd try to keep the vehicles in a convoy this size fifty metres apart. Controlling and protecting a formation more than a kilometre long was where the fun really began.

Sierra-Two led us down the road towards the leaking sewer, after which we would turn left at the next roundabout and head towards the tank trail. The air-conditioned interior of the armoured truck insulated us from the worst of the stench, although the guys manning our PKM wouldn't be so lucky. The other twenty-seven vehicles behind us started to creep away from the roundabout like a giant, slow motion conga line.

'Sierra-Five, moving, out.'

That signalled all the vehicles were off the grid. Once more into the breach.

★

Route Tampa, or Highway 1 as the Iraqis knew it, was a main supply route that ran for hundreds of kilometres from the Kuwait border in the south to the Syrian border in the northwest. Camp Taji was perched on the east side of the highway fifteen kilometres north of Baghdad. For us, it meant missions started either with a left turn towards Baghdad or a right turn to the north. Whichever way we went could be a drama; the road was blighted by IED attacks and ambushes all along its length.

Convoys tended to stay on the main routes due to the less awful road surfaces for the heavily loaded lorries and for security reasons. It meant route selection was limited at the best of times. For everyone at Taji, being lucky on Tampa became an essential part of the arsenal when you deployed outside the gate.

We reached the main road at 05:40 with the rest of the convoy closed-up in single file behind us. Sierra-Two pushed north towards the nearby bridge that ran above the road while we took up a position blocking the highway to the south. When the lead lorry bumped onto the road tarmac and turned north, we were relieved by one of the sweep vehicles.

'Go Jeeves,' said Ryan, throwing a mock American salute to Jamie in Sierra-Three, and we spurted past the trucks and security vehicles now spewing out of the tank trail to take our position in front of the lead truck. Kemal's two 'technical' pickups joined us.

We rolled forward slowly to allow all the vehicles to get out onto the road without opening a huge gap. It was a vulnerable time even though traffic was light this early in the morning. As a precaution, Sierra-Three would hold back any early risers until we were finished and on our way. A couple of Suicide Vehicle-Borne IED attacks had wreaked carnage at Taji's front gate in the past, so none of us wanted to hang around any longer than necessary.

'*Sierra-Two, IP call sign on the bridge.*'

'*Five, roger IP on bridge.*'

A flatbed pickup with blue and white Iraqi Police markings had rocked up and stopped on the bridge 150 metres ahead. In the grey dawn light before sunrise, the growing tail of dipped headlights turning onto the highway must have caught their interest.

That wasn't necessarily a good thing. Most of the Shi'a and Sunni death squads terrorising the country were card–carrying members of the security forces. Much better for us if no one had been around to witness our departure, composition, and direction of travel.

We probably looked a handy outfit, especially with Kemal and his two huge machine guns driving either side of us at the front of the line. But as trucks continued to bump across from the tank trail exit onto the road, I experienced the first twinge of doubt. It's one thing to plan for a twenty-nine vehicle move, it's quite another to see the scale of it in the flesh. 'I wonder who tipped those fuckers off?'

'Maybe they're just up early to do their bit to help the war on terror,' replied Ryan, with a humourless laugh.

'Yeah, and maybe there's a bus load of Narvik nurses coming to Taji for my fortieth birthday party.'

'Forty, eh?' said Ryan. 'All downhill from there.'

'Cheers, mate. That's your invite to the party lost in the post.'

CHAPTER 4

0600 HOURS

By 06:00 the entire convoy was nose-to-tail for 700 metres on the highway, straddled below the watching IP vehicle on the bridge, and finally ready to move. A cluster of civilian vehicles were being held at the rear by Sierra-Three and Sierra-Five. Ryan instructed they be allowed through and, once they passed us, we set off.

'Sierra-One, moving, over.'

'Sierra-Five, roger moving in front, out.'

By now the sunlight was pouring over the desert scrubland and would soon begin to heat the day into a predictable furnace. It almost made me glad for the changeable British weather back home.

I donned my Oakley ballistic glasses – the clear lenses for night ops swapped out for the cooler-looking black sunglasses style – and tightened the head strap. Next, I popped in my Sonic ear protectors. They allowed in regular sounds but would protect my hearing in the event of an IED blast, even if the rest of me might be a little the worse for wear.

Then I dipped my hand into my top left admin pouch and checked my plastic, gobstopper-sized 'lucky eyeball' was there. After it fell out of a Christmas cracker years earlier, my eldest daughter Natalie had presented it to me prior to a Northern Ireland tour, with a solemn instruction. 'It's your good luck charm daddy, so keep it with you. Promise?' Said as though she were a princess awarding her colours to a knight before a joust.

Once back in the province, I declared to the lads I was invincible due to my new-found protection. Two weeks later I was lucky to survive a vicious tangle with the IRA. Before future patrols, it became a running joke that my lucky eyeball was part of essential team kit.

Now only held together with 'Harry Black' masking tape, I'd carried it with me ever since. I wasn't superstitious but it didn't hurt to hedge your bets.

I ran a hand through my crewcut hair and sighed with relief that the mission was underway at last. Despite being against company SOPs, my helmet was attached to the grab bag instead of on my head. As the country manager it wasn't the greatest example to set, but I'd always hated wearing them since joining the military while the old-style, never-worn tin lids were still in fashion.

I shrugged my body armour into a more comfortable position, adjusted the seat belt so my Glock and AK stopped digging into my hip and thigh, and settled in for the ride.

★

'*Two, US call sign opposite carriageway.*'

'*Five, roger US call sign.*'

The MRAPS and Humvees of the US clearance patrol rumbled past in the opposite direction without so much as a wave or any acknowledgement of our flashed headlight greeting. After spending the night wombling down Tampa searching for IEDs, I'd probably flip us the bird as well.

For a large convoy we were making good speed: Sierra-Five reported 70 km/h at the rear. A concertina effect was inevitable with so many lorries, despite the spirited efforts of the sweep vehicles to keep the distances between each truck down to fifty metres. They also needed to stay alert, ready to chase off any cars that tried to cut into the line from adjoining roads.

If we kept this up, we could have the 350 km first leg completed by lunchtime. That would provide enough time for the mission east to Erbil – 100 km or so – and for Ryan and the empty trucks to return to Q-West before nightfall. I'd be in Erbil in good time for my meetings, and the others would be able to punch out early the following morning for the tricky move to Mosul, then on to Tal Afar.

I had meetings scheduled the following day with two international oil companies, an American oilfield services company, and the operations manager from a large British engineering firm. Based on the recent revenue and the forecasts I'd compiled, we desperately needed new clients in addition to the US military.

The company owner wanted to concentrate on clients in Baghdad and the south, but I wanted to harness my good contacts in the Kurdistan Region, of which Erbil was the capital. The environment in Kurdistan was completely different to the rest of Iraq. The military and security forces worked with the support of the local population to stamp out the slightest inkling of insurgent activity. In my opinion, establishing a foothold there in the oil and gas industry, or in a large engineering project, was both desirable and achievable, and would transform the company's fortunes.

The trip to Erbil also gave me a great opportunity to meet with old friends from the region, including a senior Peshmerga general and a handful of other guys I'd worked with in the past. They had helped me out in some scrapes, including a crazy situation three years earlier involving Coalition counter-terrorism forces and raids in Mosul and Diyala Province. They were driving over from their home city of Sulaimaniyah and we would all be meeting for dinner and a catch up. And maybe the general would have some ideas for developing new business.

Ryan also seemed optimistic about our progress. 'I don't want to jinx it, but we're making good time here. The first dodgy spot will be around Tarmiyah, coming up soon. It's a bit early for the nuggets who usually take a pot-shot, so let's hope we can keep this up.'

'Yeah, better if we can get decent scran at the DFAC in Q-West before pushing out for Erbil.'

Ryan snorted and said in mock outrage, 'We'll have no more of that bootie talk. You may be the country manager but this is my team. We'll be eating scoff, not scran.'

I laughed. 'Keep this pace up and you can call it whatever the hell you want. I'm a long time away from all that inter-service rivalry shite.'

'Moi aussi, boss. Moi aussi.'

Like many soldiers, I was intrigued with the mystique of the French Foreign Legion. 'You'll have to spin a few dits about your time in the Legion someday. As long as you don't get all misty-eyed about your white kepi and start singing.'

'Aye, when we get a chance to grab a beer. Too late for you now though, for the Legion. Forty and that.'

'Not much chance of a beer anytime soon either. Although I might be able to sink a couple while I'm in Erbil.'

'You never know, boss, what with your birthday coming up. And I haven't forgotten you mentioned Narvik nurses either.'

'Seriously, Ryan, don't let the guys do anything stupid with booze. This company has been in enough trouble recently and we need to keep our noses clean.'

General Order Number One for the US Military equalled no alcohol on camp. The whole of Taji and every other military establishment in Iraq was dry. And woe betide any soldier or contractor caught in possession of the demon drink.

What Ryan didn't know – or at least wasn't supposed to know – was that our QM supplied bottles of Johnnie Walker Scotch whisky to the American senior NCOs at Taji in exchange for vehicle spares, repairs, and the occasional replacement tyre. Our one-eyed mechanic needed all the help he could get, and it was about the only thing keeping our fleet on the road. Our whisky supplies had dwindled, so we'd soon need to smuggle in another small shipment unless we could eke it out until the next decent splash of money arrived.

'Two, IA call sign static right.'

'Five, roger IA static right.'

We had a few waves from the Iraqi Army soldiers parked up in a lay-by on our right-hand side. Thirty-five minutes after getting underway, we were now a couple of kilometres south of the town of Tarmiyah.

There had been regular sniping and bomb attacks against Coalition targets on this part of Route Tampa going back months. The US military intelligence officers in Taji reckoned the same cell kept having a go because the timings and MO remained consistent.

If it was the same guys, they had earned my grudging respect. They might be the enemy, but it took some balls to keep taking on the US military and heavily armed outfits like ours on a regular basis. It would only be a matter of time before they came a cropper. I certainly wouldn't be doing any retirement planning in their shoes.

Attacks on this stretch could come at any time, although the previous pattern indicated a group that liked to get into position around mid-morning before shaking the dice and seeing if today their luck ran out. My watch showed 06:38. We should be too early for their fun and games.

We sped past the turn-off for Tarmiyah and continued north without incident as the sun lifted into the sky to our right. Our bullet-proof windows always remained closed and the air conditioning meant we wouldn't feel the heat of the day inside as the temperatures climbed towards fifty degrees by midday. Instead, we observed a deceptive vision of summer bliss while remaining detached from the dreary mix of small settlements, desert scrub, and cultivated land that flashed past on either side and had to suffer the blazing daily onslaught.

Five minutes later came a message with a potential red flag.

'Two, checkpoint empty.'

'Five, roger checkpoint empty, speed sixty-five.'

We roared past the improvised trappings of a small, empty checkpoint. No men or vehicles in sight.

'Might still be having breakfast or maybe shagging their wives,' Ryan said without conviction, 'but this place is normally manned.'

'Two, static vehicle right, two up.'

'Five, roger static vehicle two up.'

Then an unmistakable American voice over the net: our medic, Jamie. 'Sierra-Three, one hundred gap opened at truck ten. Slow down in front to allow catch up.'

'Sierra-One, roger Sierra-Three. Slowing down in front, speed fifty, advise when complete.'

'Sierra-Three, roger, out.'

Jamie had deployed to Taji soon after my arrival when our burnt out South African doc disappeared on R&R. He had been a Navy Corpsman medic who completed the Special Operations Combat Medic course and served with the US Marines Special Operations Command.

Although I hadn't previously known him, I had worked with his Green Beret brother during my immersion in counter-insurgency operations in 2005. The special forces team leader from that adventure had tapped me up earlier in the year to see if I could do my extended American family a solid.

Jamie was more than qualified for a small outfit like ours and my SF buddy had assured me he was a great guy and a capable operator. 'Remind him he got the job on my recommendation,' he said on hearing Jamie was inbound for Taji. 'Tell him he'd better not screw up.'

He needn't have worried; Jamie had fitted in right from the off with his easy-going manner and obvious professionalism. The crew of Sierra-Three welcomed him into their fold. Manned by our sole Fijian and our only pair of Gurkhas on the road, they already regarded themselves as orphans amongst the more numerous Brits and Sri Lankans on the convoy team. An American paramedic slotted in as an ideal vehicle commander to replace the holidaying South African doc.

Now Jamie would be harrying the local driver in truck ten to close the gap. All the trucks had number IDs fixed to their cabs and tail gates to help us with control and situational awareness.

I peered into the static vehicle as we drove past. Two men parked at the side of the road early in the morning in the arse end of nowhere. I didn't like it.

'What do you reckon?' I asked Ryan

'I reckon I've got a bad feeling about those guys.' He reached for the radio mic.

'This is Sierra-One. Eyes peeled guys. Report anything suspicious, out.'

'Sierra-Three, spacing complete, over.'

Good effort, Jamie. He was proving to be a safe pair of hands.

'Sierra-One, roger, speed to seventy in front, out.'

After a brief pause with no increase in our speed, Ryan's head turned towards the driver. 'Come on, Jeeves, step on the gas. Seventy yes?'

'Yes sir,' replied the diminutive Jeeves as we spurted forward.

Ninety seconds later we heard: *'Sierra-Five, speed sixty, over.'*

'Sierra-One, roger speed sixty, out.'

'Drop to sixty-five,' Ryan told Jeeves.

'Sierra-Two, static vehicle right at culvert.'

'Five, roger static vehicle right.'

Culverts could provide a handy place to insert IEDs. Ever since my first operations in Northern Ireland twenty years earlier, I'd always regarded them with caution.

Ryan shifted in his seat. 'Another static vehicle. I really don't like that.'

Only 150 metres behind the scout vehicle, we passed over the first of two irrigation culverts as Sierra-Two reported reaching the second. A thunderclap rang out from ahead and a black cloud shot across the road where Sierra-Two had been.

'IED. Sierra-Two, contact.'

His panicked voice indicated Ashen had survived the blast, which quelled my instinctive vision of charred bodies and severed limbs.

Ryan reached across and pressed the panic alarm located in the central console. 'Here we fucking go.'

CHAPTER 5

0646 HOURS

CONTACT

I jolted against the seat belt as Jeeves went heavy on the brakes. Wrenching my attention from the fast-approaching, billowing cloud, I focused on unclipping my helmet and getting it onto my head asap. Would there be a secondary attack?

'*Sierra-Two still mobile.*'

Thank fuck for that. Ashen's vehicle was still on the road and driving. Hopefully, he and his crew had avoided serious injury.

'Sierra-One, all call signs push through. Get off the X.'

Five seconds after the initial contact report, we entered the dissipating dust cloud. Sierra-Two was 200 metres ahead as we accelerated past the static vehicle, which had catastrophic damage to its rear only. Either an IED hadn't fully exploded or it had been an EFP attack firing a molten armour-piercing slug of copper – and failing to take out its target.

As I processed that thought, a terrific blast sounded from behind and our gunship wobbled. Shit.

The armour-plated compartment behind the cab blocked my view, so there was no way of seeing what had happened. I pulled the metal stock of the AK into my shoulder and scanned the terrain through the nearest window. Past the sandy central reservation and the opposite carriageway, a thin line of trees caught my attention. An ideal ambush position, but it slid by on our left with no sign of occupation.

'Slow, slow, slow,' murmured Ryan as he peered into the passenger wing mirror. 'Fuck. That was a big one. Trucks are still coming through it though.'

'This is Sierra-Three, IED strike. One vehicle down: a semi. Others going through. Stopping to provide assistance, over.'

'Sierra-Four this is Sierra-Five, stop, stop, stop. Sierra One, rear of the convoy is stopping south of the explosion. Half a dozen trucks and the spare heads, over.'

'Christ.' Ryan clicked the pressel switch. 'Sierra-One, roger your last Sierra-Three and Sierra-Five, break. Sierra-Three, confirm only one vehicle hit, over.'

'Sierra-Three-Alpha, roger, one vehicle hit.' The personal call sign and gulped breaths indicated Jamie had already dismounted to check the driver. *'Cab is seriously damaged.'*

'Sierra-One is stop, stop, stop. I'm six hundred metres north of the blast site. At least ten trucks with me, break. Sierra-Two, come to my location now. Kilo stop here.' Ryan indicated with his hand through the passenger window to Kemal's vehicle which had pulled alongside on our right.

When we stopped, I pushed open the heavy armoured door and stepped onto the uneven tarmac: five-metre checks for signs of IEDs, then twenty-metre checks; scan the treeline for movement; note the slowing train of lorries stacking up behind us. I tried not to focus on the large smoke cloud obscuring the contact point and the rear half of the convoy.

A worried Indian face peered down from the cab of the lead lorry as it drew to a halt by our bumper.

Ryan stepped out from his side and shouted across to me with accompanying hand gestures. 'John, how about you stay here with Sierra-Two and one of Kemal's technicals? I'll roll down with Kemal to secure the tail of our group and assist Sierra-Three.'

No, that didn't work for me. 'I've got a better idea. Leave Hamoodi to control Kemal's number two and I'll come down with you. We might need all hands if Mike is stuck securing the back end.'

Without hesitation Ryan agreed. 'Okay. Let's do it.'

'Lone-Wolf, this is Sierra-One, come to my location now.' Hamoodi's ride in the second truck had stopped, and Ryan was beckoning to the big Iraqi even as he radioed the message.

Sierra-Two arrived and Ashen jumped out. Ryan gave him quick instructions before turning to Kemal and a panting Hamoodi. Kemal wasn't happy with Hamoodi having de-facto control of his second pickup but agreed the vehicle commander would vacate his seat and help secure the tail. We mounted up, leaving Ashen in control at the head of the convoy with the second Kilo vehicle in support.

Our lorries were using both lanes to get as far from the seat of the explosion as possible. Control would be easier with them compacted, but right now it meant we had to use the rough ground of the central reservation to get past. There was no time to check ahead for IEDs, so it was fingers in ears time and hope for the best.

The crackle of small arms fire opened up from the direction of the blast, muted by our reinforced glass.

'Sierra-Three-Alpha, contact east, small arms fire, over.'

'Sierra-One, roger, inbound your location now. Sierra-Five, send sitrep over.'

'Sierra-Five, seven trucks and two spare heads secure two hundred and fifty metres south of the blast. Sierra-Four is controlling the rear. I'm heading up to support Sierra-Three-Alpha, over.'

'Sierra-One, roger, out to you. Kilo, stop here.'

We'd reached the end of our group of trucks. I'd counted twelve, although the last one had a '13' panel fixed to the cab. By the time they nestled together, this group would be crammed into less than 100 metres of highway.

'Sierra-Three-Alpha, two of us are dismounted and pinned down next to the disabled truck. Sierra-Three still mobile and the gun is returning fire, over.' Jamie must have taken one of the Gurkhas with him and left the machine gunner and one other with the vehicle.

'Sierra-Five, contact right.' Mike's calm voice belied bad news. He'd reported his last position as 250 metres south of Jamie. This appeared to be an organised and substantial attack.

Ryan dismounted and spoke with Kemal while pointing at his big 12.7mm machine gun and then towards the reported enemy locations. With the long-range weapon, Kemal and his team could stay here in a dual role of fire support and protecting the rear of the front group of trucks. Ryan climbed back in and chopped his hand towards the south. 'Go, go, go.'

He threw a handheld VHF radio to me. 'Channel five. I'm One-Alpha, you're One-Bravo, okay?'

'One-Bravo, got it.' I switched it on and wedged it into a pouch on my upper chest. Instead of a radio check cluttering the net, I hit the pressel switch and heard the static on Ryan's set. He did the same. We were good to go.

'Three-Alpha, this is Sierra-One approaching your location from the north. Dismounted will be myself, One-Alpha, and Charlie-Mike is One-Bravo, over.'

No response. Judging from the intense gunfire, Jamie and his team had their hands full. Because everyone used Soviet weapons, it was tricky to tell how much was enemy fire and how much originated from Sierra-Three. But seeing as our guys only had three AKs and a PKM, most of the ordnance had to be incoming.

The heavy report of Kemal's 12.7mm anti-aircraft gun opened up from 300 metres behind us. That would give the attackers something to think about.

'*Sierra-Four in contact. Close. They're very close.*'

The last time I'd heard Ravi on the net he'd been protecting the rear of the convoy. His message reinforced the notion of a sizeable ambush hitting the entire group south of the explosion.

'*Sierra-Five, I'm dismounting at the front of our group. Four, dismount all except gunner and take cover. Driver stays in vicinity of vehicle. Engage confirmed enemy targets. Mind your RUF.*'

There didn't appear to be any houses or other civilian presence around here, but I was pleased Mike had reminded the guys to follow the Rules for the Use of Force. Decisions, even in the heat of this chaos, needed to be justified later. And nobody wanted to shoot anyone innocent.

We barrelled down the road towards the lorry crippled by the IED. The cab was wrecked and one of the front wheels had collapsed, but the forty-foot container still sat on the trailer behind. We'd been lucky so far: the explosion had only winged one vehicle, albeit I had no idea of the driver's condition. He might not have read the situation quite as positively.

The satellite phone chirped in its cradle and Ryan grabbed it. As my focus zoomed back into the vehicle, I became aware of the ringtone from my local mobile phone.

'John Pierce, can I call you back?'

'Boss, it's Hutch. Are you guys okay? Both panic alarms are activated, and the ROC can't get hold of Ryan.'

I caught snippets of Ryan communicating a sitrep.

'I'm pretty sure Ryan's on the sat phone with the ROC now. We're in contact after an IED hit one of the local lorries. Twelve trucks now grouped north of the blast, nine grouped south, I think. Being engaged by small arms fire at the centre and south.'

When rounds pinged off the left side of the F350, the percussion from our gunner opening up from the turret vibrated through the cab.

'Gotta go mate. I'll get you a sitrep when I can.'

'Okay boss. Sounds full on. Good luck. Get back to me when…'

I hung up as we skidded to a halt in front of the stricken lorry. The incoming rounds were coming from the left, so I shimmied over to the right-hand door and threw it open. 'Down ramp out troops,' I shouted with a manic laugh.

'…king Royal,' said Ryan as he passed me and moved to the rear of the F350. 'Chris, you're with me,' he shouted in competition with the outgoing PKM bursts.

I shuffled in a crouch along the front right wing and peered into the bushes and scabby trees where the enemy was firing from. A mixed smell of fireworks and eucalyptus hung heavy in the air with remnants of smoke. I didn't spot any muzzle flashes and the sound of battle seemed to be dying down here and rising a few hundred metres to our south where Mike held sway.

Seeing Jeeves still in the driver's seat I signalled for him to join me. Vehicles are bullet magnets in an ambush, so he needed to remove his silhouette from the front seat nearest the action. He slithered across the seats and fell out onto the floor behind me. 'Stay there. Wait for instruction. Listen out to the radio, okay.'

'Yes, sir,' he replied, getting his AK into the shoulder and shifting up behind the tyre.

I checked left to see Ryan and Chrishantha in a similar position at the other end of the vehicle.

'Can you see Jamie?' Ryan shouted before he fired two shots in quick succession.

'Negative. I'll move to him now.'

'We'll cover you.' Both Ryan and Chris popped up and engaged with their AKs.

'Three-Alpha this is One-Bravo, coming round the front of the cab.'

'Three-Alpha, roger. Careful, we're in a crater immediately off the tarmac. Incoming fire reducing.'

I sucked in a couple of deep breaths and charged forward around the front of the truck. Jamie and one of his Gurkhas were ahead five metres to my right firing into the scrub and I aimed towards them, landing with a crunch a metre to Jamie's left.

Pain flashed in my ribs. I caught my breath and used my thumb to move my sticky safety catch down two notches from safe to single shot, ripping my nail in the process. 'Bastard! Too old for this shit.'

'Motherfuckers let rip as I opened the cab door to check the casualty,' Jamie said, as I scanned the treeline hiding the enemy shooters. 'The driver's door is jammed, so had to come this side.'

Two figures carrying Kalashnikovs darted right fifty metres in front and I loosed off two rounds. One of them stumbled, his momentum taking him out of sight. 'Fucking have that.'

Jamie whooped and added, 'Go Marines.'

Ryan and Chris flashed into my eye line on the left, taking cover behind a rockpile before coming up on aim.

For the first time I looked south and saw Mike's smaller group of trucks the other side of the first culvert. An F350 at the front spat rapid fire from its turret in controlled bursts.

The cacophony of the skirmish had now rolled onto the southern group, although a shot pinged off the forty-foot container on the lorry behind us – a reminder we were still in the fight.

'Cover me. I'm going to check the casualty,' said Jamie.

I couldn't see any movement in front, so I put down a rapid three rounds into bushes I didn't like the look of, then slowed to a shot every three or four seconds. Paresh, the Ghurkha on my right, followed suit.

'Sierra-Five-Alpha, any support available, over?'

'Five-Alpha, this is One-Alpha, en route to your location now, over.'

'Five-Alpha, roger, out.'

Ryan and Chris sprinted back onto the road and into the vehicle. 'Mount up, Jeeves,' Ryan shouted. 'John, stay here with Three-Alpha.'

I lifted my hand in acknowledgement. 'Will do.' Another round pinged off metal behind me and I responded with more shots at the enemy bushes.

'One-Alpha, if we set up fire support fifty metres to your north. Can you mount up and punch through to the main body, over.'

'Five-Alpha, roger your last. As soon as you get their heads down, we'll be on our toes. We've got trailers with shifted loads, but we'll push them through.'

'Kilo, this is One-Alpha, can you move south four hundred metres? To my location, over.'

'This is Kemal, Kilo, yes, we come.'

Meanwhile Jamie had yanked the passenger door of the crippled truck open and disappeared inside with his rucksack full of med kit. 'Casualty is conscious but losing a lot of blood…'

The rest was lost as a whoosh pulled my attention south. An RPG missed Mike's group and exploded in the treeline across the road. Thank Christ for that.

My relief didn't last long.

'Man down, man down. Four-Alpha, man down.' One of Ravi's team.

Kemal's truck raced past our position to join Ryan to provide fire support so that Mike's group might break out of contact and join the main body. The battle appeared to have left us.

I shouted, 'Jamie, I'm going to leave Paresh and your driver here and take Sierra-Three to support Mike, okay?'

'Roger that but keep an eye on us here.' Jamie yelled back.

Paresh, ten feet to my right, looked over.

'You stay here and protect Jamie, okay. I'll send...who's the driver?'

'Samir, sir.'

'I'll send him to you. You tell him, okay?' I gestured towards the trees and bushes out in front of our position.

Without waiting for a reply, I hauled myself up and ran past the container on the trailer. I jinked right to go round the bonnet of the F350 to the driver's side. 'One-Bravo is commandeering Sierra-Three and moving to join Sierra-One, over.'

'Sierra-One, roger One-Bravo, out'

I yanked the heavy door open, helped Samir and his weapon out, and indicated his buddy's location. 'Go to Paresh.'

After adjusting the seat for more legroom, I selected reverse and stamped on the gas while yelling 'Hang on Briyan' to the big Fijian manning the PKM. The top-heavy gunship rocked as I spun the wheel and the nose pitched round to the right until we faced south.

Two football pitches distance away, Sierra-One and Kemal's pickup were stationary, facing southeast into the scrubland and trees. I threw the Ford into drive and we shot forward.

A mush of radio transmissions squawked from both the vehicle set and my handheld radio. Voices became clear once I turned the volume down on the handheld.

'...go left round the convoy, over.'

'Sierra-Four, roger.'

I shouted, 'Engage the enemy, Briyan. Suppressing fire into the treeline if you can't see any targets.'

The gunfire grew deafening, especially when I lurched to a halt next to Kemal's big gun putting down a murderous barrage. He and two of his guys were kneeling next to the pickup firing their rifles. And Sierra-One's machine gun shuddered as it kicked out plenty of lead down range.

Ryan and Chrishantha were crouched behind sparse cover ten metres to my front left. I threw the door open and raced out to join them as glass smashed behind me. A dive to the ground resulted in another crunched landing. More bruises. With only vegetation to shield me, I adopted a prone firing position.

'One hundred and fifty metres, ten o'clock, large bush at edge of tree cluster, seen?' asked Ryan

I scanned the terrain. 'Seen.'

'Last RPG fired from that location.'

'Roger, I'll cover it.' If the rocket firer showed his face again, I'd be ready to ruin his day. For good measure I fired two shots into the area and then two more. Having lost count of my remaining rounds, I loaded a fresh thirty-round mag with an accompanying shout of 'Magazine.'

Spewing diesel fumes and the hiss of air brakes indicated the convoy group was on the move. I remembered my handset volume was turned down and adjusted it.

'…*vehicles are moving. Sierra-Four leading, Five in rear. Five will go firm at the main body, Four will take casualty to the front, over.*'

'*One-Alpha, roger. Enemy fire decreasing. We'll follow you up. Sierra-Two, send sitrep, over.*'

'*Sierra-Two, all secure. Traffic held in front, over.*'

'*One-Alpha, roger, out.*'

Shit. I'd forgotten about Jamie. 'Three-Alpha this is One-Bravo, send sitrep, over.'

Nothing.

'Three-Alpha this is One-Bravo, send sitrep, over.'

Come on Jamie, come on.

CHAPTER 6

'… *Three-Alpha, hands full. Quiet here, over.*'

'One-Bravo, roger, out.' As I sighed with relief, a torso appeared by the RPG bush. I fired four rounds in quick succession – not my most accurate shooting. The marksmanship principles went out the window that time, but the torso had disappeared.

Lorries rolled past gathering pace. Sierra-Five and the two spare tractor-heads geed them up from behind by alternately surging forward and braking, like learner drivers bunny-hopping down the road.

Some of the trailers were loaded with strapped-down plant vehicles, at least two of which leaned awkwardly over the sides. The straps must have come loose due to hard braking or taking evasive action when the IED went off. They wouldn't get far like that.

The unmistakable sound of a Nokia ring tone cut through the battlefield noise as I shuffled left in case anyone had zeroed in on my last firing position. The prominent sound of the phone indicated the contact was dying down again.

Surely, the enemy wouldn't be able to manoeuvre past and hit the main group or the crippled truck at the blast site. I offered up a silent prayer that there wasn't another assault group near Sierra-Two. On occasions like this, comms with the big guy came naturally.

'Fuck off and leave me alone,' barked Ryan. Hopefully, he hadn't yelled that down the phone to the ROC or I'd be fighting off more complaints.

Another RPG arrowed out from the treeline and shot between the two spare tractor-heads. Not from my assigned target area though. I assumed the gunners behind me had seen the firing point because the volume of outgoing fire cranked up before suddenly falling quiet.

'STOPPAGE.'

That was all we needed. But the back marker, Mike's Sierra-Five, had almost reached us. I could see scars from bullet strikes down the passenger side and also on the nearest lorry as it lumbered past.

'Mount up, John,' shouted Ryan.

'Roger, moving.' As I ran to Sierra-Three, I could see Briyan struggling to clear a stoppage on the gun.

Kemal's Dushka fired a short burst and went silent. Only a couple of distant shots took up the slack. I pulled my door shut and spun the wheel to the right as I accelerated through a 180-degree turn, narrowly missing Chris's left heel as he and Ryan crossed in front of me to reach Sierra-One.

I followed Sierra-Five and the line of escaping trucks until pulling over next to the busted-up cab of the IED-damaged lorry. Mike stopped his F350 twenty metres ahead. When I exited the car, both Sierra-One and Kemal's pickup screamed past, forcing me up against the silver bodywork with a face full of dust from their slipstream.

Good job I hadn't stepped out. A bit embarrassing to be run over after surviving a full-on contact like this one. I could just imagine the talk around the bazaars: *Did you hear about John Pierce? Knobber got out of an ambush and then stepped in front of his own vehicles.*

'Jamie,' I shouted. 'You okay? Need any help?' Through the spider cracks of the shattered front windscreen, he appeared to be hunched over the seats.

'Man, this is one lucky dude,' came the reply. 'He's fucked up, but he'll live.'

'Three-Alpha this is Sierra-One, friendly casualties requiring assistance at my location asap, front of convoy, over.'

'Jamie, you need to leave this guy. Mike will sort him out. Let's go.'

Jamie dropped onto the tarmac, his jacket now splattered with blood, and removed a pair of bloody surgical gloves. 'Good job I've got plenty of these,' he said, balling them up and stowing them into a waste bag inside his rucksack side pouch.

'One-Bravo, en route with Three-Alpha. Sierra Five now at the blast location, over.'

'*Sierra-One, roger, out.*'

Mike arrived on foot with his bullet-scarred silver F350 rolling slowly behind him, the gunner in the turret scanning for enemies and poised, ready to engage again.

Jamie gave a quick handover of the casualty. Provided they didn't break the wound open lifting him out of the cab, it sounded like he'd be okay. Like me, Mike had recently attended a Combat Life Saver course given by the US military at Taji, and we'd both taken plenty of battlefield medical courses over the years.

Paresh and Samir swapped out from their defensive duties with two of Mike's team, and we mounted up and set off with some trepidation towards the front of the reconstituted convoy.

'My radio's down, so I'm out of the loop,' said Jamie. 'Any idea what casualties we've taken?'

Sierra-Four approached us head on as it returned to help Sierra Five hold the contact point and protect the rear. I scanned the faces inside.

'I think someone in Four was hit, but Ravi and his driver look okay. Maybe one of the gunners.'

When we reached the chaotic gaggle of our once-organised convoy and swerved down the left flank, we passed Hamoodi commanding Kemal's number two vehicle. He stood barking orders at his new charges and shot me a wide grin as I acknowledged him. His day had improved, even if others had just experienced a life-changing or maybe life-ending ten minutes of bedlam.

I'd been too preoccupied to notice my thumping heart rate until now; it was still high but dropping with every beat. Fatigue washed over me as the adrenaline tap switched off. My bleeding thumbnail needed a clean, my ribs hurt, and I didn't remember hitting my throbbing left knee on anything.

'Okay, stop behind Sierra-One,' Jamie said to Samir as we arrived at the head of the convoy – Sierra-One between the front lorry and the central reservation; Sierra-Two on the opposite carriageway with Ashen's team spread out stopping oncoming traffic and covering the flanks.

I took a deep breath and willed a new burst of energy before climbing out to survey the aftermath, conscious we could still face renewed attack even if it now seemed less likely. Ryan had informed all call signs the US Military had sent out support from the large nearby base, JSS Balad, and to also be alert for the appearance of Iraqi police or army units. My money was on our attackers being long gone by the time support arrived.

Jamie rushed over to Ryan behind Sierra-One, who was knelt over a prostrate figure laid on a flimsy stretcher. Deepak remained conscious and moaned with his eyes screwed shut. I could see a mess of damage to his right shoulder and upper arm, but nothing else obvious under the huddle now working on him.

Raised voices sounded from Kemal's Hilux on the other side of the front lorry. With my AK in the shoulder, I approached the commotion while scanning eastwards into the trees and broken terrain. To the right, Chris and Jeeves were already monitoring that flank, so I turned my attention to the pickup.

At my appearance, the Turkmen team fell silent. A leaden Kemal stood by the tailgate. Drawing closer, I could see one of his men laid in the rear of the truck. He'd suffered a catastrophic head wound that made bile rise in my throat. Opened-up, the human body can horrify.

'My brother-in-law,' said Kemal. 'Ryan checked but…' He finished the sentence with a shake of his head.

At that moment, any words would be insufficient; the man was clearly dead. And with the situation not necessarily contained, practical issues were the priority.

'Do you have any other casualties?' I asked, aware how heartless it sounded to ignore the lifeless figure in front of me.

'Nothing serious,' Kemal replied. 'How is your man?'

I glanced back at Deepak. 'He's conscious. They'll keep him alive until medevac arrives.'

The calm around the pickup simmered with an underlying tension. All other sounds faded into the background. Pockmarks showed the truck had seen a lot of incoming rounds in its time. No doubt some from today. Four cheerless faces studied me.

'I'm sorry for your loss.'

A guilty thought popped up as I thanked fate the ambush had occurred before the turn off for Kemal's alternate route and not after.

'Thank you, guys. You fought well. You helped make the difference. Shukran.'

'We'll go soon,' replied Kemal. 'Not many bullets left, and we must bury my brother.'

I hesitated, wondering how easy it would be to transit through checkpoints all the way to Tal Afar with a dead body in the back of the truck. My practical side also engaged – what about the crane we needed?

Some quick thinking was required. 'Of course. We'll see you when we reach Tal Afar for the crane. And to pay our respects to your brother. Now our brother.'

I wasn't big into displays of warrior brotherhood and all that jazz, so hated myself for using those words to manipulate Kemal to assist completion of the mission. But I did feel genuine sorrow and regret. This was the first man who had ever died under my command so to speak, and I didn't even know his name. I had encountered painful deaths of comrades before, but the senselessness of what had happened on this insignificant stretch of nowhere hit me hard.

Kemal bowed his head in response and unclipped the handheld radio from his belt. As he handed it over, it burst into life with a message that the injured driver had been lifted out of the destroyed cab by Mike's team. As the saying went: *it's all fun and games until someone gets hurt.*

We shook hands and Kemal leaned forward to embrace me. Desolate, dark-rimmed eyes broadcast his grief; anguish accentuated by gaunt features and grey-flecked stubble, and the grime of the morning's exertions. He seemed to have aged as though a twenty-year time lapse had struck since the previous night.

'Thank you, Mr John.'

CHAPTER 7

1000 HOURS

Three hours after the attack and we had yet to move. The American military had arrived first to provide welcome support. Their natural suspicion of private security companies, especially those skirmishing in their neighbourhood, softened due to Jamie's presence. An outburst of inter-service banter between him and the army soldiers turned scowls to smiles.

After a protracted negotiation, they agreed to escort our convoy via the back roads into their large base ten kilometres up the road in Balad. There we would be able to assess all our vehicles and the safety of the loads.

Two run-flat tyres on the F350s had been struck and needed to be changed. Apart from that, our vehicles sustained little more than superficial new battle scars. Only the lorry hit by the IED suffered extensive damage – that would need to be shunted off the road. Fortunately, the accompanying trailer and forty-foot container remained serviceable. Although the struggle to hitch them up to a spare tractor head was the reason for the lengthy delay.

In the end, an enterprising selection of local drivers, Sri Lankans, expats, and judicious use of a large hammer by our friendly giant, Briyan, bodged together a work-around. A joint effort also heaved, pushed, and utilised ingenious improvisation to secure three transported vehicles hanging dangerously from their mounts, and two others with snapped and sheared restraining straps. Good enough to rumble the short distance up the road to safety.

It wasn't all seamless cooperation. Three of the trucks near the explosion had collided, causing them and those behind them to stop during the contact. Once the firefight died down, a furious Indian driver had to be restrained from assaulting the local drivers front and rear who had sandwiched his vehicle with their braking, swerving, and all-round careless driving – as he put it. I admired his devotion to the cause but the lorry he drove was leased by us, not owned by him. Any necessary repairs would be another headache I'd have to face – with the potential to hit our profits from the mission.

The Iraqi Police showed up fifteen minutes after the Americans and not long after Kemal and his two vehicles slipped away. They showed little interest in investigating our attackers. Instead, a tall, self-important senior officer strutted about the place and accused our reaction to a 'minor show of local disapproval' of being heavy-handed and disproportionate.

Hank, the army captain commanding the Americans, gave him short shrift and the frustrated Iraqi officer eventually gave up trying to order our team to the local police station. With the traffic tailing back in both directions, he then surprised me when he made himself and his officers useful by organising a diversion on the opposite carriageway to get all the disgruntled drivers moving again.

Occasional shots sounded throughout the morning, twice close enough that we moved into stand-to positions in the growing heat. But the local scallies probably thought better of antagonising the firepower assembled on the road.

A Black Hawk medevac helicopter arrived, and both Deepak and the injured local driver were flown to the US CSH military hospital in Baghdad. The driver's comrades had begged me not to allow a local ambulance to take him away; they were convinced he would never be seen alive again.

Using Hamoodi to create a poor man's 'good cop, bad cop' routine, I negotiated their commitment to complete the mission. Not that we'd have let them slink off but having them working with us was far preferable to against us.

As we trundled up the rough minor road to JSS Balad my phone rang. Hutch.

'Boss, the big boss has been on the phone and he wants you to ring him asap.'

'Any idea what he wants?'

'He's concerned about the attack of course. And he didn't seem happy you're out with the team again. I think he wants you down in the Green Zone for something.'

I bit my lip. Better not to rant about the company owner to the other guys. 'Okay mate, thanks. I'll try and give him a call now.'

After a few deep breaths failed to cool my annoyance at the anticipated conversation, I dialled the security company owner in the UK.

'Ed, it's John. How's things?'

'I should be asking you. I know there's been an IED and you're with the team. What's happened and why are you there?'

Another deep breath. 'Bottom line? We got hit with a complex attack. EFP that pretty much missed, followed by an IED secondary attack situated right where they probably expected us to go static if the EFP had taken out the lead vehicle. Oh, and that was combined with a nasty small arms ambush. With all that waiting for us, we got lucky the way it worked out. Most of the convoy pushed through the contact point. Only seven trucks and the two spare heads got caught in the rear ambush.'

'Lucky? Were any of the gunships damaged? And tell me, why are you there in the first place?'

That riled me. 'We were lucky, yes. Even with one of our friendly Turkmen security killed, one local driver injured, one of the team, Deepak, with gunshot wounds, various minor injuries including a ricochet strike to a leg, two cases of heavy bruising after hits to body armour, and one lucky escape when a helmet deflected a round. Plus, a sprained ankle.'

Silence.

'Yeah, I'm sorry, John. Obviously, the casualties are the most important thing. But remember I'm not there, so it isn't as clear from sitting here in the UK. I am sorry though.'

'No, that's fine. To your question about the gunships, we have some bullet strikes to bodywork but nothing too serious. A couple of the run-flats need to be swapped out and there's a cracked windscreen that's workable for the mission but will need replacing. We do have a spare back in Taji. Also, one wing mirror shot off that I know about. Happened right behind me.'

'Okay, not too bad. It could be worse. What's happening now then? And why are you with the team. I need you in Baghdad, not gallivanting round Iraq. That's what we pay the guys for.'

The anger bubbled again. 'I'm on my way to Erbil for the meetings with the oil companies and a couple of others. I did mention those meetings in my management report last week.'

'You buried it in the weekly report? I've told you before, I want you in Taji or going into Baghdad to meet with the Contracting Officer. Getting new business, not fucking around wasting time on the ground. You know very well how the financial position looks.'

The red mist was descending. I had to end the call before I said something that would lose me my job. 'Ed, now isn't the time for this conversation. I'm going to head back down to Taji on Space A and call you from there.'

Ed sighed. 'I don't mean to be a prick about this, but you're the country manager, John. That's where you need to be.'

I moved the phone from my ear and glared at it. 'I'll ring you later.' And terminated the call.

Things had changed since Ed had been out here setting up the company operation in 2006. I'd tried to tell him you couldn't meet with contracting officers anymore, not unless there was a witness present. Rumours of corruption and sudden recalls to the US were doing the rounds. Whispers of prosecutions and jail time. The rules were tightening up and Iraq was no longer the Wild West.

The meetings in Erbil were a great chance to explore business that didn't rely on the DOD. Prices on our US Govt contract were being driven through the floor due to intense competition. Security companies were struggling, getting close to going bust. I reckoned we were close to going bust.

But underneath squirmed pangs of guilt. Ed wasn't far off the mark. Catching up with old Peshmerga friends had been a primary motivation for setting up meetings in Erbil. I also loved escaping the office and getting out on the ground. Not all the time – convoys were usually boring as hell – but occasional missions sated my adventurous needs.

It didn't stop me being pissed off with him though, pissed off with the insurgents, and pissed off with turning forty years old in a few days and still struggling with money.

I needed to ring General Rashid and tell him our get together in Erbil was off, then drag my arse back to Taji and try to find a way to dig Ed's company out of its financial mess – if only to make sure he could keep paying me and the others.

Any sense of disappointment about my involvement in the mission being curtailed was well and truly snuffed out by the administrative clusterfuck that ensued when we arrived at JSS Balad. There was no way 'on God's green earth' that the base security officer would allow any of our local drivers to be admitted to the camp, so it was a good job we had our in-house Indian crew.

With most of the lorries confined to the 'dust bowl' outside the base and guarded by three of our security vehicles, any trucks with loads that needed to be re-secured were driven onto the camp by our Indians for begrudging assistance from KBR with their crane and other Material Handling Equipment. That risked another bollocking from our COR, or Contracting Officer Representative, the army senior NCO who monitored our performance on the contract.

Only the week before, similar use of a KBR crane at Besmaya Ranges led to an angry phone call. We had to price the provision of all necessary MHE into our mission quotes, so having to borrow a crane at the destination was frowned upon to say the least. Today wasn't our fault though. He should cut us some slack even if he'd likely suspect we had somehow got one over on him and the government. Fingers crossed the crane promised by Kemal's people in Tal Afar remained available, otherwise that slack would be reeled in fast.

After the usual excellent lunch at the DFAC, Ryan dropped me off at 'Catfish Air', the helicopter operations terminal for troops buzzing around theatre on the swarms of Blackhawks that criss-crossed from camp to camp above the carnage playing out on the ground.

'Good luck, mate. Wish I was staying with you, but…needs must.'

'We'll be fine, boss. Touch wood, we'll get up to Q-West tonight without any more dramas, then an early start for Erbil and back. Depending on how that goes, we might have to overnight again at Q-West and punch out for Mosul and Tal Afar the following day. Then bring the backhaul down as fast as possible.'

'Anything you need, give me a shout. I know friendly forces in Erbil and their influence extends to Mosul. Just hope we don't need to call on them.'

Ryan smiled as we shook hands. 'The guys will be relaxed now. Now that Mr Jonah isn't with us.'

I shook my head. 'Twat.'

'Au revoir. Drive on Jeeves,' said Ryan, slamming his door shut. As they drove off, I noticed several new strike marks decorating the dusty silver bodywork.

'Space A', or Space Available, was the system used to fill up spare capacity on the Black Hawk helicopters with individuals needing to move around theatre. I registered at the counter and immediately ran into trouble because of my AK and sidearm.

It took a descriptive – and some might say sexed-up – version of the morning's events to persuade the heli ops guys to let me board without the dispensation form they thought I needed. Folding the AKMS into my rucksack and stowing the Glock cemented the deal after I assured them we'd 'greased some Qaeda' just down the road from the base.

Ninety minutes later I was airborne on my way back to Taji, forty-five kilometres to the south. As the Black Hawk flew over the fence line soon after take-off, I peered past the door gunner and saw our convoy forming up in the dust bowl.

A sense of desertion surfaced. I was leaving, but the four walking wounded had all volunteered to continue the mission after minimal patching up and handfuls of strong painkillers. That was despite their obvious discomfort, including two with pronounced limps.

With Kemal's team gone, the move to Q-West would only have our usual five-vehicle security team to escort the remaining twenty-one lorries. The morning had shown the value of the extra firepower from the Turkmen security team. The guys wouldn't have that luxury if they got whacked again, and twenty per cent now carried injuries that would impact their ability to react effectively.

Shortly afterwards, I spotted the culverts where we'd been attacked. One with the half-destroyed saloon and the other now marked by a devastated lorry cab. Both tagged with newly scorched tarmac. We'd performed well but also been lucky. Nothing I could do about the rest of the mission except hope Ryan and the team stayed lucky without me.

CHAPTER 8

CAMP TAJI – FOUR DAYS LATER

Sweat flowed and my legs weakened as I struggled to maintain the usual pace on my early morning run. Laughable, but it felt like my fitness levels had plummeted in just two days since my last outing. The route was nothing out of the ordinary: a four-mile circuit around the soulless roads and roundabouts on the Iraqi side of Camp Taji. But today was my fortieth birthday. Maybe an internal switch had been activated to make everything harder in celebration of the inauspicious date.

Unless you encounter a dust storm, June in central Iraq is guaranteed to be hot – blast furnace hot. That's why I ran before 7.00 a.m. Much later and the climbing temperatures meant I wouldn't have bet on reaching forty-one. The other expats tended to go in the evenings, if at all, so I usually ran alone.

Two of our F350s had overtaken me with blasts on the horn and obligatory piss-taking while en route to a big breakfast at one of the DFACs on the US side. The only other witnesses to my race with old father time had been the slouched figures of various compound gate sentries giving me an occasional half-hearted wave.

The first three miles had skipped by as my thoughts wandered around the primary issues filling my in tray. But this last mile, my body's warning systems had overridden all that clutter to point out that dragging my forty-year-old carcass round the sweltering streets of Taji might not be quite as easy from here on in.

The attack near Balad had spawned a family tree of incident reports, insurance forms, and other paperwork, along with a myriad of phone calls from various interested parties – some of whom I knew beforehand and others I didn't.

Meanwhile, I had managed to win another, much smaller mission on our DOD contract scheduled for tomorrow. The team had returned from the big convoy mission to Tal Afar the previous day without any further serious incident, although a small IED had almost caught Mike's tail-end Charlie vehicle as they sped through Mosul. They didn't bother with the panic alarm but informed us by phone later and let Hutch notify the ROC.

The casualties were on the mend: Deepak had been flown to Ramstein in Germany and transferred to the Landstuhl Regional Medical Center where specialists could work on his shattered shoulder and ribs; our walking wounded had soldiered on without complaint, treated and monitored by Jamie; and the local driver had been transferred into the care of a hospital near his home neighbourhood in Baghdad. When the latter disappeared into an admin vortex for twenty-four hours, his company was quick to call and accuse me of handing him over to a Sunni death squad. Not so quick to ring back with an apology once he turned up in the care of Baghdad's finest though.

In Tal Afar, Kemal had taken time out from family mourning to provide the agreed mobile crane needed to unload the team's final shipment. So apart from the attack, the mission could be deemed a success.

That thought prompted images of Kemal's dead brother-in-law, Yusuf, laid broken and lifeless in the back of the dirty pickup, Deepak lying in a German hospital bed, and dead and injured insurgents scattered amongst the scrub.

How many insurgents? The estimate stood at six enemy killed and a dozen wounded, but the American record with suspect body counts since Vietnam coloured my view of that report. One death is a tragedy, a million deaths is a statistic – pretty sure that was a quote from Stalin or someone similar. Not far off, whoever it was.

Only 500 metres left, and the thought distractions had seen my struggles forgotten. Running, like most sports, was a mental as well as physical endeavour. I increased the pace.

Experience had taught me to run the route anti-clockwise, so the finishing straight could be attacked in private. Clockwise meant a gawping audience from the compounds down the main drag while breathing the ever-present fumes of shit from the ruptured sewer just as my lungs needed maximum oxygen. Coughing and spewing my way across the finish line wasn't the best way to lead by example.

My thoughts strayed to my running partner at home. Taz was a twelve-year-old black Labrador-cross whose white toes had now spread into a grey-flecked coat that gave her a ghost-like appearance. She'd slowed down over the years from the manic puppy I fondly remembered. It was doubtful we'd be running together much longer.

Christ, all this morose retrospection and musing about death. I'd turned forty not eighty. Time to get a grip. I pumped my arms faster to encourage my legs to follow suit for a sprint finish. Lactic acid burned in my quads and calves and sweat sluiced into my eyes. Suitable punishment for being a miserable git.

Sitting at my office desk forty-five minutes later, I troughed two yogurts and a banana as the company-issue laptop booted up in its own good time. Despite a cold shower and my efforts to cool down, a light sheen of sweat lingered in defiance of the rattling aircon.

'Looked good this morning, boss,' said Hutch as he walked in from next door. 'Making the rest of us look bad. Okay if I join you tomorrow? As long as we keep a sensible pace.'

I glanced up to gauge if he was taking the piss. 'I was breathing out of my arse, mate. Dig out if you want to come along. We can stick to chatting pace.'

'Sounds good. Any more about the new mission and this scanner bollocks?'

'I'll see if anything's come in since last night. As far as I know, we need to designate a half hour slot for arrival at the scanner. I'll forward the details when they arrive, and you can arrange it with the Battle Space Captain at BIAP.'

The new mission involved escort of a single forty-foot container to Baghdad International Airport, but it needed to go through a specific checkpoint that had a special scanner. Our winning bid for the task had been well under $10,000 and it was the only mission on the board. Not enough – not nearly enough.

The old days of making money hand over fist delivering gravel to the multiplying US FOBs around Iraq for $120 per cubic metre were long gone. The figures in the spreadsheet didn't lie: the company was hurtling towards failure unless we won a lot more work.

The phone rang. 'John Pierce.'

'Picked up anything new?' said the unannounced but instantly recognisable voice of the company owner.

I rolled my eyes and flapped a hand in Hutch's direction. He took the cue and returned to the ops room.

'Morning Ed. Nothing new yet but it is only eight o'clock. The new client is calling me later. Let's hope we get our first tasks from them asap.'

Ed had demanded I try networking in the Green Zone after my return from Balad. I had shaken off my annoyance at his efforts to micromanage from the UK and hopped on a Black Hawk flight into LZ Washington the previous day.

An impromptu meeting with an American contracting outfit had made the trip worthwhile. I already knew their general manager and walked through his door on the right day. The firm had won a DOD project in restive Diyala Province and needed a security provider. Although the other meetings Ed set up proved a waste of time, I had to admit that his networking idea had paid off.

'You see? I told you we needed to concentrate on DOD and the contractors in Baghdad. I need you to push them to give us all their work, all their moves,' said Ed with a hacking cough.

His first cigarette of the day, maybe? I didn't remember if he even smoked. His time in the UK was two hours behind: 6.00 a.m. The strain showed through the 'I told you so' theme in a mixture of relief and messianic hope.

I only had access to the local operational figures for income and expenditure and that was enough to conclude the company couldn't survive much longer in its present state. There were sizeable debts and loans of which I had no sight. It was little wonder Ed was feeling the strain.

'I'm pretty sure they will use us for everything, but it's not clear how much work that will entail. And US Mil is hardly putting any new missions out through our contract.'

'I'm working on something here. Finance. Just keep pushing the business development hard.'

Ed had been working on new finance ever since I'd arrived. I couldn't tell if he had partners or investors – he kept that side vague – but everything I heard indicated the original capital had run out. Launching and running a security company was an expensive business and the work was petering out.

I changed tack to a more pressing matter. 'What's happening about pay?'

'Why? Is there a problem again?'

'No one's refusing to work if that's what you mean, but you told me last weekend the pay would be transferred at the start of this week. It's still not arrived for anyone, me included.'

The replying thump suggested his phone had been put down. A distant female voice spoke, followed by an urgent, muffled conversation.

'Sorry about that, where were we? Ah yes, pay. It's coming. I'll be able to transfer yours and some of the other expats, but I'm still waiting for the Yanks to pay three invoices. We definitely offered discount terms?'

'The normal five per cent for payment in fifteen days.'

'Right.' Followed by stage-whispered calculations. As if he didn't know when the incoming funds were due to arrive.

'Everyone will be up to date by next week. I'll start the transfers today.'

My reply was instant. 'Not just the expats. If you need to make the transfers over a few days, then pay the guys as well. One expat salary would be about six of the team instead. It will head off problems if you begin payments across the board, including the guards.'

My own financial situation wasn't brilliant, and it was the same for some of the others. On the face of it, the tax-free salaries presented as 'rock star' wages but that didn't tell the whole story. Normal rotations – two months deployed in Iraq followed by a month on unpaid leave – evened the monthly average to $10,000 for me.

Just my luck that the pound was stronger against the dollar than it had been for years. Once exchanged, that $10,000 equalled £4,750 give or take. Not bad money if you kept to less than ninety days per year in the UK and qualified as non-resident for tax. But hardly a fortune for risking your life running convoys in Iraq and spending nine months of the year away from your family.

Private security contracting had enabled me and Claire to recover financially after a disastrous business venture in the Kurdistan region forced us to sell our house in 2006 to stay afloat. Now renting a smaller house for a much higher monthly cost, we had disposable income every month and had even been on holiday with our three girls earlier in the year. However, alongside eye-watering debt repayments there was no safety net – no savings, no assets, no margin for error.

'Shall I delay paying yours?' asked Ed, pointedly.

I had personal outgoing payments that would bounce without immediate funds, including £2,000 rent.

'That's not what I'm saying. Make the payments as you see fit, but I recommend you spread them through the team or we may lose the goodwill of the guys. Without them we can't run any missions and we don't want phone calls from the DOD investigating payment problems.'

Ed's voice took on an edge of certainty. 'You're right. I'll begin those payments this afternoon and include the senior team members. Yours will be paid today.'

I wasn't going to argue. If anyone was getting paid then it might as well be me. 'Thanks. I'll let you know when I've spoken with the new client.'

The phone clattered as I dropped it wearily onto the desk. While I ditched my breakfast gash in the bin, Hutch reappeared at the connecting door.

'Good news about pay?' he asked with faux innocence.

I hesitated and tried to replay my side of the conversation to figure out what he would have heard. 'It's coming mate. A slight delay while Ed waits for invoices to be paid, but the payments will begin today.'

'Okay,' said Hutch, sounding unconvinced.

Best to assume he'd heard everything.

'I've told him to begin paying management and the team. If the team refuses to soldier then we're screwed, and we'll all end up looking for new jobs.'

Concern flashed across his face. 'Shit. Are things that bad?'

'I don't have access to all the accounts, mate, so I don't know the full situation. But I do know we've got money inbound, and we've just completed that mission and invoiced for another three hundred grand yesterday. We're okay for the time being, but we've got to keep this show on the road. I'll get everyone together later and brief them with an update. But if anyone asks, keep it positive, yeah?'

'Sure thing, boss.'

Even $300,000 wouldn't go far. Monthly salaries in Taji alone needed $150,000 to catch up, and they'd be due again in two weeks. The leased Kuwaiti trucks and local truck rentals added up to a tidy sum; the Turkmen needed to be paid for their services via Cal and Mehmet; then there was Ed and his office in the UK, plus operating costs for Taji and payments towards outstanding debts. Plenty coming in, plenty more going out by my calculations.

My phone rang again. The caller ID showed *Cal Simmons*.

'Cal, you're up early. What can I do for you?'

'Morning, John. Early bird and all that. Are you alone?'

'No, why?'

'Away from prying ears would be better. I've got an update about Africa for you. Things have moved at last.'

My office and the rest of the HQ could be like Piccadilly Circus at this time in the morning with the team on camp. 'Give me five minutes and I'll call you back.'

I locked my door from the inside, walked into the ops room, and secured the connecting door behind me. 'I'm just dealing with something. If anyone wants me, I'll be back in ten,' I answered in reply to Hutch's unasked question.

CHAPTER 9

I fired up the AC in my cabin and nipped into the wet room-style bathroom. The walk from the HQ and the lingering humidity from the earlier shower combined to fight my attempt to stay cool. Before sitting down at the small writing desk, I opened my arms and basked in the cold blast of air – eighteen degrees, the lowest temperature setting.

I pulled out the local Nokia and rang Cal. He continued the conversation as though I'd unpressed a pause button. 'The broad terms for a joint venture to develop the concessions is agreed in principle, but I really think you need to go down to Guinea and finish it off with Manny. He is your guy after all.'

True, Manny was 'my guy'. Half-British through an English father and hailing from Sierra Leone, Emmanuel, to give him his proper name, had first contacted me in 2005. He'd found my homemade company website and was looking for a job. I was focused on developing business in Iraq at the time, but I encouraged him to explore opportunities with the great contacts he claimed to have in Sierra Leone and the surrounding countries.

After I returned to the UK, we'd met for the first time in London and struck up an easy friendship. We had maintained frequent contact ever since, which included many lengthy discussions about potential business opportunities that cropped up. None of them were goers though – until now.

A year earlier, he'd approached me with information about six mining concessions in the Republic of Guinea, a Francophone country neighbouring Sierra Leone on the western edge of the West African coastline. Paperwork had been duly produced that all looked impressive but none of my business contacts showed any interest in exploring investments for virgin concessions in one of the poorest countries in Africa.

My only previous experience with mining matters had been advice from the CFO of a UK-listed mining company during a boozy lunch with mutual acquaintances. 'Whatever you do, never invest any money in diamonds. Quickest way to lose everything.'

Sage advice I'm sure, but of little relevance for someone without a pot to piss in at the time. Not that I had much more now.

Step forward Cal Simmons, he of the Turkish security contacts and numerous other similar relationships around the world. Difficult to tell how well he was connected in the intelligence world and political in-crowds. He played up an image that his phone contained plenty of decision-makers on speed dial, but I wasn't convinced; a bit too much of the showman about him.

Still, there had been nothing to lose by passing over the mining opportunity to see what he could do with it. The concessions weren't going anywhere in my hands, so when I deployed to Iraq, I introduced Manny and Cal and wished them all the best extracting some value out of the whole affair.

'You're going to need to roll back a step. I'm way out of the loop with Guinea now. What joint venture?'

'I can't really go into it on the phone. I'll send you a briefing note on secure means to your Hush.'

'Okay. I'm busy but I'll be able to pick that up today.'

Cal sounded pleased with himself. 'Good. But what I need to know pretty much right now is – are you interested in deploying to Conakry for this? You're still due back from Iraq before the end of the month?'

'Yes. Flying back in the last week of June. But we're planning a family holiday, so it depends what dates you're talking about. Now Becky's at school we have to fit around their calendar.'

'John, this is a huge opportunity. Once in a lifetime stuff. I'm telling you now, you won't want to miss it. And I need you to keep Manny onside down there. Him and me don't exactly hit it off, otherwise I'd go again myself.'

I smiled to myself. 'Must be your sparkling personality, mate. How long are we talking about for this trip?'

'One week. Ten days tops.'

'And the money's good?'

'The money's fantastic and there's a great chance for a big payday and a long-term gig. Trust me.'

Based on past experience, his use of the phrase 'trust me' increased my wariness.

'Can I tell them you're in? I've got a meeting with the board in twenty minutes.' Cal sounded like an enthusiastic salesman trying to close a deal.

'Err, I guess so. But I need to see the terms and these details you're sending over. If I don't like it, it'll be a thanks but no thanks.'

'Don't worry, you'll like it. All of it. I'll get something over to you today and you can fire back any questions on secure, okay?'

'Okay.'

After he rang off, I sat at the small desk with the air conditioning humming above me and the sounds of distant shouts and laughter from the guys turning-to for the morning parade.

Africa – not a continent I knew well by any means. I struggled to recall any visits other than an all-inclusive beach holiday to Tunisia while on R&R from Bosnia over ten years before. On the plus side, surely it couldn't be any worse than the current mayhem here, and the financial prospects sounded promising. I'd just have to review the details when they arrived and make up my mind then.

Cal would encrypt his email using a programme called TrueCrypt, then send that message to my encrypted Hushmail account from one of his own for another layer of security. Even if anyone had a back door into Hushmail they wouldn't be able to read our correspondence without the TrueCrypt keys only the two of us possessed. Overkill for our normally bland communications, but Cal was a careful guy.

I'd met him during the ill-fated project in Kurdistan that had cost me almost everything I had. It turned out he had put plenty of his own funds into the same project and when the whole enterprise collapsed due to a pair of devious bastards from the City of London, we both lost out.

Since then we'd collaborated on a few bits and pieces, the latest being his utilisation of Turkish contacts to help with the convoy to Tal Afar. I liked the guy to have a drink with but didn't fully trust him. He'd have called me an idiot if I said I did.

CHAPTER 10

LATER THE SAME DAY

After three rapid knocks, the connecting door to the ops room opened. I'd known my productive afternoon in the office wouldn't last.

'Boss, you coming to the DFAC?'

I lifted my head and met Hutch's expectant gaze. 'What's the time?'

Before I could check my watch and answer my own question, he chimed in, 'Seventeen forty-five. Come on, the lads are waiting.'

The half-finished document on the screen in front of me could wait till tomorrow, but I clicked into my work email to check for any notable late afternoon messages. Only one stood out as requiring prompt attention. I rubbed a crick in my neck and reached for the AC remote to switch it off. 'I need to deal with this. You guys go on and I'll follow.'

'No, come on, it's your birthday. The lads want to help you celebrate the big four-oh.'

'Not much to celebrate.'

He pointed at the laptop in front of me. 'That can wait till later or the morning. The cars are outside. Come on.'

I pulled a face but couldn't avoid breaking into a smile. 'Big eats' at the DFAC with good friends wasn't the worst way to spend your fortieth birthday.

'That's more like it,' said Hutch. 'Let's go.'

After I locked my office doors, we strolled towards Sierra-One and Sierra-Three. Fresh scars of battle punctuated the freshly polished silver paintwork in the late afternoon sunshine. Eight of us crammed into the two F350 pickup cabs. I couldn't help laughing at the sight of three burly men crammed into the rear of Jamie's twin-cab. Scouse remonstrated with Briyan and shoved against one of his beefy shoulders, prompting a big Fijian paw to raise in apology.

Looking left I saw the ops room door remained open. We didn't have anyone out on the ground so Hutch could have shut up shop, but he hadn't.

I gestured towards our shared metal office building. 'Who's manning ops?'

'Ashen,' replied Hutch. 'He's studying the mission plan for tomorrow and having a go at creating his own set of orders for practice.'

'That's good. He's keen to learn and he's a good operator. Useful if we can get some of the lads up to decent TL or 2IC level.'

Hutch grunted in agreement.

Ryan and Mike chatted in the front seats as we drove out of the gate. Hutch leaned over and murmured, 'Any idea if the pay went in today?'

'No mate. Still time over there though. It's two hours behind. I'm going to check my account this evening.'

I recognised the finishing straight from my morning run; not the usual or even a direct way to the DFAC on the US side of camp. 'Taking the scenic route, Mike?'

'It's a nice evening for it.'

Hutch couldn't keep a big grin off his face and Ryan flashed a smirk in my direction.

'Okay lads, where are we going?'

'Don't you worry, birthday boy, you shall go to the ball,' said Mike.

A selection of options for a potential destination flicked through my mind. Other contractors with more opulent surroundings perhaps?

I opened my mouth to speak, but Hutch beat me to it. 'Don't fight it, boss.'

'Where are you fuckers taking me?' I said and laughed. 'Not another goat's head stew I hope.'

'If we'd left you in camp, that's what you would have faced,' said Ryan. 'The Ghurkha lads are disappointed they couldn't give you a feast tonight.'

We turned down a rough narrow track between two large compounds. Not somewhere I'd ever been before.

'Well, I'm grateful for small mercies. Just hope I haven't spoken too soon.'

We entered a small, neat compound with a single main building which had an appearance not dissimilar to an American homestead. Cow horns, furs, a coiled whip, and a large sign pronouncing 'Southfork Ranch' added to the unexpected slice of middle America in Taji's back yard. Completing the image, a limp Stars and Stripes hung from a twenty-foot flagpole by the entrance. We pulled up and Mike sounded the horn.

The homestead door swung open and a cowboy boot-wearing woman in her late forties or early fifties sashayed onto the porch with a smile and a wave.

Mike turned from the driver's seat. 'That's Helen. She's a contractor. Been here ages and has this place set up just how she wants it.'

Leaving both our vehicles parked out front, we bimbled over to the porch. Helen embraced Mike and invited us in with a warm southern drawl. 'Come on in boys, come on in.'

Everyone else greeted her like an old friend. She wore a red checked shirt and tight stonewashed blue jeans. Slim and with a smiling face framed by messy blonde hair, she would have been a real looker in her day. That was unfair, especially since I'd now joined the forty-plus club. She was an attractive woman. Handsome you might say, although this was the first time I'd thought that word might suit a woman.

She fixed me with a welcoming smile as I reached her. The others had all filed in through the door ahead. 'You must be John, the boss,' she said. 'It's nice to finally meet you.'

'Likewise. It's Helen, yes?'

'That's right. You've got some great boys there. They've helped me around the place this last year or so. It's only right that I can give 'em a place to relax and forget about all this.' She threw her hands out towards the fence line and what lay beyond.

'To be honest, I didn't even know you were here,' I said, suddenly suspicious of when the guys had made time to slope off and help out.

'Well, now you do, welcome to my home and be sure not to be a stranger.' Helen held out her dainty hand.

I shook it and smiled. 'Of course, thank you.'

Mike's head popped round the doorway. 'Come on, boss, put the poor lady down.'

Helen laughed and ushered me inside. I found 'the boys' already sat round a large wooden table in the centre of a room decorated with knick-knacks, mementos, signs, flags, photographs, and movie posters.

'Happy birthday, boss,' said Ryan, handing me a can of Budweiser. Most of the others around the table already had a Bud on the go.

I took it but shook my head. 'What did I say about alcohol, mate?'

The room went silent save for the tap of Helen's cowboy boots as she walked up behind me. I flipped the ring-pull. 'Cheers.'

Answering cries of 'Cheers' mixed with laughter as Helen appeared on my right holding a half-full wine glass in salute. I took a long swig of the ice-cold beer and damn it tasted good. For a couple of seconds there was silence again as we all supped our drinks. It was soon broken by shouts of 'Happy birthday, John' and 'Happy birthday, boss'.

I'd never been a stickler for the rules.

We stayed for an hour and a half – two beers each for some of us, although Jamie and Briyan drank Coke and both Ryan and Mike only had the one beer each. They were all on the BIAP mission first thing in the morning.

Helen served up a cracking meal of T-bone steaks, fries, and crunchy salad, ably assisted by Mike and Jamie. Mike then appeared with a fancy chocolate birthday cake, decorated with 'Happy Birthday Royal – You Old Git' and a single candle.

They must have swung a deal with the DFAC, although I guessed Helen may have had some input. I was moved by the effort everyone had gone to. And moved in other ways by the warm breath on my neck that accompanied Helen's birthday kiss as she wished me all the best for the next forty years.

'Enough of that,' interrupted Mike. 'Mustn't forget the main event.' He placed a ten-inch long, thin, rectangular, gift-wrapped present next to the cake and picked up a fierce-looking kitchen knife. 'You open that, while I cut the cake. Who wants some?'

'Thanks guys, you shouldn't have.'

I ripped off the wrapping paper to reveal a plain white box. When I opened it, my stolen pointer lay inside. Laughter rumbled round the room.

'Ahh, you didn't.' I swung it towards the chief suspects. 'I knew one of you fuckers had it. Now where's my piece of cake.'

When we left, I thanked Helen for a great evening and vowed to drop in again soon – meant in the moment but unlikely. As we drove to our camp in the darkness, thoughts of Africa crept in. Ryan, Mike, and Hutch were three men I'd be happy to work with anywhere. With his service in the Legion, Ryan would know Africa well. Mike too probably, from his lengthy spell with special forces.

'I might have something coming up in Africa,' I offered into the car to no one in particular.

Mike caught my eye in the redundant rear-view mirror. 'Keep me posted. You never know how things turn out,' he said.

'Aye, me too, boss,' said Ryan.

'And me,' added Hutch.

'Will do, guys, will do. And thanks for tonight. It's really appreciated.'

CHAPTER 11

Alone in my cabin half an hour later, I decrypted Cal's email.

Subject: Project Thorin

Background

Pinnacle Mining Corp. has an agreement in principle with Sapro Mines SA to sign a Joint Venture for the development of six mining concessions at different locations in the Republic of Guinea (Iron Ore, Zinc, Copper, Uranium, Gold, Diamonds). Having introduced the deal, Cal S. is being employed by the board of Pinnacle to oversee the contract formalities and the operational elements.

1. Primary Objective
   Secure a signed JV agreement in terms agreeable to the Pinnacle investors. Draft terms to be advised.

2. Secondary Objectives
   - Identify physical assets, Conakry HQ base location and suitable local national personnel to support PMC mining operations in Guinea.
   - Conduct reconnaissance of concession locations and complete appropriate threat and risk assessments, together with assessment of logistic support requirements.
   - Reinforce existing relationships with key security forces officials and identify additional political, military, intelligence and police figures

that could provide 'top cover' protection and valuable support to PMC operations.

- Identify in-country competitors and assess capabilities, strengths and weaknesses.
- All the above factors to be included in a comprehensive Concept of Operations plan to be presented to the board within 7 days of PMC team arrival back in the UK.

3. Provisional PMC Team & Travel Arrangements
    John P. & Manny I. to travel to Conakry on or about 5th July 2008 to conclude agreement with Sapro and conduct information gathering and site reconnaissance. Trip duration – max 14 days. JP will have power of attorney to sign deal on behalf of PMC and open local bank account (SocGen).

4. Compensation
- JP £500 per day – Success bonus £2,500 once contract signed
- MI £200 per day – Success bonus £1,000 once contract signed

5. Additional Task
    A potential deal for the purchase of 10,000 carats of highest quality diamonds has been offered. The origin of the stones is unclear, but the sellers are willing to meet in Conakry to open discussions. The team is to investigate the viability of the deal and report to CS for further instruction. Shares in any successful deal that results shall be as follows: JP 5% profit share. MI 1% profit share. This is a potential $10 million USD deal!

    Any questions?
    CS

Cal didn't do things by halves. I noted the maximum duration of the trip to Guinea had extended to fourteen days, but on a daily rate of £500 it would only mean more cash in my pocket. If it did run on that long, then it would be touch and go for the family holiday. Although if it all went well, maybe I wouldn't be returning to Taji anyway.

I reread the email. At face value it could be an incredible opportunity. Provided it wasn't all bollocks of course. Only one way to find out – get on that plane to Conakry. I should have run it past Claire first, but it wasn't as if she would say no. Not unless she'd picked the winning lottery numbers this week.

I typed out my email reply.

Subject: Re: Project Thorin

Your email well received and understood.
Timings and compensation workable. Subject to appropriate MUF.

Rgds,
JP

I went through the encryption palaver and pressed send. Any other questions could wait. The main thing I wanted to know about was MUF – Money Up Front. Everything else would come out in the wash.

I Skyped Claire straight after, although it was Becky's face that filled the screen almost right away. 'Daddy, when are you coming home?' she demanded. 'You've been away for ages.'

'Soon,' I replied. 'Less than two weeks.'

'How many days is that?'

'Fourteen days. Less than fourteen days.'

Satisfied, she tried to encourage a few words in my direction out of her baby sister, Daisy, before giving up and vanishing off screen with a shout of, 'Bye, love you.'

'Daddy, love you.' said Daisy, waving a biscuit-filled hand. Then she too squealed and ran off, with Taz in hot pursuit. The wily old hound no doubt sensing a good opportunity to swipe a biscuit-sized snack.

Claire and I didn't make video calls very often. The Internet wasn't usually up to it. Instead, we used Skype to chat by text. The image scrambled soon after Becky and Daisy disappeared, so we reverted to our usual flow. After catching up about bills and my frustration that Ed's promised payment still hadn't arrived at the bank, I mentioned Africa.

John: Might need to travel to Africa while on R&R. Paid though! Good money.

Claire: For how long. You're coming home first??

Claire: Please

Claire: I miss you x

John: Home first but might need to fly after a week. Back in time for the holiday with plenty of cash x

Claire: If you're sure. We all miss you xxx

Claire: Natalie says hi + can you pay the last instalment for the college field trip. It's very late and she's mortified about it. Sorry x

John: Pay should be in shortly. Tell her I'm sorry and it'll be sorted in the next couple of days.

The connection dropped. My cabin relied on the VSAT Wi-Fi from the office and managed a couple of strength bars most nights. Any problems normally occurred when an internal security breach leaked the main Wi-Fi password to the convoy team and guard force. The connection at their accommodation was okay but the sheer number of users meant I was often inundated with complaints.

If the password for the quieter connection over here was compromised, before you knew it clusters of Sri Lankans and Ghurkhas could be found huddled around the HQ and surrounds sucking up the bandwidth. Resetting the router would achieve that. I suspected Ashen's earlier stint in the ops room had not been without cost.

I stood up and swiped at a hardy mosquito that hadn't been put off by the room's Arctic temperature. Time to find out if I was right and a password reset at the HQ was required. I wouldn't have this problem in Africa. Or would I? Would I even have access to the Internet? A flicker of excitement ran through me. Iraq suddenly felt mundane and organised compared to pitching headfirst into the unknown.

PART II

RECONNAISSANCE

CHAPTER 12

JULY 2008

CONAKRY, LA GUINÉE

Along with the other tired and stiff passengers, I yawned and stretched as we disembarked from the Air France jet in disorderly fashion. Nearly midnight, a blast of heat and humidity accosted me as I jostled my way through the aircraft door. Twenty metres opposite the rusty mobile aircraft steps, a decrepit bus squatted on the cracked tarmac.

It beat me why flights into these places arrived in the middle of the night. Maybe so no one could see what a shithole they'd just landed in. The morose faces of the soldiers flanking the plane and the bus did nothing to lighten the atmosphere.

We waited by the bus for the doors to open. A frazzled mob. Heat radiated from the close-knit bodies as passengers pushed from the back and the gaps between everyone grew smaller. Angry shouts in French pinged back and forth as heels were clipped and elbows dug into ribs. I inched my way out to the right to escape the crush. Squeezing onto the ancient tin can sweatbox in front of us had lost its appeal. Hopefully, a more roadworthy example of passenger comfort would be along to mop up any excess passengers.

After ten minutes, more shouts. This time from a military officer with three yellow bands decorating the epaulets of his drab, dark uniform. A line of passengers began to drift towards the shabby, dimly lit terminal on foot, like a column of knackered ants. Female cries of frustration or desperation rose from those near the doors of the stationary bus. I didn't understand the words but agreed with the sentiment. I trooped off with my fellow suffering travellers, anonymous in the crowd – if I hadn't been the only blond-haired, blue-eyed guy on the flight.

The city of Conakry, capital of the Republic of Guinea and home to a population of 1.5 million, protruded from the Atlantic coast of West Africa. I'd peered out for a first look at my new stamping ground as the plane circled prior to landing. A fifteen-kilometre finger of illumination jutted out into the inky blackness of the city's watery borders. Lights from a handful of ships reminded me Conakry was a port city. A more subdued and gradually patchier light show indicated the commuter-belt shanty towns of the poorer residents. The glowing blob stretched back beyond the airport into the hinterland for a few kilometres before breaking into smaller clusters and finally fizzling out into the darkness of the jungle.

As we reached the terminal, a corridor of armed soldiers directed us with silent stares. My phone had failed miserably to detect even a whiff of a signal, so I was relying on Manny being at the right place at the right time: waiting outside arrivals when I made it through. Either that or I'd need to dust off my limited schoolboy French and make my own way to the digs Cal had booked at the oceanfront Novotel hotel, nestled somewhere near the tip of the Conakry peninsula.

First, I needed to get past immigration armed with the unimpressive letter acquired the previous day at the faceless Guinea consulate office in West London. My name had been on the list, so within an hour, and after payment of ninety quid, they produced a poorly worded, offset, smudged document which, they assured me, would facilitate entry to the country.

I shrugged my rucksack higher, wiped the sweat from my forehead, and slapped my right shoulder with my left hand. Bastard mosquitos already. Or maybe not.

A flash of pain indicated I'd struck the site of my recent jabs. Earlier in the week, I'd walked into a medical centre at Waterloo station and received a cocktail of inoculations that rivalled the worst efforts I experienced in the military. A civilian version of *'we haven't got your records, so we'll assume nothing and puncture both arms like a pin cushion, unless you'd prefer some elsewhere, Sergeant Pierce?'*

I took my chances with the multiple stab wounds to both arms. The last time I received an injection in my buttocks – for 'Woodbury rash' during commando training at Lympstone – I hadn't been able to sit comfortably for a week. Economy seats on two packed Air France flights for 5,000 kilometres were enough of an ordeal without a sore arse.

By the time we reached immigration, I was one of the first in the queue. Groups of passengers carrying, wheeling, and pushing ridiculous amounts of 'hand' luggage had fallen by the wayside amid squabbles between husbands, wives, grandparents, and crying kids.

A question in French from the surly immigration officer, followed by a sneer when I asked if he spoke English. Consulate letter barely acknowledged, passport stamped, and on my way.

I had changed planes at Charles De Gaulle Airport in Paris. Provided my luggage had made it onto the Paris-Conakry leg of the flight, and not been offloaded during a technical stop in Dakar, I didn't foresee any issues – ours was the only recent arrival.

I took up a position in the gloom next to the conveyor belt. Over the next forty-five minutes, my brightly dressed fellow passengers shuffled up to join me, collected their luggage from the wheezing conveyor, and toodled off on their merry way.

Just my luck to have the last bag off the plane. Not that any new luggage had tumbled down the chute recently to join the last of the orphan cases making circuits of the terminal.

When the final remaining passenger dragged his bulging suitcase onto a squeaking trolley and nearly tripped over in the process, the belt stopped and didn't restart. Shit. I recalled the contents of the rucksack on my shoulder, relieved that my habit of packing hand luggage on the assumption everything else would be lost had finally paid off. Relieved maybe wasn't the right word. Then I looked around at the last few officials yet to depart the largely empty building to gauge which one might offer the best customer service experience. Not an obvious choice.

I collared the nearest one and subjected him to my excruciating French. 'Bon soir, monsieur. J'arrive on le Air France…flight. Mais mon…luggage n'arrive pas avec moi. S'il vous plaît.'

The man glared at me and barked something over my shoulder that I couldn't understand, apart from the word 'chercher' thrown in the middle. 'Search', if I remembered correctly, so he seemed to have got the message. The military officer who had led the exodus from the plane appeared and said something I didn't catch but, combined with his hand gestures, clearly meant *come with me.*

I felt uneasy as he led me down a dark corridor, but after only five metres he opened a door on the right and the mystery of my bag's disappearance was solved. We'd interrupted three men as they rooted through my clothes and equipment under an anaemic lightbulb.

One of them examined my Leatherman multi-tool. Next to it sat my folding Ka-Bar knife, mosquito net and repellent, medical kit, water filtration pump, and a pair of jungle boots. Another shone weak torchlight inside the empty Karrimor bag and ran his fingers along the seams. The last and fattest of the silent, sweating trio handled my spare clothes and only pair of smart shoes like he was at a jumble sale.

I didn't know what these clowns thought they might discover, but fat boy going through my clothes certainly wouldn't find anything that fitted. I looked at my escort, spread my palms and gave my best impression at a Gallic shrug and 'what the fuck is going on?' look.

Maybe my French communication was improving. He snapped at the three comedians defiling my kit and they began to shove everything back inside the bag in quick time.

The sour-faced guy held up my Leatherman and Ka-bar with a smirk of anticipated ownership. His face fell when my new best friend spat out a reply that made him toss them both into the bag and add my boots on top.

'I'll do it. Here, don't worry, I'll do it.' I motioned them all out the way and rearranged everything so I could at least zip the bag shut. One of my shirts looked as though they'd mopped the floor with it. I hoped the hotel had a decent laundry service.

My relief was short-lived. The officer poked at my daysack and made it clear the bag needed to be checked. Bollocks. The oppressive heat closed in and coated me with a fine sheen of perspiration. I swirled my tongue to try and moisten my parched mouth, to little effect.

The daysack held a selection of spare shirts, trousers, socks, and knicks to get me through a few days without my grip, but it also contained higher value items – kit that I couldn't afford to lose: Thuraya satellite phone, Garmin GPS, and my Sony laptop.

All the work information on the laptop was encrypted and hidden in image and video files. But I didn't want this lot – or any other muppets – trawling through my personal files and photos. There was also the small matter of it being my only computer. I hadn't yet earned enough for the luxury of deploying with a dedicated, clean device.

A prickle of anger pierced the layer of wearied annoyance. I'd experienced fun and games at other airports in the past with attempts to seize sat phones, GPS, and weapon ancillaries. I didn't possess anything linked to weapons, but neither did I possess a shred of documentation that said I was here to negotiate with the president's people and to fuck off and leave me alone.

Different strategies to dissuade them from conducting an intrusive search ran through my mind – crazy considering I was here legitimately.

In my laptop bag I did have a power of attorney letter for the mining company. Alternatively, perhaps I should dig my DOD badge and Letter of Authorization out of the hidden pocket of my daysack if things became tricky. Although only valid in Iraq, they did imply an official status. However, even that might work against me here. Guinea Conakry was a former French colony and half-failed state like its next-door neighbour Guinea Bissau. Not a renowned friend of the United States.

'This has already been through scanners at London City Airport and Charles De Gaulle. I'm not carrying anything banned, so can I go now.'

'Monsieur, posez votre sac ici.'

I understood that meant to put my bag down, even without the jabbed finger and raised voice. An inward groan as I envisioned the potential threat to the $3,000 in a money belt under my moistening shirt. Not the best time to consider removing my lightweight jacket either. There was my phone in one of the pockets and my wallet with more cash, credit cards, and ID in another.

'D'accord. Mais vous ne trouverez rien d'intéressant.' *Okay, but you won't find anything of interest.*

I don't know who was more surprised by my sudden recollection, him or me. A synapse or two must have fired up and dredged some 'O' Level French out of my memory banks. Shame it probably wasn't true.

'Nous verrons,' he replied quietly. No idea what that meant but I expected the worst.

It didn't take long. 'Ahhh.'

No need for any translation as he pulled the sat phone out of the bag, followed by the GPS. His eyes shone with the righteous zeal of officious bastards the world over.

'GPS and sat phone. Un problème?'

'Oui, c'est un problème.' The reply I'd expected.

Voices echoed from down the corridor and through the open door. A deep booming laugh approached. The officer stopped and looked towards the doorway.

A glimmer of recognition as another voice became clearer. Speaking French, but I knew that guy. Manny. Just in time.

A beaming barrel of a man rolled into view and ducked his head below the low doorframe as he entered the room. He stopped in front of me and a fleshy hand grabbed my own and began to pump it.

'Mr John. I've heard all about you. Welcome to Conakry.'

He had a hat covered in scrambled egg, a lanyard of gold braid, and a pair of stars on his shoulder epaulets.

'Thank you...General?' I looked towards Manny for guidance as he hovered by the door taking in the scene.

The big man laughed. 'General Ndidi, that is right. I will see that your stay in our country is a pleasant experience.'

He turned to the officer holding my GPS, stared at the device, and then switched his attention to the satellite phone on the table. His smile dropped. A burst of angry French saw the officer's eyes widen and my kit returned into the top of the bag tout de suite.

The general scowled and spat vicious admonishments at all four of the uniformed men as he prowled the room. The soldiers shrank against the table as he circled them, and all seemed to hold their breath in fearful expectation until he stopped, gave a satisfied sigh, and turned his attention back to me with a renewed smile.

'Forgive me that you had to experience this.' He shot a dark look at the search team. 'Sometimes my colleagues can be a little… enthusiastic in their work. Come, I will drive you to your hotel.'

We swept out of the room and Manny winked as I caught his eye.

'Emmanuel, did you say it was the Novotel?' asked the general.

'Oui, Général.'

'Please, please, English for our friend. I like to practice for when I go to London. My wife loves Harrods, but everything is so expensive.'

I liked this guy already.

Beyond the terminal doors all looked calm. No evidence of the earlier commotion that would have played out as taxi drivers vied with each other to attract the exhausted travellers from my flight. But it wasn't completely dead outside. A few shadowy figures moved around, although in the half-light I couldn't tell if they were passengers, staff, or simply denizens of the airport car park.

Once outside, smartly dressed soldiers dived out of two high-spec Toyota Land Cruisers and opened the nearest passenger doors. General Ndidi directed me into the rear of the front vehicle to sit alongside him. He dismissed Manny to the other car.

Traffic was light as we drove through the city. The darkness couldn't disguise the ramshackle state of the areas we traversed, hide the rubbish and junk that littered every surface, or soften the sullen glares we received from groups of young men as we swept past. The general ignored it all and kept me occupied with a barrage of questions about where I lived in London and, finally, what I needed during my stay in Guinea.

Conspicuous by its absence was any question about what I was doing in the country. I assumed he was completely au fait with the reasons for my visit, but I didn't offer any information about my plans. I hadn't had a chance to say more than two words to Manny, so I couldn't be sure where the general fitted in. And I had long ago learnt the truth in the saying that 'assumption is the mother of all fuck ups'.

'Of course, you will need a car. Baldé…' – the soldier in the front passenger seat turned – '…you will accompany Mr John throughout his visit. Take Demba and the white car and report when and where Mr John tells you.'

The general leaned over. 'Caporal Baldé is one of my best men. A rising star. He will take care of you and see to it that nobody interrupts your business. Here, take my card. It has my personal number on it, and you can call me anytime, day or night.'

I took the gold embossed card and nodded in appreciation. In many places acceptance of someone's business card is a cultural minefield, so I played it safe. An impressive card it was too. Probably sourced from a posh printer in London's West End.

'Thank you, General. That's very good of you. I should really speak to Manny first though, because I'm not sure what arrangements he's already made.'

A spy in the camp might not be the best idea. I needed to check with Manny before agreeing to anything. I hoped the general wouldn't take it the wrong way. But of course, he did. He instantly bristled and his smile vanished.

'Mr Pierce, your safety during your time in our country is my responsibility. Baldé will accompany you to make sure that I discharge that responsibility effectively.'

I ran up an instant white flag. 'Of course, General. I'm sorry. I didn't mean to cause offence. I simply wanted to make sure that our support is coordinated. Your assistance and that of your man, Baldé, is very welcome, thank you.'

A satisfied sigh and we were back on track, all smiles again. Note to self: try not to piss off the volatile local general immediately on arrival in-country.

By now, the buildings either side were a mixture of office blocks, shops, and restaurants – downtown Conakry. The windows in the car had been opened a few inches and the welcome airflow brought with it the faint tang of the nearby ocean mixed with a stronger scent of decomposing rubbish. I'd have dearly liked the AC to be going fall blast, but I reconciled that my current discomfort helped with acclimatisation if nothing else. I desperately needed a shower; I knew that much.

CHAPTER 13

Half an hour after leaving the airport, the general pointed out the Conakry Port entrance as we drove past. 'The Novotel isn't far from here. It's a fine place, although next time you should consider the Hotel Camayenne. My friend is the owner and will give you a good rate.'

'Where is it? Nearby?'

The general slapped the top of his thighs with both hands in obvious irritation at an opportunity missed. 'We came along the direct road because of the time. The Cameyenne is also by the sea but on the north side of the city, along Corniche Nord. A very nice location. Near where I showed you the Botanical Garden and the Grand Mosque. Not in downtown, but close to the diplomatic quarter and nearer the airport.'

'It's always useful to have alternatives. The Novotel was booked for me and I'm sure it will be fine. But if not, I'll take a look at the Cameyenne. In fact, I need to check out all the options, so I will go and see it at some point.'

The general beamed. 'Baldé will take you tomorrow.' He then instructed Baldé in French that the Hotel Cameyenne would be on the morning's itinerary. I let it slide. No point antagonising him again.

As long as my room had Wi-Fi, hot water, and aircon to keep the mozzies at bay, I'd be happy. The online reviews hadn't been glowing, but the consensus seemed to be that the Novotel was as good as it got in Conakry.

We turned into the hotel car park and passed a range of luxury cars and SUVs filling the spaces in front of two connected main buildings. The United Nations logo adorned a pair of older Land Cruisers, and other NGO and corporate logos indicated the big boys were in residence. It meant the place had passed their routine checks.

A standard seven or eight floor rectangular structure stretched a hundred metres to the left. On the other side of the central entrance stood a modern-looking wing sweeping down like a rollercoaster ride from over ten floors above us to perhaps four floors at the other end, eighty-plus metres away.

We pulled up under the circular canopy outside the main doors. Baldé hopped out and opened General Ndidi's door before scooting round to pull mine further open, even though I was already halfway out. A flash of wariness as he shot a look over to the general. He caught my eye and transmitted a silent plea. Next time I'd wait for him to open the door for me. Not that the general had noticed. He was already chatting with Manny next to the other car.

The general didn't hang around. He shook my hand and said we'd meet in the coming days, reminded me I had his card, and said Baldé would be here with the car and driver at ten o'clock to take me to view the Cameyenne. Then he directed a menacing stare at a hotel porter before climbing back into his seat with a fresh order on his lips for Baldé and the driver.

'A useful guy to have onside.' I said to Manny as we watched the gold-coloured car depart.

'He helped at the airport, but I don't know how much we'll see of him.'

'He's sending his car for us tomorrow. We can use it while I'm here. Baldé as well.'

Manny thought for a moment. 'Good. That gives us some security. One less headache for me to arrange. But I've got another car ready if we need to travel anywhere without the general's knowledge.'

I nodded as we matched conspiratorial smiles. 'Anyway, how are you, mate? It's been a while.'

'Keeping busy. Your friend Cal is not like other people I've met. You work closely together?'

Our first conversation alone and straight into it. The question must have been on his mind and came with an implied note of caution.

'Not at all, mate. Wouldn't trust him as far as I could throw him. But he's paying the bills and I've got some money up front with me. It's more than you and me managed to secure in the last couple of years.'

He looked relieved. 'I thought you'd say that. Some of his contacts here, they are not good people. We need to be very careful.'

Why didn't that surprise me?

★

'No sir, we don't have any booking under the names Pierce, Simmons, or Pinnacle Mining.' The hotel receptionist spoke with certainty despite giving the ledger in front of him little more than a cursory glance.

'It's for seven days. Already paid. It has definitely been reserved by my company in the UK. On the computer perhaps?' My reasonable tone belied a growing desire to grab this prick by the lapels and drag him over the counter.

He regarded the computer as though he'd never seen it before. 'No.'

Manny had a go in French as I stepped away from the desk before I lost my temper. A sign on a glass door indicated the business centre. It consisted of a handful of desks crammed together in a small office. I peered inside and decided I'd rather work in the privacy of my own room.

My first impressions of the best that Conakry had to offer weren't good. What were the chances of a workable Internet connection upstairs?

Manny joined me. 'He looked again, but he doesn't have the booking in any of our names.'

'Does he have a seven-day booking for a guest that hasn't arrived?'

'No. He says the hotel is full. Only one or two rooms left.'

'Find out how much for a room for one night. I'm not pissing around trying to ring Cal this late. I'll just have to pay up for now and sort it out with the manager in the morning.' My watch showed 1.30 a.m. 'Later *this* morning.'

One hundred and twenty dollars later I waved off the haggard porter who attempted to commandeer my duffel bag and stomped along to the lifts. I considered the stairs but fatigue won over. If the lift got stuck, someone would suffer when I got out.

Manny was staying with one of his local contacts, Condé, who he assured me would be a great help during our trip. Tonight, the general's second car gave him a lift home. In the morning, Condé would drive them both to meet me for breakfast in the hotel at 9.00 a.m.

CHAPTER 14

By the following morning I'd been dealt a full house of disappointment – kicked off by a terrible night's sleep under constant bombardment from one or more elusive mosquitoes as they droned past my ear with annoying regularity. Nothing breeds irate guests and poor Trip Advisor reviews quite like having to haul yourself out of bed at 4.00 a.m. to rig a mozzie net in your supposedly three-star hotel room.

Any help from the aircon to keep the flying bastards at bay could be discounted. Not content with a pathetic air flow, the rusty antique served only to warm the stifling room until I turned it off in disgust. Instead, I opened a window to get the benefit of the sea breeze. The bugs could give it their best shot once I lay drenched in sweat and dog-tired under my trusty net.

Come daylight, which had arrived with a welcome dash of freshness, I'd written off the chances of decent Internet even before I discovered the Wi-Fi in the room was non-existent. A quick test in the business centre proved little better: a signal yes, but hardly workable; and an insufficient number of fixed LAN connections to inspire confidence.

The tepid shower had a flow like it was suffering from plumbing prostate cancer. No wonder this room was one of the last to be released to paying customers.

The duty manager proved no more helpful than the receptionist the previous night. He remained adamant the hotel had not received a reservation request for me and certainly not received any payment.

I retreated to the restaurant under a cloud of doubt, trust in Cal's declaration about the accommodation arrangements shaken. My phone still hadn't picked up any local networks, so the answer would have to wait until I fired up the sat phone or obtained a local mobile. One positive: the quality of the buffet in the bright and sunny restaurant was a pleasant surprise. But my mood darkened as I ate breakfast alone. Manny was late.

I checked my watch before pouring another cup of strong coffee to jump-start the day. As I returned to my table, Manny and a shorter companion entered the restaurant. Nine forty-five. *This had better be good.*

Manny held up his hands as he approached. 'I'm sorry. The traffic is terrible. I managed to get you the local phone you asked for, but I know we are late.'

A smile crept onto my face; my anger punctured. As reasons went, that was plenty good enough. 'That's fine. Thanks for getting the phone. I need to ring Cal and find out what's happened with this hotel booking.'

He handed me the opened box. 'It's from Orange and there's one hundred dollars credit already on it, just like you asked.'

Although we'd known each other for over two years, we had only met a handful of times and never worked directly together. I was predisposed to trust him due to his military background – he'd served with the Sierra Leone army during the catastrophic civil war of the late 90s and alongside the British military in their intervention in 2000. Even so, first impressions count, and Manny had come up trumps so far.

'This is Condé. He can help us whenever we need. He already got us a good deal on the phone through his cousin at Orange. Doesn't speak English though.'

Condé was short and stocky. He had a shaved head and wore a frayed check shirt, battered jeans, and trainers. A smile creased his face and reflected in his eyes.

'Condé, hi. Comment ça va?'

'Ça va bien,' he replied with an even brighter smile.

'Unfortunately, that's as good as it gets. Mon francais n'est pas tres bon.' No point in pretending my French was anything but limited.

Condé disagreed. 'Tres bon, tres bon.' But then he'd only heard my day one, week one stuff so far.

The two men helped themselves to the buffet while I sat down with my coffee and pulled out the new Nokia. I signalled hello to a pair of tanned guys as they walked past, both wearing cargo trousers and shirts designated with UN logos. Scandinavians at a guess from their blonde hair and Viking features. Perhaps a bevy of Narvik nurses might join them. That would be worth a photo for the lads in Taji.

I'd used my ever-handy 'combat' iron to press my lightweight shirt and trousers. Together with a decent breakfast, hot coffee, and now a working phone, it helped me feel human and organised again after my long journey and broken night. I hated turning-to looking like a bag of shit in crumpled clothes.

Manny also looked smart in his fitted shirt, black jeans, and leather shoes. At around six foot, he was an inch or two taller than me. Younger and thinner as well, with a physique that might not be gym-honed but came from putting in the hours with the family business.

He owned a part-share with his half-brothers in two fishing boats based out of Freetown in Sierra Leone, 125 kilometres to the southeast. Plus, he spent time wheeling and dealing around the region, trying to sniff out shares in lucrative import/export deals – with mixed results.

More recently, he'd been kept off the boats by this mining project in Guinea. With his mixed-race heritage and dual British-Sierra Leonean nationality, Manny could move in circles that others perhaps couldn't.

He said it had both pros and cons.

On the plus side, he could adopt either an African or a British persona depending on the situation. His casual but expensive appearance today was a good example: combined with his meticulous English we could pass for executive colleagues just arrived from the UK together. He reckoned I would never recognise him in his fisherman's garb and in full cry with the natural Krio of his homeland.

On the negative side, he said he wasn't fully accepted into either camp. Allowed in by both, but not quite 'one of us' in either.

Over the top of a plate stacked with food, Manny explained that Condé was one of his fishing industry contacts here in Conakry, with his own boat and a similar family business. He assured me Condé had a variety of excellent connections throughout Guinea and could be trusted not to betray our confidence. I nodded and smiled. If Manny trusted him, it should be good enough for me. However, I'd be keeping things on a need-to-know basis. And right now, Condé didn't need to know anything about our plans.

Come to think of it, I needed to get my comms set up and establish exactly how much Manny knew. I trusted him more than I trusted Cal, but I might still have to manage the information flow. I excused myself as they demolished their hearty breakfasts and sought some privacy to try out my new phone.

'Keep an eye on my daysack while I make a call.'

As I left the restaurant with my concentration on the phone, a guy with Slavic features slammed into my right shoulder as he and a thickset companion barged their way in. 'Smotret' yego,' he snarled.

I half turned with the impact. 'Alright mate, fucking hell.'

He stopped and glowered at me from six feet away. His mate also studied me, a wisp of a smile on his face.

My temper flared. 'What? Look where you're going.'

The guy I'd clashed with said something else I didn't understand – sounded like Russian – and the two of them laughed and turned towards the hotplates. I resisted the temptation to retaliate, despite a flash of rage. Great start that would be – getting into a fight at the breakfast table.

The duty manager ducked away in comical fashion as I walked through reception still simmering. I'd deal with him in a minute. Outside the front entrance I peeled off to the right and pressed call on the Nokia. After a hiss and squelch, the UK ringtone sounded. 'Hello?'

'Cal, it's John.'

A crackle and silence.

'John. Good to hear from you. This your number?'

'Yes mate. My UK mobile is u/s for some reason. I'm at the hotel, but they don't have any record of the booking. You've paid for seven days, yes?'

A few seconds of distortion before: '…so sorry about that. They should have the original reservation though.'

'Say again mate. Did you say the room's been paid for?'

'No. There was a problem and the payment wasn't made. Reserved for seven days but not paid.'

My shoulders fell. 'The room's shite anyway and the Internet is crap. I'm having a look at another place soon, so I may well move.'

'What's that? Did you say you're moving?'

'Probably. I met General Ndidi last night. Your contact?'

Cal's voice was suddenly loud in my ear. 'Let's keep anything work-related to secure, mate. Or sat phone if we need voice.'

Touchy about the general then.

'Roger that, mate. I'll be in touch once I've got my comms set up.'

'I've sent another briefing note with some amendments the board wants for the contract. Acknowledge when you've seen it and fire over any questions if there's anything needs clarifying.'

'Okay. Speak later.'

After cutting the call, I glanced around the car park. Spaces had appeared as people left for their daily routines and I noted many of the cars weren't quite as new or immaculate as they'd seemed last night.

A figure caught my attention climbing out of a gleaming white Land Cruiser that had pulled into a space twenty metres away. Baldé. Smart in his pressed barrack dress and black beret and carrying a slung AK-47. 9:55 a.m. – five minutes early. I walked over.

'Le petit déjeuner?' I gestured to him and Demba, the driver. They'd both had late nights and I wanted to make sure they started the day fully charged and fighting fit.

'Non, merci,' Baldé replied.

'Oui, come on, come on. Allez.'

Five years of French at school and I could hardly string a basic sentence together. The perils of a misspent youth.

Despite his reluctance, I persuaded Baldé to accompany me into the hotel. The driver remained with the vehicle, as of course someone should. I nodded with approval. 'We'll bring some food out for you.'

Demba gave me a blank smile in return.

★

After some confusion it became apparent that General Ndidi had done more than arrange for me to view the Hotel Cameyenne. He had secured me a booking 'at a special rate' with his friend the owner and instructed Baldé to ensure I moved hotels. I surrendered to the idea without a fight. It wasn't like the staff at the Novotel had gone out of their way to impress me.

I took great pleasure in telling the manager I was checking out; a moment made even sweeter after he produced a seven-day reservation in my name with a flourish. I dropped my room key onto it with a satisfied smile. 'Next time perhaps.'

The fawning manager of the Hotel Cameyenne introduced himself when we arrived at reception. He gave a full sales pitch as though I might want to buy the hotel, not book a room.

Quality-wise there wasn't much difference to the Novotel and room Wi-Fi wasn't even an advertised feature. However, the business centre was more spacious and workable for my needs – privacy while working being one of them.

The room had a large bed with a decent mattress, hot water on demand, and efficient air conditioning. It ticked most boxes and had a balcony with a sea view. And it wasn't as though I really had an option to throw the general's help back in his face.

Once checked in, I grabbed my daysack – now minus the spare clothes and plus various kit from my hold baggage – and rejoined Manny and Baldé in reception.

'Where to now then?' I asked. 'Do we have a time to meet the president's people?'

'We have a meeting at three,' answered Manny. 'It's not far from here. Fifteen minutes.'

My watch showed 11.20 a.m. 'That gives us enough time for a look around the city so I can get my bearings and change some money. Then back here and I'll check my email before the meeting.'

Conakry was a riot of colour, discarded trash, angry traffic jams, and noise. All steaming under a relentless sun and energy-sapping humidity. The main arteries linking the city together were jammed solid, but the traffic moved more freely on the smaller roads. Demba proved a competent driver and Baldé navigated from the passenger seat to avoid the worst of the hold ups.

Sat in the back, I took the opportunity to catch up with Manny as the sounds and mixed aromas of the city wafted in through the open windows. From habit, mine was wound down less than six inches. Acclimatisation was all very well, but I had been instilled with years of guarding against a grenade landing in my lap. I couldn't help myself, even though there was no recognised threat and a football could have flown in through the other windows.

The road noise, music on the car radio, and shouts from street hawkers offered a shield for a discreet conversation with Manny. I kept my voice low and he followed suit. The loyalty of Baldé and Demba wasn't in doubt – they were General Ndidi's men.

'Do you know who will be at this meeting?' I asked.

'The general manager of Sapro is Édouard Touré. I don't know who else.'

'Have you met him?'

'Once.'

'What's he like?'

'Same as all those others who've grown fat on the president's favour. Arrogant, rude, easily offended, unpredictable.'

'Sounds like a right charmer. What's your take on the state of negotiations? Are we close?'

Manny rubbed his chin before answering. 'Very close if Pinnacle agree to all Sapro's terms. They already produced a draft contract, in French. Have you seen it?'

He gave me a doubtful look as I nodded. He was right – translating it and understanding the subtleties of the original language were two different things.

'Not so close if changes need to be made,' he added.

The clauses of the draft joint venture agreement were standard fare, and I wasn't too concerned about the language differences. However, the bigger picture terms could prove a problem.

The Guinea company – the president's company – wanted a 50-50 split. They'd provide the exploration licenses for the six concessions and Pinnacle Mining would have to plough in all the investment.

I doubted whether Sapro had paid more than a token amount for the concessions, which meant all the capital investment and financial risk for these unproven, virgin sites would be on the investors i.e. Cal's friends at Pinnacle.

Understandably, Pinnacle wanted to either alter the percentage ownership or demand an investment contribution from Sapro. The last three months had seen no movement on the issue, hence our two-man team sent into the lion's den to argue Pinnacle's case face-to-face.

Now we'd arrived, I had a sense of why Cal sent me rather than return himself. According to Manny, Cal's last visit in the spring had concluded without progress after increasingly fractious meetings.

'The last visit, did Cal meet with the same guy, this Édouard?' I asked.

'Yes. By the end they didn't get on very well. I don't think Cal understands when you can negotiate and when you need to stop pushing. He doesn't listen and it caused a big problem. We shouldn't make that same mistake.'

'When we get back to the hotel, I need to pick up some new amendments from London. I'm going to try and strike up a rapport with Édouard before we get into the details. Cal already said we need to get their share down or their investment up. Sounds like that will be hard enough without any more fuel thrown on the fire from London.'

We crossed the causeway onto Tombo island at the head of the peninsula and into the old city. Manny changed into tour guide mode and pointed out the Palace of the People, various ministries, and the French Embassy, before gesturing at a guarded entrance.

'Behind that gate are the presidential offices. Sapro is based from there. Probably one small office. But we're meeting at Édouard's place near your hotel. You recognise this area?'

I checked my bearings and caught site of the top floors of the Novotel. 'I think we must have come through here last night.'

Manny nodded. 'That's right. This time we'll go along by the coast road, then find an exchange so you can change some money.' He gave instructions in French to Baldé.

We passed the Novotel entrance and took the coast road heading anti-clockwise around the perimeter of the four-kilometre-long island. I looked out to sea and noticed land a few miles offshore to the southwest. 'Where's that?' I asked, pointing across Manny and through his open window.

'Those are Îles de Los. Nice beaches for tourists. There's a ferry. If we have time one day, we could go.'

We cruised past a tatty beachcomber-style bar-cum-café with early patrons out on the sun-drenched deck. Colourful, faded signs suggested a welcome atmosphere if not a hipster hangout. Next to it, long wooden fishing skiffs were tied to a pier in front of a rock-filled, muddy shoreline. People lazed in the shade under the palm trees dotted along the road at the back of the beach.

'Maybe we'll leave the sunbathing. I hope the beaches over there are better than this one. If not, the Guinea tourist board must have a magician in charge.' Not that I imagined many tourists travelled this far off the beaten track.

If I had changed much more than $200, it would have needed a wheelbarrow to carry the bundles of scruffy Guinean Francs back to the car. I used a wad of notes to buy coffee and provisions from a French supermarket to bolster the meagre supplies in the hotel room and add to my emergency rations.

After stopping for a drink in a pleasant café downtown, we wound our way through several districts to complete an anti-clockwise, sight-seeing loop of the city: past the airport, through busy neighbourhoods filled with two-storey houses, and along the edges of shanty towns. Seas of corrugated iron roofs topped small dwellings built with foraged materials. Colourfully dressed women fussed around playful street urchins and steaming pots as their dejected menfolk wallowed in the hopeless poverty of one of Africa's poorest countries. Then up to the colonial mansions of the diplomatic neighbourhood that hugged the north side of the peninsula, before swinging southwest to the Hotel Camayenne.

When we reached the hotel at 1:45 p.m., I stopped off in the business centre to pick up the latest emails from London. Their tone suggested a strength of negotiating position that sounded optimistic based on my conversation with Manny.

CHAPTER 15

Édouard Touré stood over six feet tall, wore wire-framed glasses, carried a slight paunch, and had an annoying habit of tilting his head to look down his nose when he spoke. At a guess he was mid-forties, although his bald head might have added a few unearned years. Manny hadn't exaggerated his lesser qualities and he was every bit as much of a prick as I'd imagined.

My diplomatic efforts to counter a natural dislike for the man and foster a spark of mutual respect might have been working, but he came across about as sincere as I felt so it was difficult to tell.

It was already clear that Édouard, and I assumed the president, believed the terms of the contract to be settled. My efforts to probe Édouard's willingness to offer concessions in the negotiations weren't getting far.

Instead, he focused on the administrative and logistical requirements of the JV between Pinnacle and Sapro: branch company or subsidiary registration for Pinnacle in Guinea; selection of a headquarters office; instruct one of the recommended local solicitors; account opening at French bank Société Générale; a field visit to the nearest of the six concessions.

The itinerary he proposed for me did not set aside any time to finalise the contract terms with good old-fashioned, sleeves-rolled-up, eleventh-hour negotiations. He just wanted me to sign the draft already on the table and agree to provide him with a €15,000 monthly salary for the duration of the project. Getting this deal over the line wouldn't be easy.

His large two-storey, brick-built house looked very pleasant from the outside. A well-maintained roof, smart paintwork, immaculate windows, hanging baskets of colourful flowers, and an impressive deck at the rear. We'd come through a side gate and sat in the garden at a wooden table under a sunshade that could double as an umbrella if a rain shower rolled over. Trees and bushes surrounded a lawn so green it looked as though it had been painted. Sprinklers stood idle.

We had already experienced one twenty-minute downpour on the way here, so the leaves dripped, and a moist, earthy smell engulfed the three of us as we traded forced pleasantries. The faint sound of traffic hummed in the distance, if you listened for it.

As I sipped at a long glass of orange juice, I imagined the house was furnished to a standard that General Ndidi's wife would appreciate. A world apart from the meagre lifestyles we'd driven past earlier.

'Can we go back to the contract terms? There are still various areas we need to discuss. Parts of the draft you submitted don't match with the risk appetite of the investors in London.'

Édouard's eyes narrowed. 'I discussed the terms with Mr Simmons when he was here. If you are referring to the fifty per cent equal shares, that is non-negotiable. Just as I told him.'

I interrupted as he took a breath. 'I understand that will be an issue, so let's focus on the costs and capital investment requirements.'

He tried to speak over me, but I steeled my voice.

'The current draft is too open-ended and places all the burden on Pinnacle. We need to insert a backstop that limits the initial agreement to the exploration phase only, plus modify the clause that could be interpreted to give Sapro the right to dictate the scope of the exploration operations.'

I ignored his emphatic head shaking and continued.

'If Pinnacle is funding this entire project, then decisions as to the scope of the exploration phase must be made by the Pinnacle management, in consultation with Sapro of course. These six concessions cover a vast area spread over different parts of the country. The potential liability if the decisions are made by anyone else, including the Ministry of Mining, could be crippling. No investor would agree to your draft as it stands.'

Head tilted back, Édouard looked through his glasses and down his nose at me before turning to Manny on his left and waving a finger in my direction.

'Allons-nous avoir le même problème avec ce gars?'

Something about having a problem.

I answered. 'No, there won't be a problem. We'll find an acceptable solution in the coming days. My job here is to reach agreement with you and to prepare for Pinnacle to operate in Guinea. I'm authorised to begin those preparations immediately, even before we reach final agreement. That's an indication of Pinnacle's commitment to get this project off the ground.'

Édouard took off his glasses and placed them on the table. 'Mr Pierce, Pinnacle Mining PLC is a new company, an investment vehicle for this specific project, am I right?'

'That's right.'

He nodded sadly as though I was a naive fool about to be imbued with great wisdom. 'Sapro Mines has acquired six of the best prospects in Guinea. The iron ore concession is adjacent to Rio Tinto's Simandou project. The gold and diamond concessions already have renowned potential among the alluvial miners. If your company doesn't want to form a joint venture with us, then…c'est la vie.

'But you need to tell me now. If I am wasting my time, then you must say so right now. Your company needs to understand that it only has this chance *because* it's making the investment. Taking the risks, as you put it. Otherwise, we have Russians, Chinese, even the French who we could partner with. If you're serious, then speak to your people in London, speak to Mr Simmons, and get permission to sign this contract.'

I controlled my rising temper and mulled over a couple of possible responses before replying in a measured tone. 'As I said, Pinnacle is committed to the deal. We have funding from Fortis Bank ready to finance the project. But the terms of the contract still need some work.'

Édouard gave a heavy sigh and then rose to his feet. 'I think that's enough for today.' He turned and garbled a stream of French at Manny.

After a stiff goodbye, we returned to the Cameyenne.

★

'I really doubt they're going to move much. He spoke about Russians and Chinese being interested. And he said Pinnacle was only in the deal because we were offering the investment they wanted.'

There was a delay before Cal's distant voice responded, reflecting the thousands of miles it had travelled across the Thuraya satellite network. 'That's bullshit and Édouard knows it. We're in because no one else will agree to pay him a small fortune for doing fuck all. They don't want to get too close to more Russians with their private business. As for the Chinese, not for this deal. Keep pushing John, I know you can get this done.'

'I'll try mate, but I'm not so sure. The board may need to make concessions.'

'You've only been there one day. Only had one meeting. These things take time. Send me a full report about today on secure. When are you meeting with Édouard again?'

'Tomorrow morning at ten.'

'Send me a report when you get back from that and we'll review their position. He may be the general manager, but he's just the messenger. He'll be reporting your meeting today and getting his own instructions. Push on with the logistics and stay wary of the general's men. He'll know everything they see and hear.'

'And the general, where does he fit in?'

'He's close to the big man, so gives us some top cover. But he doesn't directly control many troops. We'll need other generals and unit commanders on side. There's a couple of others we've reached out to, but it's a murky pool over there. Some unstable characters. Leave that to me and concentrate on the contract and the company stuff.'

I brushed a mosquito from my arm. Forgetting to reapply mozzie repellent before I came out into the hotel garden had been an oversight. Fortunately, I didn't tend to attract too many bites and the daily dose of doxycycline countered the malaria threat from any nasties that did get through.

I lifted the sat phone back to my ear and winced as the sweat already smeared on the earpiece squelched loud and unexpected.

We assumed all GSM calls in-country were monitored. One thing authoritarian governments usually excelled at was subjugation of their populations and tapping phone networks could be accomplished with ease through compliant telecoms operators.

Interception of satellite calls was a whole different ball game. It required specialised, expensive, and tightly controlled equipment, together with the necessary expertise. Cal reckoned the Guinea security services had no capability, so we'd agreed to communicate everything project related via satellite phone and double-encrypted email only.

The Thuraya phone needed line of sight to the satellite, and I had considered making the call from my room balcony. However, it was impossible to tell who might be within earshot on other balconies nearby. That had led me to take an ill-advised trek round the hotel grounds as dusk crept in and the insects came out to play.

'One more thing,' Cal said. 'I should have an update about the other business by tomorrow night. I'll send that via secure.'

The other business – the diamonds. I'd almost hoped they'd gone away, but now I had an inkling how difficult it might prove to close the mining deal, perhaps these diamonds would be the better opportunity. When anyone started talking telephone numbers about the dollar value of a deal it was normally a bad sign, but the potential size of the commission on offer with these diamonds couldn't be ignored.

I'd play it careful and see what happened. Once the next update arrived, I'd let Manny know about that side of my trip.

A growl of complaint from my stomach was a reminder it had been over eight hours since breakfast at the Novotel. I closed the aerial on the phone, stowed it in my daysack, and wandered past the pool and into the large thatched-roof bar which overlooked a rocky outcrop into the sea.

There was only one other customer – a casually dressed Westerner sat on a bar stool with a beer in his hand. I acknowledged him from the other side of the bar and dropped my eyes onto a menu before he was encouraged to start a conversation. The picture of steak and chips made my mouth water.

'Sorry, monsieur, no steak today. And no frites, sorry,' said the local barman.

'Fair enough.' I turned the page to another appetising image. 'I'll have the chicken then.'

The barman's smile faltered. 'Sorry, pas de poulet monsieur.'

I changed tack. 'So, what do you recommend?'

His face lit up and he flicked forward a couple of pages. 'Barracuda, monsieur. C'est très bien.'

Barracuda. First time for everything. Much as I wanted to be careful with what I ate and drank to avoid going down with anything, I did have form with fish dishes. To my wife's exasperation, when eating out I had a habit of choosing the most exotic-sounding seafood on the menu at the last minute. In the UK that rarely amounted to anything unusual, but on my travels I'd chanced many dishes that came with health warnings. So far, I hadn't been caught out.

'Okay, barracuda it is. And une bière, s'il vous plaît.'

The flight, the previous night's broken sleep, and the heat and humidity of Africa had taken it out of me, but I needed a beer to relax.

The lights had come on around the bar, swimming pool, and garden, and the gentle rasp of waves breaking on the nearby rocks serenaded me. I could imagine settling in for a session. Tonight though, it would only be the one drink because I needed to write that report for Cal.

'Merci.' The frosted neck of the Heineken bottle had me salivating. I waved away the glass and pointed towards the empty tables on the far side of the rectangular pool.

Once settled at a table, I took a long swig of the chilled beer before reaching into my daysack and pulling out the laptop. With no one else around I began composing the report. I needed to write and encrypt it first before accessing the Internet in the business centre. Once online, I would send it via my Hushmail email account.

Cal had arranged a Virtual Private Network for me to use when accessing the Internet. It provided a layer of anonymity and security on top of our double-encryption method. It had been slow when I'd accessed it earlier that afternoon, but it was workable.

Another security layer hadn't been a success. My first effort to get online via TOR, a secure method of accessing the Internet and deep web, had failed miserably: fifteen minutes twiddling my thumbs followed by an error message. I'd give it another go tonight but there had to be trade-off between security and functionality.

All too quickly the beer was finished but so too, almost, was my report. I looked around to see a smattering of other patrons now occupied the bar and a few had drifted to the tables on the other side of the pool. With more people arriving by the minute, it was time to put my work away. A waiter approached carrying a tray. 'Barracuda, monsieur?'

'Oui, merci. Et une autre bière s'il vous plaît.' One more wouldn't hurt.

The barracuda was fantastic. Juicy flesh, a flash of pepper and spice, and not too many bones. And despite the earlier claim none were available, it came with a side order of French fries.

By the time the waiter whipped away my plate and empty beer bottles, a hubbub of noise and people filled both the bar and the tables by the pool. Time for me to depart, send my report, and retire to bed for a good night's kip.

I saw trouble approaching from the other side of the pool. The two girls showed acres of rich brown skin barely augmented by their short skirts and flimsy tops. They teetered on high heels as they locked me in their sights and homed in.

There are times when I've enjoyed having the craic with working girls; not sleeping with them, but chatting, flirting, taking the piss. But not tonight. I was way too busy and too tired. They loomed over the chairs at my table, poised to strike. When they asked in French if they could sit down, I played dumb. 'Je ne comprends pas le français.'

They both giggled and sat down. That worked a treat then.

Both were pretty with smooth skin, corrupting curves, and doe-like eyes, possibly sisters. And they both looked young – very young. I thought of my eldest daughter, Natalie, and wanted to ask if their parents knew where they were. I needed to knock this on the head asap before they, and anyone else, got the wrong idea.

Two male figures stepped into the light and I looked up. Manny and Condé. Manny glanced from me to the two girls, then shot me a questioning look.

I raised my hands. 'I'm glad you've turned up. These ladies have just sat down, and I think they have the wrong idea. Can you ask them to leave for me?'

Manny hissed angry French at the girls. Their faces fell before they picked up their tiny handbags, hurled a couple of insults, pouted, and tottered off, muttering over their shoulders.

'Take a seat, guys.'

An unsubtle grin passed between them as they settled down.

'Honestly, they'd just sat down after appearing out of nowhere. I tried to tell them I didn't speak French.'

Manny laughed. 'Well, that's almost true.'

The guys had come to check I'd settled in at the hotel. We drank a beer together – another one, but my report was almost finished – and they refused my offer for dinner on the company before leaving an hour later. I headed into the empty business centre once they'd gone.

CHAPTER 16

Re-energised by a comfortable, uninterrupted seven hours sleep, I cracked through sets of press-ups, sit-ups, squats, and lunges before enjoying a high-pressure shower. The hotel gym had proved a mythical beast so far; nice pictures in the brochure but no one could give me directions.

I always travelled with multi-purpose soap to hand-wash my clothes if necessary and took the opportunity to use it on my worn pairs of socks and knicks. There is something cathartic about scrubbing your own clothes clean, occasionally. For my grubby shirts and the trousers now adorned with a greasy barracuda stain, I filled out the form and slipped them into the hotel laundry bag to test their service. Then added the shirt soiled at the airport during my shakedown.

Downstairs, the business centre was quiet as I connected the LAN cable and went online via the VPN. I'd given up on TOR for good after another frustrating attempt to use it before sending my report the previous evening. After reading the latest short message from Cal, I confirmed my plans for the day and powered down. Breakfast time.

As I sat down to eat in the first-floor restaurant, Manny and Condé arrived. 8.50 a.m. – ten minutes early. I gestured for them to join me.

Manny wore smart casual like the previous day, but Condé was noticeably better dressed. Last night's conversation about employment prospects might not have registered.

'He knows we don't have a job for him today?' I asked Manny while filling a croissant with strawberry jam.

Manny stopped attacking his own mountainous plateful to answer as he chewed on a pastry. 'Yes, but he might be useful, so I thought it better for him to come inside and check.'

'He can't come to the meeting with Édouard.'

'That meeting is cancelled,' said Manny, looking down.

'Since when?'

'Édouard called me last night and said the meeting is rescheduled for tomorrow morning. Today we should go to the solicitor about the branch company. And we have an appointment to look at a house this afternoon.'

I fought the urge to swear but couldn't stop the sarcasm. 'Thanks for letting me know what I'm doing today.'

I considered the email traffic with Cal over the last twelve hours where we'd agreed the strategy for the morning's meeting with Édouard.

'Last night? So why didn't you call me?'

He shrugged his shoulders. 'It was late.'

I sighed. 'Just call me next time. I'm keeping London updated with regular progress reports, so I need to know as soon as anything happens or changes.'

A rueful look replaced Manny's smile. 'I understand. Next time I'll call you straight away.'

We ate in silence for a couple of minutes.

'Is the meeting rearranged for tomorrow morning at ten?'

'Yes.'

'Same place, his house?'

'Yes.'

'Okay, good. Let's make the most of today then. Is the solicitor expecting us?'

Manny's smile made a cautious comeback at the edges of his mouth. 'Yes. His office is in the city and we should be there at eleven.'

Baldé and Demba were due to pick us up at 09:30. We might get there early, but better than being late.

'And it's the same bloke you met with Cal last time? Fozzie something.'

'Monsieur Leclair. He's the best in Conakry, the best in La Guinée.' He laughed. 'No one can buy him and even the government is scared of him.'

'Good. And Cal seems happy to trust him.' We'd soon find out if we couldn't.

'What about this house we're seeing? Where is it and what time?'

Manny's smile completed its return. 'In the diplomatic quarter, not far from the hotel. It's a very nice place; the old Vatican Embassy. And it's by the beach.' He grinned. 'I know you like the beach.'

I laughed. 'It'll need to be a better beach than anything I've seen so far. What time did you say?'

'Three.' He hesitated and glanced at Condé. 'Condé knows the owner. I think it would be a good idea…'

I interrupted and finished the sentence '…if he came along.'

I looked at the two eager faces now studying mine. 'Okay.' I held up two fingers to Condé. 'Ici à deux heures et demie.'

They both chuckled.

'Two-thirty, here. That was right wasn't it?'

'Parfait,' said Manny. *Perfect.* He turned to Condé and said something about Mr John and his impressive French and broke into a laugh. Both me and Condé joined in.

★

The former Vatican Embassy nestled in a peaceful spot in the Conakry district of Dixinn, home to various foreign embassies. Five kilometres along the coast northeast of the Cameyenne, the neighbourhood nearest the beach became a small, leafy suburb of walled compounds, empty roads, and striking calm compared to the bustling city streets.

After we returned from our morning excursion to see the solicitor, I'd told Baldé we didn't need him and Demba for the afternoon, but he insisted they had orders to escort us at all times. Not wanting to cause trouble, I agreed. So much for trying to give the guys some time off.

As we waited for the owner outside the peeling metal double gates, I retreated under a tree by the compound wall. Before retrieving my water bottle, I cracked a five-metre check for any nasties hanging off the branches. I hadn't seen any spiders or snakes, but it didn't mean they weren't around.

Ten minutes after we arrived, Condé pulled up in his battered but clean, classic-style, red Mercedes saloon with the property owner in the passenger seat. If he was trying to impress, it was working.

Inside the compound stood a pair of large, white, two-storey buildings surrounded by a gatehouse and several small outbuildings. Each floor of the main house comprised three bedrooms with en-suite bathrooms, two huge reception rooms, and a kitchen. Plus additional storerooms and toilets. I pictured desks, room dividers, conference tables, communications suites, wall-mounted screens, and an assortment of expat and local operations personnel in the cavernous reception rooms.

The tall, latticed communications tower next to the main building was an obvious attraction for our purposes. Signal range promised to be impressive given the right kit. The smaller building also contained three bedrooms with en-suites on the top floor, while the ground floor included two large integral garages alongside a couple of reception rooms and a kitchen.

All in all, there was plenty of room for the headquarters operation I envisaged. Additional hard-standing areas in the grounds, complete with sunshades, could accommodate numerous vehicles.

As I walked down a sloping path lined with saplings and thick bushes leading to the rear of the property, a beach came into view through the foliage and excited shouts peppered the air. I reached a padlocked wrought-iron gate adorned with the same security spikes that ran along the top of the fence line and walls around the entire compound.

The dark, sandy beach stretched fifty metres to the light Atlantic surf. To the right, it was bordered by a rocky headland that protruded into the water. From the left, a football bounced across in front of me.

A young, barefoot lad in a team shirt darted after it and brought it deftly under control before rolling it under his foot to evade a flying tackle from a larger opponent.

'Can we open this and go onto the beach?' I asked

After an initial 'no' – the default answer – a key appeared, and we all stepped gingerly down the crumbling, narrow, five-metre-long concrete slipway that led from the gate onto the beach. The bootneck in me added boat hops and seaborne extraction to the available options menu.

Now I could gauge the size of the beach. A hundred metres to the left, above and behind a group of twenty or more local youths playing football, the unbroken walls of another compound grew out of the rock and jutted into the sea like a small cape. The roofs and aerials of a handful of SUVs could be seen above the walls and there were at least two tall buildings within the compound, although distant enough that they didn't infringe the privacy on this side.

Time to get down to business. 'How much is he asking?'

Manny consulted with Condé, who in turn spoke with the owner.

'Six thousand Euros per month,' Manny said with a whiff of embarrassment. 'But we can get it lower.'

'I should hope so,' I coughed back.

'There's another place we can look at. Condé called the landlord and he's on his way. It's close by.'

I couldn't fault his keenness. Probably working on commission.

The ball rolled close and I took a step forward and chipped it back to the nearest player. My wave to acknowledge his thanks prompted a chorus of yells and beckoning hands from the other players encouraging me to join the game. We would do well to beat this location for a corporate office.

Back in the compound I wandered around making notes and taking photographs. The more I saw, the more I thought it would make an excellent HQ. And who would we need to man the operation? Faces of the lads in Taji and a selection of other capable guys from past jobs sprang to mind. This would be an attractive number if the contract with Sapro could be agreed and signed. A shame there were still considerable hurdles to cross.

The solicitor we'd met that morning was different to how I expected, both in appearance and attitude. Greyer, older, and with a knowledgeable and confident manner – not quite how I pictured a 'Fozzie'.

He perched on his armchair with an owl-like face and a toad-like body; wore a well-tailored, blue, pinstriped three-piece-suit and immaculate brown polished brogues; and worked from a fussy office with a large picture of the Eiffel Tower on the wall like a window overlooking downtown Paris.

His forthright declaration in booming French of the primacy of the law in Guinea – and the ability to take on the government if necessary – were at odds with my understanding of the realities of a dictatorship. He gave examples of previous successes against the state, but I wasn't convinced it amounted to a sensible strategy for anyone seeking to live out a long and happy retirement.

As a former French colony, Guinea used the French legal system along with French-style governance. I'd read that France had never forgiven Guinea for being the first colony to gain independence and there didn't appear to be much love lost between the two countries, but a shared culture runs deep.

Monsieur Fauzi Leclair, Fozzie to his friends only, suggested that rather than incorporate a Pinnacle branch company in Guinea, it might be preferable to set up a Joint Venture company with Sapro to bind ourselves together tighter than a more easily breakable contract.

The six mining concession licenses could be placed into this JV company, and the director appointments and issued shares would provide a clear indication of the relationship between Pinnacle and Sapro.

It would still need a shareholder agreement to address the question of responsibilities for the financial side, but his ideas gave a tangible structure to how this could work.

From a negotiation standpoint it did little more than shift the areas of contention from a document – the existing draft contract – to a corporate structure, but it might provide new impetus to reach an agreement acceptable to both sides.

It would be interesting to hear Cal's reaction when I reported the idea later.

Interesting too would be Édouard's response to our last meeting, when he deigned to show up again. Did he have a real say or were we in fact trying to play hardball with the president himself?

The 73-year-old president had seized power in a military coup in 1984. Since then, he had survived several coup and assassination attempts and kept tight control of the country through a series of disputed elections and an iron fist. An archetypal strongman leader, he'd vowed to serve until the next election in 2010 but rumours of serious illness bubbled away.

Guinea itself was a country blessed, or some said cursed, with rich deposits of natural resources, including gold, diamonds, copper, iron-ore, and aluminium. An indication of the problems faced to harness this potential wealth could be seen in the Transparency International corruption index: Guinea rated as the second most corrupt country in the world after Haiti.

Foreign investors needed to be either brave, stupid, or well-connected to risk money here. Maybe all three. I hadn't yet figured out which applied to Pinnacle.

It also rated as one of the poorest countries in Africa, dogged by high unemployment, crippling poverty, a stagnant economy, and the regime's heavy touch.

Over the last two years Guinea had been rocked by riots, general strikes, and widespread unrest, all of which had been savagely suppressed by the security forces.

International agencies reported that South American drug cartels had a firm grip in the country, having expanded from its narco-state neighbour, Guinea Bissau. The collusion of Guinean naval, coastguard, and other security forces in smuggling drugs from South America to Europe via the Sahel land routes was strongly suspected by foreign observers.

But where there is chaos, there is opportunity. If Guinea was a beach paradise under the West African sun, then Cal and his friends at Pinnacle wouldn't stand a chance of winning the kind of extensive deal currently on the table, and I wouldn't be there earning £500 per day. The key was to make sure we could navigate the chaos. So far, I hadn't seen much to worry me, which was a concern in itself. The dark forces were out there, and I didn't know where. I needed to tread carefully.

'He's here.' The shout from Manny pierced my thoughts and I made my way to the front gate through the first heavy drops of rain.

'Just in the nick of time.' I waited for the owner of the old embassy to lock the gate behind him, then shook his hand. 'Merci beaucoup. Au revoir.'

He told me I was welcome and shot me an odd look as he clambered into Condé's car.

'He's coming with us,' said Manny.

Our two vehicles set off behind an old banger driven by the owner of the next residence on the expanding list. All his money must have gone into his land assets. My posse had grown to eight including the new addition and his sidekick. Any more property viewings after the next one and at this rate we'd need to hire a bus.

Less than ten minutes later we stopped outside a pair of grey gates engraved with a large decorative logo. Like the Vatican Embassy, the property within had plenty of room spread through two buildings. However, it didn't have access to a sandy beach and covered a smaller area with less open space and outbuildings. Worse, the red glass slathered across the balconies and rooftops of all the buildings gave it a gaudy look that reminded me of Afghan warlord villas in Kabul. I had to smile at the first owner taking a good mooch around. Checking out the competition perhaps.

'How much is this guy asking?' I called out to Manny.

After a quick exchange with the scrawny owner and his sidekick, he replied, 'He doesn't know. He's not the owner.'

An unexpected answer. 'Who is he then? And where is the owner?'

'The owner's French. This guy looks after the place for him. The caretaker. He'll ring him and let us know the price.'

We trooped out back to our cars. This time we had a round of goodbyes before Demba took us back to the Cameyenne. Just before we left, I learned the monthly rental would be €5,000. For one of the poorest countries in the world, these landlords tossed out some big numbers.

CHAPTER 17

Maybe I turned up for dinner too early, because the only dish on the menu again that evening was spicy Barracuda. No fries this time, so I risked a side salad. After eating at one of the tables inside the circular bar-cum-restaurant, I cut away to the business centre before the rush and before any of the scantily clad 'night fighters' could intercept me.

The business centre was packed, but I snurgled into a corner that provided a shield from any prying eyes on my laptop screen. Skype indicated a recent missed chat message from Claire. Guinea operated on Greenwich Mean Time or UTC as it was now known. It meant Claire was one hour ahead of me in the UK on British Summer Time – 7.15pm.

Claire: Are you there?? Haven't spoken for ages x

Claire: :(

John: Just logged on x

Claire: Video? The girls would love to see you xxx

John: No privacy here right now. Maybe later. How are you all?

Claire: :(((we're all fine. Missing you x

Claire: Looking forward to the holiday. We're still going? Please x

John: Getting a lot done, so should be back in time. Looking forward to it. You keeping an eye on last minute deals?

Claire: oh yes! Natalie's college work should be fine. She doesn't seem to go much anyway.

John: By the end of this week I should be able to let you know about

dates. Need to finalise a contract, but home by end next week I
reckon x

Claire: :) ;) How is it there?

John: Hot and humid. Poor. Place is a shithole even compared to
Baghdad. Next job in the Bahamas maybe.

Claire: Well take care. Tried to message you but it didn't go through.

John: I'll send you my local number. Need to write a report, but I'll
text you if I'm online when it's quieter later xx

Claire: Love you xxx

John: xxx

I checked out my fellow scribes as I rolled my shoulders, stretched the
muscles in my back, and rotated my head to try and undo a niggle in
my neck. It hadn't felt quite right since I'd woken in an uncomfortable
position on the flight. Snippets of French and Russian drifted around
the room as the mainly expat patrons fought to sign off from work
before dinner.

At a guess, I would have placed nearly everyone in the room as an
engineer; one suited local and two furtive Asians being amongst the
exceptions. And me of course.

No one showed any interest in me, not even the foxy blonde
laughing with her deeply tanned male colleague, despite us exchanging
passing smiles a couple of times since I'd checked in. South African by
the sound of it.

The latest message from Cal showed as decrypted and drew my
attention back to work. And talk about sensitive topics. I shook my
head while responding in bold underneath his points. I rounded off
with details of the meeting with Fozzie and the HQ villa options.

From: JP
To: CS

Subject: Re: Cancelled Meeting

> 1. Any explanation yet for the cancelled meeting? Is tomorrow's
> meeting definitely going ahead? Does MI have a view on what this
> might mean?

No explanation yet. Meeting tomorrow is on as far as I know.

> 2. You need to discreetly establish the strength of our legal position in
> the event the Big Man dies/is incapacitated or removed from power.
> Rumours of serious illness are growing. Aim to establish any truth
> to them.

Rgr – understood. Will need to be VERY careful about this. Any talk about the president or his family is whispers only. FYI have heard rumour his eldest son is heavily involved with drug smuggling

> 3. We have received a report that the recently appointed Prime
> Minister does not support our project. Any indications regarding the
> veracity of this report would be valuable.

Will probe Edouard about this.

> 4. Secondary objective update to follow this evening.

Rgr – Will check secure at 21:45 Local. Business Centre shuts at 22:00.

PMC Corporate Structure in Guinea

Met with solicitor Fozzie today to discuss the above. He suggested rather than incorporate a branch co, instead to incorporate a JV company with Sapro to lock in relationship. Issues regarding financing responsibilities & investment to be addressed by way of shareholder agreement. Based on the discussion with Fozzie, I recommend we explore this option. If we present a new structure, we can also present our version of the shareholder agreement. Set the agenda.

Comments? Should I mention in tomorrow's meeting or wait until we have draft docs prepared and ambush them?

If nothing heard, I'll keep quiet for now.

Potential Conakry HQ Locations

See attached reports and photographs detailing two properties in the Dixinn district visited today.

You'll see the prices are high, but MI is confident we can reduce both by €1,000. My preference of the two is the old Vatican Embassy. Reasons given in the summary.

Rgds,

JP

Cal would know that asking after the president's health and investigating the prime minister's views was a recipe for trouble. Easy requests to make from distant shores. Christ knew what the jails in this place were like and I had no intention of finding out. The secondary objective had to refer to the diamonds – a deal that might prove more straightforward. *Bring it on.*

I left the business centre to the die-hard corporate slaves and continued to work upstairs in my room after another refreshing shower. Free from the distractions of email and Internet, it provided an opportunity for a careful reread of the project paperwork and background research.

I had no idea what Édouard might throw at me tomorrow and wanted to ensure a good handle on the political and ethnic factors at play in the country and in the leadership circles. Start asking too many of the wrong questions to the wrong people and who knew what the consequences might be.

Most of the information originated from open sources and the rest from the briefing notes Cal had provided. As to the provenance of Cal's information – unspecified. The assertion that Pinnacle was ultimately negotiating a partnership with the president for these concessions had no basis in any of the documents I had received. That made sense – no one would want an audit trail like that – but it was also an assertion I couldn't rely on 100%.

And what if we weren't with the president? Who were we negotiating with?

I could have kept going around in circles but in truth I didn't have all the facts. Better to concentrate on the objectives as directed by Cal and try not to overthink it. However, forgetting Cal and London for a moment, I was the guy exposed on the ground if this went south, so it would behoove me to play things extra careful from here on in.

At 21:40 I received a text message from Cal that simply said *MAIL*. I returned to the now empty business centre, logged on, and retrieved the latest encrypted message.

From: CS
To: JP

Subject: Strategy 1

1. Make no mention of JV structure plan to E. We're working a draft here, but useful if you obtain copies of all the incorporation documents, statutes, articles, and shareholder agreements as recommended by Fozzie. Take photographs of everything and encrypt to send secure by these means. I'll supply revised drafts with our terms included within 24-48 hours. Meanwhile, focus on the admin and logistics. When are you going out to the Copper concession near Forecariah?
2. Continue with previous instructions regarding president's health and PM position.
3. Secondary objective – A representative from the seller will meet with you tomorrow evening at your hotel restaurant. Simply a 'getting to know you' meet and press the flesh. No direct business discussion. No mention of the stones. Timings TBC – will advise tomorrow PM.

Rgds,
CS

My reply:

From: JP
To: CS

Subject: Re: Strategy 1

All points acknowledged.

JP

By the time the manager closed the business centre at 22:05, there'd been no sign of Claire on Skype. I shut down the laptop and went to bed a little deflated.

CHAPTER 18

THE FOLLOWING DAY

Édouard placed an envelope on the table. 'This is authorisation to travel to Forécariah with your military escort. Two cars. For tomorrow.'

A look inside revealed a sheet of headed paper covered in ink stamps and expansive signatures.

Édouard spoke in French to Manny. Something about a second vehicle for the 100-kilometre road trip the next day. Manny nodded as he responded.

The morning's meeting had been a cagey affair. Neither of us referred to the contractual issues. After a sanitised progress report of my meeting with the solicitor and the viewings of the two properties, the conversation lapsed while we finished our drinks in his garden.

I downed the last of my orange juice, wiped a stray piece of pulp from my lip, and launched my opening gambit. 'As I explained when we first met, my role with Pinnacle is focused on due diligence and risk management.'

After a delay, Édouard acknowledged my comment with an irritated, 'Oui. Yes.'

I chose my words carefully. 'This deal. Between Pinnacle and Sapro. How will it be affected if the president doesn't stand for re-election in 2010.'

His surprise was evident. 'It will have no effect. Why do you think…? What happens at the palace is politics. It is not our concern.'

'So, if anything was to happen…' I paused to consider the right phrasing. 'My understanding is that Sapro operates from the presidential offices. Therefore, my concern is that if anything were to interrupt… that if there was a change of president, we might face issues.'

Édouard's initial look of shock gave way to one of suspicion. Fuck it, now it was out there I might as well keep digging.

'If the president is involved, and he should be – these concessions will be of strategic importance to the country once developed – then I need to know if our deal is safe. Whatever happens.' I glanced at Manny. His wide eyes and paler shade suggested I'd gone too far, but it was done now.

'Non, le president n'a aucune implication. Je suis le directeur de l'enterprise.' His voice raised a notch or two and he stood up. 'Qui t'a dit ca?'

My brain was translating his speech in slow time and I lost track. It must have showed.

'Who told you this?' He then fired an angry stream of rapid French at Manny.

I stood and held both my hands in a surrender gesture. He hadn't stopped gobbing off to Manny, so I spoke over the top of him. 'Nobody's told me anything. It's my job to look at all scenarios. All the what-ifs.'

He stopped talking and glared at me.

'It's my job at Pinnacle to look at these issues. Understand and plan for all eventualities. I do the same in every country. Like in Iraq where I've just come from.'

He remained standing, but his arms dropped and he relaxed into a less hostile stance. The glare remained.

'I'm asking you because I trust you. Because we are partners and because you are the general manager at Sapro. The government must have an interest, but I don't care. Pinnacle doesn't care. It's your country and we just want to make sure we understand how best to operate here. With your help. As partners.'

Whether he could see straight through my arse-kissing attempt to retrieve the situation or not, he seemed to lap it up. His face relaxed and he motioned for me to take my seat before he straightened his tie, shot his cuffs, and sat down. It was thirty degrees plus and humid as hell – I was roasting in shirt sleeves.

He laced his fingers together on the table and spoke deliberately. 'These matters are not for companies. Not for foreigners. Talk of these things can be…' he searched for the word '…mal interprété.' He looked at Manny who had yet to recover from my diplomatic faux pas.

Manny looked between us. 'Err…mal interprété – misconstrued.'

'Yes, misconstrued,' continued Édouard. The thin smile on his face had no warmth. 'Please be careful, Mr Pierce.'

It probably wasn't a good time to follow up with a question about the prime minister.

When we got back to the car, Manny was flapping. As soon as the doors of the Land Cruiser had shut, he rounded on me.

'John, you can't say things like that. You know this country's history.' He glanced towards Baldé and Demba up front and lowered his voice. 'If you talk like that to people…' He threw his hands up. 'Anything could happen.'

'Yeah, I know it's sensitive, but London wanted to know the answers. Better to be straight up and ask Édouard than sneak around the place and risk really getting into trouble.'

'You should have told me.' said Manny.

'So, you know the answers then?' I asked.

He sank back into his seat and shook his head. 'No, but I would have told you not to ask the question.'

'Well, it's done now. And I don't think it's caused any harm.' I pulled myself forward and changed the subject. 'Baldé, two cars for tomorrow. To go to Forécariah.'

Baldé asked Manny what I wanted to know. After a three-way discussion about the arrangements to visit the concession the next day and a phone call to his boss, Baldé said, 'Oui monsiuer, le deuxième véhicule a été arrangé par le général.' The cars were sorted.

Along with skimpy arrangements for an 8.00 p.m. meeting about diamonds, courtesy of Cal, that was tomorrow arranged. Now we needed to crash another appointment to see Fozzie and instruct him to prepare the draft incorporation and contract paperwork.

125

CHAPTER 19

Only Manny joined me for an early breakfast the next morning.

'Where's Condé today?'

'You said we didn't need him.'

'No, we don't. I just wondered where he'd got to. Parking the car?'

Manny shook his head. 'No. I came by taxi. Condé is on the fishing boat since early morning, working with his brothers. He won't be here again for two days. That's alright isn't it? You don't need him?'

'No, that's fine.'

Today we'd be driving east to the copper concession with Baldé, Demba, and the extra vehicle. And because Cal had arranged for the diamond guy to meet me here at the Cameyenne later, I wouldn't need to sneak off anywhere in Condé's car to avoid compromising our extra business activity to all and sundry. I decided not to mention tonight's meeting to Manny for now. Might as well see who turned up and what they said first.

'But when you hear from him again, tell him to come along the first morning he's back. Just in case.'

Manny nodded and said something lost in an eruption of pastry flakes from his mouth.

I hadn't brought much field kit with me but what I had was packed into my daysack and waterproofed. I even had my lucky eyeball in the inside flap, just in case.

★

The two soldiers in the extra vehicle weren't a patch on Baldé and Demba: both scruffy, dirty, and with poor attitudes. Plus, the nearest AK shone with copious orange rust. Maybe I'd been spoilt, but there was no way I could have put up with the sneering, lackadaisical tosser commanding the new car for more than five minutes. Good job we weren't sat together or I'd have kicked off.

Our vehicle led the way as we harassed a path through the heavy traffic. Demba's liberal use of the horn garnered attention. And Baldé, standing tall on the running board and wedged in the half open door, ordered everyone in the vicinity to make way. With his black beret, dark glasses, and slung AK on his back, he looked the part. Not the lowest profile move, but it was effective. Demba cut through the city snarl with skill and one or two 'brave' manoeuvres.

Both Baldé and Demba had loosened up since we'd first met. I think they enjoyed our relaxed atmosphere and probably understood quite a lot as Manny and I chatted about all sorts of random shit: London, women, football, and Sierra Leone were our regular topics. We kept work talk away from the car as much as possible. The guys might have chilled out, but they were still the general's men.

Once we left the city behind, the roads were empty. The surfaces weren't in the greatest condition although still better than I'd expected. The humidity and daily monsoon-style rain would give the best-laid highway a run for its money.

The weather was sweltering but with the windows down and warm air blasting through the vehicle a grin spread across my face. This was what I loved – getting out on the ground and seeing a bit of the world. And I'd dispensed with the six-inch window gap routine. Time to loosen up a bit myself; this wasn't Iraq.

As we shook off the urban sprawl and congestion of Conakry, thick forest and lush vegetation provided a glimpse of natural Africa. Vivid greens and browns and splashes of colour replaced the uninspiring drabness of the city.

Twenty-five kilometres and ninety minutes after setting out, we turned southeast at the town of Coyah and began to pick up speed.

The hills and high ground on our left gradually dropped further into the distance as we approached the town of Mafarenya a further twenty kilometres down the road.

I encouraged Baldé to keep going rather than stop for a break at one of the roadside cafés. Once through the town, the forest and countryside became more prominent than the intermittent settlements and small pineapple and mango plantations.

Shortly after driving through a small village where smiling and waving barefoot kids ran alongside the cars, a huge vicious-looking boar with curled tusks shot across the road in front of us; the first large animal I'd seen in the country.

Guinea had diverse wildlife but if I hoped to tick off encounters with the big five this was the wrong country. My research of what might lurk in the undergrowth had indicated a chance of seeing the African Forest buffalo, a relative of the big five's Cape buffalo, but the odds of spotting a West African lion or an African forest elephant were worse than those of winning the lottery.

The atmosphere in the car brightened when I announced we could stop for a break once we reached the town of Forécariah, capital of the prefecture of the same name. From there it would be another twenty kilometres along minor roads and tracks to the south-west corner of the fifteen-square-kilometre concession.

I aimed to reach it by 12:30, spend an hour or more getting a feel for the place, then return to Conakry. That meant we should make it back by six, well in time for me to greet the diamond seller at the hotel at eight. Unless we hit major problems, it ought to provide enough leeway for any delays.

An hour at the site should be enough. I didn't expect any earth-shattering revelations because the concession was virgin exploration territory. With no mining activity underway, the infrastructure and terrain should be similar to what we were seeing around us.

I made notes as we drove and took position data with the GPS. Details of the road condition, traffic levels, towns, prominent landmarks, rivers, security checkpoints, medical clinics, and any areas of potential concern: tactical, flood risk, traffic bottlenecks, and similar. All useful information to help plan the logistical aspects of future operations.

The other concessions were much further afield and would require local support hubs – or forward operating bases if I wanted to get all military about it. The time this journey took over decent roads would be a basic guide to work with. Although up-country I expected the road conditions to be far worse, especially during the rainy season.

Outside a small village as we neared Forécariah, a group of armed soldiers lounged in chairs at a checkpoint. They made no effort to stop either vehicle, but their aggressive stares followed us as we passed.

'Manny, who are those guys, locals?'

Manny spoke to Baldé in French and then answered. 'He says they are a different unit, but we have the authority from Conakry, so there won't be any problem.'

'Any problem like what? He's the general's man. Surely, we shouldn't have any issues moving around even without a piece of paper.'

Manny and Baldé had a further exchange that I couldn't follow, before Manny lowered his voice and said, 'He won't say too much, but I think there's rivalry between some of the generals. Big rivalry. The Beret Rouge are the presidential guard. No one fights with them. But those guys' – he waved his hand in the direction of the checkpoint now behind us – 'they were regular army.'

He opened his mouth again as though to speak but closed it without saying anything. Then he smiled and said, 'It can be the same everywhere, I think. I remember in Freetown in 2000, the British parachutists telling me bad things about your Royal Marines.'

'A bit of banter is one thing, mate. Dishing out the evils and causing issues on the road would be something else. Should we be looking at having Beret Rouge with us in the future? Even though they have red berets like the paras.'

His smile cracked wider. 'You have green beret, yes.'

'Green commando beret, mate,' I said with mock seriousness.

Baldé turned, pointed at me, and asked, 'Es-tu un commando?'

Even I understood that one. 'Oui, je suis un commando. Well, not anymore.' I turned to Manny. 'Tell him I was a commando but not anymore. I don't want the general stringing me up as a spy.'

Manny cringed. 'Careful the words you use. He understands more than we think.' He then explained to Baldé that I was no longer a soldier and my work in Guinea involved mining.

A minute later Manny said, 'If the contract is signed, then maybe they will give us some Beret Rouge. But I like these guys.' He pointed at Baldé and Demba.

'Yeah, so do I. We'll try and keep them with us if we can.'

★

The two dickheads in the other vehicle moaned and pouted when I chivvied everyone to get going after a sandwich at the side of the road in Forécariah town.

Baldé had stopped us outside a sit-down restaurant, so I wasn't sure what kind of beano this crowd thought we were on. And you'd have thought the take-out sandwiches I bought were filled with broken glass from the way they all reacted when I handed them out.

Now I was losing my rag.

'Tell them to get in that fucking car and start driving,' I said to Manny.

His face scrunched in clear disapproval.

'What? What is it? Tell me.'

Manny considered his words. 'These people are more relaxed. This weather, the attitude – it's just more relaxed. Not like the UK.'

I sighed and shook my head. 'Okay. Can you tell them we need to get a move on otherwise they'll be no time for a break on the way back.'

I pointed at my watch. 'The clock's ticking.'

Finally, we set off again. The guys frustrated at the short stop, and me frustrated at the guys. We'd crossed a dilapidated 200-metre-long bridge over the river to enter Forécariah. Now we drove northeast following the river as it snaked towards its origins somewhere beyond the escarpments looming in the distance. The jungle forest became claustrophobic in places as we navigated the rough tracks winding towards the concession area through dense foliage.

Despite several requests over preceding days, my only maps were various scales of Google Earth printouts to accompany my route card. At 12:45 I checked our coordinates again on my GPS.

'Okay gents, we're here. This is it.'

A spur of heavily forested higher ground ran north to south approximately four kilometres to the east. I directed Baldé towards it along an even rougher track than the one we'd been bumping along.

Two jarring thumps had me worried for the vehicle, but we reached the base of the spur after fifteen minutes and I signalled to stop. Unfortunately, the lack of time meant we couldn't reach the higher ground to our north and east. My map showed it ten kilometres away in each direction.

'Let's take a fifteen-minute break.'

Once out of the car, I stretched my back and rolled my shoulders, pleased my neck had stopped hurting at last. We'd halted in a secluded clearing a good kilometre after passing a hamlet of straw houses.

The few locals we'd seen since leaving Forécariah had regarded us with sullen expressions. Perhaps bitter experience had taught them to beware the portent of vehicles carrying armed soldiers. And if Pinnacle found economically reliable reserves of copper here, then anyone who lived in the vicinity would have their lives turned upside down. That would be a long way down the line, but it served as a reminder that community relations needed to feature in any operational planning.

The opportunity to get some exercise was too good to miss. A swig of water, then I corralled the team and set off yomping up the few hundred metres of rocky slope to the top of the spur. I caught the look between Manny and Baldé and their wistful glances back at the two apathetic newcomers laid on their backs in the grass in a rough approximation of vehicle sentries.

'You wouldn't want to be lazing around like those idiots. After all that time stuck in the car, it's good to get your legs moving and your blood pumping. Look, Demba's loving it.'

While I slowed to talk, Demba had gone past at an energetic pace that didn't meet with universal approval. By the time we looked down at our lifeless vehicles from the top edge of the spur ten minutes later, all four of us were sweating freely in the sticky afternoon sunshine. As I handed out water from my daysack, Manny and Baldé's scowls had been replaced by smiles of satisfaction to match Demba's.

Occasional dwellings poked through and around the distant trees and brush. Nothing moved. No cars, people, or animals. The only other sign of life in the still afternoon was the growing throng of flying insects, attracted to the four sweaty blokes who had disturbed the calm.

I brushed at the nearest beasties invading my personal space. 'Alright, let's get back. Watch your footing on the way down.'

CHAPTER 20

A closer look at the rickety bridge west of Forécariah as we trundled across the river revealed it was in worse shape than my earlier assessment. My Google Earth map showed a likely alternative fifteen kilometres to the north that would entail two river crossings: one over a bridge and the other by fording a second tributary.

Neither Baldé or Manny knew if the fording point could be used all year round or by what types of vehicles. I scribbled a note to check later and to include the northern crossings on the next recce. As an afterthought, I added a note to research Bailey bridges or whatever the correct name for a temporary crossing might be these days. Perhaps it could feature as part of a community relations strategy if any were needed.

With the time approaching 15:00, our two-vehicle convoy passed an overladen car, with what appeared to be the contents of an entire household tied precariously on the roof. Demba stepped on the gas and the warm airflow riffled through the car as we accelerated on the open road. The GPS showed a waypoint I'd marked *CP* coming up in less than a kilometre. Checkpoint. The rival military guys with the attitude.

'Checkpoint ahead.' I had to raise my voice to be heard over the wind noise.

Baldé quarter-turned his head my way and flapped his left hand in acknowledgement. Manny's eyelids drifted lower.

'Keeping you up, mate?'

His bloodshot eyes opened and struggled to focus. 'No, no. I'm awake.'

'If that phys has done you in, then you need to join me in the gym – if I ever find it. Remind me we need to search the building for it when we get to the hotel.'

'Point de contrôle,' said Baldé. Then he added 'Checkpoint' in accented English.

Three soldiers stood next to a flimsy shelter at the side of the road 250 metres ahead. As we drew closer and slowed, one of them stepped into the road and held up a hand. A single-storey shack was visible, nestled amongst trees and bushes fifty metres along a dirt track on the right. It had been hidden when we'd driven through from the opposite direction in the morning.

We rolled to a halt two metres in front of the soldier with his hand up. His AK-47 hung limply from his shoulder on a length of scrawny twine. His two oppos ambled to the right-hand side of the car. One to the front window and one to the rear. Baldé wore a crisp camouflage uniform. These guys were kitted out in olive drab which matched their demeanour and expressions.

As one soldier spoke to Baldé, the other leaned in through Manny's window, his grubby, rust-coated barrel waving in my direction.

'Fucking hell. Tell him to watch his muzzle.'

I leaned back to avoid the business end of the rifle and craned my head to see if the safety catch was applied. His grinning mug and fragrant torso were in the way.

'Get the weapon out of the car you idiot.' I pushed the barrel to keep it aimed away from my face.

The soldier's grin turned to a snarl and he spat something in French, literally. A drop of spittle landed on my cheek. Manny had caught most of the spray and put his hands on the man's left arm and shoulder as they traded angry French. Baldé and the other soldier joined in the escalating hubbub. I had difficulty enough following one person speaking slow French.

The angry face of our new friend jerked back out of the window. The third soldier had pulled him away and now followed up with a controlled slice of fast, aggressive French, aided by a finger jabbed into our spitting friend's chest.

While they caught up, Manny's hands fell open. 'What are you doing?'

'His barrel was in my face. I couldn't see if his safety catch was on and whether his finger was on the trigger.'

'His safety catch. It's on.'

'I can see that now.'

'And it won't be loaded to fire. It never is.'

'That's a big assumption to make. And not by this call sign, mate.'

The third soldier stooped and looked in through Manny's window. He barked an order and Demba turned off the ignition. The three soldiers took a step away from the car. The tallest, the order-giver, pulled a whistle from his top pocket and two shrill blasts rang out.

'I don't like the look of this,' I said to Manny. The three men all held their AK-47s loosely pointed in our direction.

'It will be fine. Just don't upset them again.'

Our second vehicle had closed right up to our rear bumper, the two slovenly new recruits showing little interest in the unfolding situation.

Baldé had an AK-47 by his side, wedged against the seat and central console. A Chinese model that I examined during the first day together, it had one magazine of fifteen rounds loaded and not made ready. He'd clearly made an effort to clean it to a high standard after I'd been less than complimentary following my previous scrutiny. Demba had a Makarov handgun because his AK was allegedly being fixed. He sounded unconvinced he'd ever see it again. The Makarov had one magazine with eight rounds. Those two weapons comprised all the firepower at our disposal.

I pulled my folding Ka–Bar knife out of its pouch on my belt and opened the black four-and-a-half-inch blade.

Manny's eyes dropped to the knife and widened. He was awake now.

'Just in case, mate.'

He shook his head. 'No.'

'Just in case. If this blows up, then follow my lead and listen in.'

Manny had been through plenty of shit in Sierra Leone back in the day. He might not want to believe it, but we needed to be ready for anything.

As he slouched into his seat, there was movement on the track behind the three soldiers. A burly figure wearing a beret and shades fastened the top buttons of his shirt as he strode in our direction, a holster bouncing on his hip. A soldier carrying an AK-47 followed at his shoulder.

As the pair approached, the officer wearing the beret ordered one of the three men near us to a position behind our two stationary vehicles, indicated by his extended arm and pointed finger. Our friend with the wayward muzzle discipline trotted away in response.

The detachment commander walked to our window, glanced in and fixed me with a blank stare, then moved to Baldé's window. The two yellow bars on each shoulder denoted him a lieutenant.

'Caporal, qui êtes-vous et que faites-vous sur cette route aujourd'hui?' *Corporal, who are you and what are you doing on this road today?*

'Lieutenant, j'escorte ce Britannique dans le cadre d'un projet soutenu par le gouvernement. J'ai des papiers d'autorisation ici.' Something about *escorting a British man in a project for the government with authorisation papers.*

Baldé began to pull the paperwork out of the clear plastic binder insert I'd given him. The officer didn't wait for them to be handed over. 'Viens avec moi.' *Come with me.*

The old car trying to impersonate a removals van pottered past with a puff of exhaust fumes that stung my eyes and tasted vile. Two much faster cars followed behind it and both pulled out to overtake on the blind bend up ahead. Confirmation that road traffic accidents promised to be the biggest risk here, as on most projects.

Baldé had stepped out of the car and left his weapon in situ. He ducked his head towards Manny. 'Ca va. Cinq minutes.' *It's okay. Five minutes.*

'What's going on?' I murmured to Manny. 'Is this normal do you think?'

Manny shrugged his shoulders. 'I suppose so. Just checking the paperwork.'

The lieutenant led Baldé up the track towards the shack with his accompanying soldier slotted in behind them. The two other troops in my eyeline hadn't moved and remained five metres away holding their rifles a little aggressively for my liking.

What-ifs began to run through my head.

'Demba, est-ce normal?' Spoken like a native.

Like Manny, he also shrugged his shoulders. 'Parfois.' *Sometimes.*

I leaned sideways to gain an angle to see into Demba's mirror, saw no traffic approaching, and opened my door.

'Where are you going?' asked Manny.

'Stretch my legs and get out of this baking tin.'

'Don't…'

I cut him off. 'Don't worry. I'll leave the knife there.' I moved the open Ka-Bar to the floor and shut the door after stepping out. Without the self-generated airflow, it had quickly grown stuffy in the car. Outside, the languid afternoon hardly counted as refreshing either.

As I walked around the rear of the Land Cruiser, I nodded at our two escorts in the second vehicle. Its engine ticked over and a trebly wail of African music leaked out of the open windows. Neither responded or altered the default mask of boredom and mild annoyance they had both displayed all day.

Manny opened the door as I arrived at his side of the car. A harsh, rising voice behind me said, 'Remonter dans la voiture.' I turned to see the taller soldier marching towards us. Something about *in the car.*

'I'm not going anywhere. Just stretching my legs.'

Manny stepped beside me. 'Nous restons ici.' *We're staying here.*

The soldier reached out and gripped my right arm with his left. His other arm holding the AK-47 on its improvised sling against his right side. As his fingers dug into my bicep and a flash of pain erupted, I ripped my arm away.

'What the fuck are you doing?' I jutted my chin towards him and squared my shoulders.

'John.' Manny then launched into quickfire French. 'Ce gar anglaise est important. Il veut seulement marcher.' *English, important,* and some other stuff I didn't understand.

The soldier bared his teeth and shouted at close quarters into my face. 'Remonter dans la voiture maintenant.' *Get back in the car now* – at a guess.

I turned away from his rancid breath. 'Okay, okay. Fucking hell.'

The other soldier had joined my new best friend and gave a stab at a menacing glare as I stepped away. Twat.

We'd need to get some special status ID and heavy escorts to stop this shit from happening all over the country. And this was near the capital. I hated to think what might go on deep in the interior.

A gunshot rang out loud and clear from close by, and an unseen bird squawked a response. All other noise evaporated as the shot hung in the air as though maintained by a musician's effects pedal. It had come from the direction of the shack. Baldé had been unarmed.

'What the fuck?' I glanced at Manny, then at the angry soldier.

He began to lift his AK with his right hand and his eyes dropped towards it as his left hand reached across.

I launched at him from a standing start and smashed a right hook into his cheek before the momentum crashed me into his body, knocking him over with me landing on top.

As we landed, the AK barrel caught me hard in the solar plexus. I sucked in a breath and brought my elbow down hard into his face. I grabbed his weapon by the barrel and yanked it, snapping the flimsy sling.

Shouted French registered and had to be ignored.

I pushed back up into a standing position and used the momentum to swing the rifle by the barrel and smash the stock into the face of Mr Menacing Glare. Teeth, blood, and bits of sunglasses exploded as it connected, and he went down like a sack of shit. That shut him up.

My eyes swept left and right. No other targets. I adjusted the AK in my hands, flicked off the safety catch and pulled on the cocking handle. It hardly moved. Stoppage. These wankers were fucking useless.

I flipped the weapon round again, took two steps to my left and prepared to bring the butt down on the head of my first victim as he tried to haul himself up. 'I don't fucking think so, mate.'

His good eye met mine. He collapsed to the floor and rolled onto his back, open hands up by his shoulders. Blood, snot, and tears decorated his damaged face. 'Non, non. Pitié, pitié.'

I hesitated.

'No, John. No.' Manny held his hands out wide.

'Take this. Stoppage. Clear it.' I thrust the weapon at Manny and ripped open the front passenger door of the Land Cruiser. 'Demba, engine on.' I simulated turning the key as I grabbed Baldé's Kalashnikov from next to the seat.

I hammered the safety catch down two notches to single shot semi-automatic and yanked the cocking handle. It snapped forward and loaded a round into the chamber. Fifteen rounds. I checked left and right again as our car engine fired up.

The faces on the two lazy twats in our second vehicle weren't on the default setting anymore. Their mouths hung open as I pulled the butt of the AK into my shoulder and lifted the barrel. The third soldier had appeared round the back of the second car.

'Arrête. Je vais tirer.' *Stop. I will shoot.*

He halted and stood still. Face taught and mouth open. His rapid-blinking eyes fell onto his oppo, spark out on the deck to my left.

'Baissez votre arme,' shouted Manny. I assumed that meant about the same thing I'd said, only better.

The soldier put the weapon down and stepped back with his hands by his shoulders, palms open. He followed the nod of my barrel by dropping to his kness.

'This is no good,' said Manny.

I assumed he meant the shitty AK. 'Get Demba's Makarov. Then put these weapons in the car.' I nodded towards the two AK's laying in the dirt. 'And tell those two to stay put.' I flicked my head at our rear vehicle.

'I mean *this* is not good.' He was behind me, so I couldn't see what he might be indicating. I had a good idea though.

'Mate, just fucking do it. I'll see what's happened to Baldé. If either of the other two AK's work, then you and Demba use them to cover these fuckers. Otherwise, grab one of theirs.' I scoped the barrel towards the rear car, causing both men inside to flinch.

A passing car slowed, and a questioning voice received a mouthful from Manny. The engine gunned into the distance as I moved onto the track.

CHAPTER 21

Deep breaths slowed my racing heart rate. Pain flashed deep inside my midriff where the barrel had caught me. The knuckles on my right hand joined in. Sweat cascaded off my forehead. I shook it off, to little effect. The crook of my right arm helped smear some away from my eyes while I kept both hands on the AK.

I could only see the far-right side of the shack and outside deck. Not the central door or more than a sliver of the right window. Mixed voices shouted inside.

The track rose up a slight incline. There was tall vegetation on the immediate left, open ground to the right. More of the shack emerged as the track bent left around the treeline. A voice called out from only a few metres away. 'Celine. Que se passe-t-il? Est ce que ça va?'

Unfortunately for you mate, whichever one of the crew Celine might be, he's not okay.

I stopped dead, butt in the shoulder, and leaned into a standing firing position with a featherlight touch on the trigger with my finger. The soldier appeared ten feet away.

'Drop the fucking weapon. Drop it. Arrete. Je vais tirer.' *Stop. I will shoot.*

He reared back. The AK-47 in his hands swung wildly. He looked down at it and reached for the cocking handle.

'STOP. Stop. Drop it.' My finger took up first pressure. The touch remained light though. AK's weren't known for a hair trigger, but I'd never fired this particular weapon before and wasn't going to chance it.

His right hand clawed at the cocking handle which didn't move.

In a flap, he'd forgotten to flip the safety catch off. He struggled with it. Of course, it might already be cocked. *Don't do it. Don't fucking do it.*

His eyes blazed wild with panic.

I advanced, almost on top of him. Barrel pointed into his face. 'DROP IT. Fucking drop it.'

He gave out a strangled yelp and dropped the rifle. His hands raised and palms open at chest height. Breaths coming in sobs.

'Get down. Get down.'

He crouched and I kicked him over. He rolled easily into a prostrated position, face down. I grabbed his AK and released the magazine. By weight, maybe half full. I stuck it into the cargo pocket of my trousers. The weapon took a graceful arc into the undergrowth.

What to do with him? I stamped hard on the fingers of his outstretched right hand. A piercing howl rang out as he rolled into a ball. That should limit his options.

'Fucking stay there.'

All this shouting and screaming meant the element of surprise was probably off the menu. I advanced, tucking in against the bushes on my left as the shack came into full view.

The yelling from inside had stopped, and a figure moved behind the left-hand window as the door catapulted open. The lieutenant rushed onto the decking and halted with a handgun dangling in his right hand. My sight picture centred on his chest.

He looked directly at me. Less than ten metres away.

'Arrête. Drop the weapon, lieutenant.'

His soldier sidekick appeared next to him, AK-47 in hand.

'Both of you. Weapons down.'

I risked a snatched glance over my shoulder to make sure my latest victim hadn't decided to enact revenge. He remained on the floor in a ball, moaning.

Baldé emerged behind the two men at the door. More alive than I'd expected.

'Baldé, come on. Yella, come on.' The Arabic came naturally. I didn't remember the French equivalent.

The two soldiers remained unmoving, both still holding their weapons although neither currently pointing in my direction. One of them had been fired recently and would therefore be made ready. I hadn't needed to shoot anyone so far. Best to keep it that way if possible.

'Put your weapons down on the ground.' I couldn't remember how Manny had said it earlier. Fuck it. Should have studied harder at school, although I doubt that phrase would have been on the curriculum.

Baldé had clearly taken in the shock of the situation and began waving his hands and spouting French ten to the dozen. His movement seemed okay. No obvious sign of injury. He turned to face the two men, his hands still bouncing invisible basketballs as he gabbled away. He had his back to me, partially blocking my view of the other two men.

'Baldé, come on. Let's go. Nous allons rapide.' *We go quickly* – the best I could do.

He started to turn my way, then stopped and instead scooted past the AK-47-wielding soldier and back into the shack. *Now what?*

The officer and soldier still held their weapons by their sides while I dropped my barrel's aim twenty degrees to the officer's feet — an attempt at de-escalation. But still ready to quickly engage if either made a move. Both eyed me impassively. Neither spoke nor altered their gaze. I could almost hear the ticking of the pocket watch in *For a Few Dollars More*, counting down until Clint and the boys let rip at each other.

I blinked rapidly as sweat stung my left eye. Not the time to adjust my hold on the weapon and provide any excuse for this pair to try anything.

Baldé reappeared with the clear folder of documents in his hand. He spoke to the lieutenant as he passed and made his way down the track towards me.

'Keep going.' I tilted my head in the direction of our vehicles, while maintaining aim towards the unmoving lieutenant and his underling.

'Nous allons.' *We go.* Baldé pointed at the two men by the shack door. 'C'est fini.' *It's finished.*

'Bon.' *Good.* I kept the weapon on aim as I stepped backwards. Cautious that the lieutenant might do something stupid if given half a chance.

From behind me a softly spoken, 'Merde.' *Shit.* Baldé must have spotted one or more of our victims. My victims.

Once out of sight of the targets, I yanked the safety catch on and broke into a jog down the track, passing Baldé who'd stopped at the whimpering figure still curled into a ball.

'Forget him. Let's go.' We might be out of sight of the shack, but the foliage wouldn't provide much cover from fire if they let rip with an AK-47.

I ran to the car, calling to Manny as I drew near. 'Tell them we'll drop their weapons fifty metres along the road. Mount up. Let's go.'

Manny and Demba sprang from their positions by the car. Demba shoved his Makarov into a belt holster as he rounded the front of the car to the driver's side, and Manny pulled his door open and spoke to the figures on the floor, a Kalashnikov tight in his shoulder. None of the three men on the deck so much as twitched in response.

'Baldé, come on,' I yelled as he trudged down the track. I still didn't know what the hell had happened, but it seemed to have ended with only a few cuts and bruises. Bruised egos as well, no doubt. The repercussions might be a problem.

Once Baldé shut his door we took off at speed. After less than fifty metres, Demba braked sharply and I lobbed three AK-47s and their ejected magazines onto the side of the road.

'Go, go, go.'

As we accelerated again, I asked the burning question. 'What the fuck happened up there?' At the same time as, according to Manny, Baldé asked pretty much the same question in reverse.

I multi-tasked as Manny translated Baldé's account from inside the shack, checking the map and the GPS for the locations of the two other checkpoints we would encounter on the route to Conakry.

Baldé said the lieutenant had asked questions about me, my business in Guinea, and the reasons for the military escort. Unsatisfied with the answers, he had drawn his Makarov from its holster and begun issuing threats while waving it around. When he crashed it against the table in anger, the pistol fired and a 9mm round almost took Baldé's head off. That prompted a heated shouting match after the initial stunned silence.

The furore was only interrupted by the sound of my shouted commands and swearing in angry English nearby.

Manny stopped talking and both he and Baldé fixed me with serious stares.

'What? Say that again?'

Manny spoke. 'He asked why you attacked the soldiers. It's a very bad thing to do.'

I met Baldé's blinking gaze. 'I thought they'd shot him, and they were going to kill or kidnap the lot of us. A fucking ND. Are you serious? Christ.'

What a mess. We had to hope the lieutenant buried the whole incident to avoid sanction for the Negligent Discharge and didn't light the blue touch paper.

Neither of the two checkpoints on the way back gave us so much as a second glance. A relief, but nothing to take too much comfort from. It's not as if I'd be difficult to find if they wanted to haul me in.

CHAPTER 22

The car had lapsed into a heavy silence after the post-mortem about the checkpoint drama. I'd rung Cal on the sat phone with an update and a warning about the incident. Our strained conversation had been brief and inspired less confidence than expected that he'd have my back if things went pear-shaped.

We'd all been on edge as we navigated two rural checkpoints and then arrived back into the crowded streets of the capital and the scrutiny of its numerous police officers and soldiers. An efficient BOLO 'Be On the Look Out' vehicle warning system might be unlikely, but it was impossible not to imagine the worst.

The sun had already slipped below the horizon when our escorts dropped Manny and me into the insect haze outside the Cameyenne. Demba and Baldé couldn't get away quick enough. As soon as the doors slammed shut, the wheels spun and they raced off. Our second vehicle had cut loose at the first junction inside the city and was long gone.

Manny watched the tail lights of the departing Land Cruiser merge into the traffic flow outside the hotel forecourt entrance.

'I guess there goes your lift home.'

He grunted, turned to me, and slowly shook his head. 'Baldé is not happy and I don't blame him. He did almost have his head blown off. And he has to live here after we've gone home.'

The annoying whine of a mosquito buzzed close to my ear and I whipped out a hand to knock it away. Manny looked as tired and grimy as I felt. The sticky heat of the evening made me long for a shower.

'I've got a meeting tonight, here at the hotel. It might be nothing, but maybe it's better if you come along. Eight o'clock out by the pool bar. If you can get here before eight-thirty and hover close by, then I'll signal when to come over.'

'Cal?' he asked with a bleak smile.

I nodded. 'Yep.'

He wiped a hand across his glistening forehead. 'Okay. Shirt and trousers?'

'I'll be smart casual after a long hot shower. No need for a suit.'

Manny looked at his watch which prompted me to look at mine. 6.15 p.m. His eyes roamed over my shoulder and locked on to an empty taxi. 'I'll be back here by eight.'

'Thanks, mate. And for today. I know it was fucked up, but you did well. Let's hope nothing comes of it.'

★

By 7.45 p.m. I was ensconced at a four-seater table in the rear of the poolside restaurant wearing my freshly laundered trousers and an equally fragrant and smartly pressed shirt. The hotel laundry service had impressed on the first try out.

My position under a ceiling fan helped to regain some of the coolness from my earlier shower. A coolness that had been overwhelmed by the sultry night as soon as I left the main hotel building.

I tried to shake off thoughts of the afternoon incident and concentrated instead on people watching while waiting for the diamond guy to show up – if he showed up. I didn't have a phone number for him, just a name. Lambert. The kind of name that could have been pronounced to sound like either an overweight British stockbroker or a French artist. I doubted our diamond dealing friend was known as Bert to his friends. Cal had provided my local number to those on the other side of the deal, so I expected a phone call soon.

I stirred my orange juice and lay the straw on the table. The umbrella had to go as well. And I couldn't tell if the piece of foliage sitting on the top ice cube was intentional decoration or had fallen from the thatched palm roof. My eyes scanned the low, natural ceiling to make sure no unwelcome wildlife might join it.

I'd requested no ice cubes as per overseas travel SOPs; not much surprise that had been roundly ignored. Good job I'd received the recent cocktail of vaccine jabs to bolster my defences.

The tables by the pool had filled up, and more diners and drinkers were arriving by the minute. Mainly locals so far. The business centre had been full quarter of an hour earlier – too full for me to find a workspace – but some of the same faces were beginning to appear. The rest wouldn't be far behind.

The tables on either side along the windowed edge of the restaurant remained empty for now. With luck they would remain unused. Better that any conversation couldn't be overheard, even if business shouldn't be on the menu.

By my third orange juice, they had finally brought me a glass without decorations or ice cubes. From the sour look on the waiter's face you'd have thought the extra measure of juice needed to fill the glass would be coming out of his wages. Perhaps it was.

My watch showed almost 8.30 p.m. Manny had arrived and sat within my eyeline on the periphery of an animated group over by the pool. But no sign of the contact. A couple more minutes and I'd ring Cal on the sat phone to find out what was going on and if we should call it a day.

Through the window, the lights of several vessels shone like lonely beacons. Fishing boats at a guess. I wondered if it would be barracuda for dinner again tonight.

Over at the bar, I spotted a spindly black guy with a shaved head and a bright taste in shirts. He craned his head to scan the assorted diners – our guy for sure.

All the tables in the restaurant were now taken and an influx of Western faces populated those around me. Even so, he fixed his gaze in my direction and walked over, holding out a hand when he neared. I stood up and did likewise.

'Mr John. Bon soir. I am Lambert.'

Lam-bear – like I'd expected. 'Bon soir. Take a seat. Drink?'

He looked at my orange juice before calling out, 'Garçon.'

The waiter placed two dishes at the next-door table then stepped across to ours.

'Whisky. You?'

With my glass devoid of its original garish paraphernalia, Lambert might have thought I'd been subtly hitting the hard stuff already. That wasn't my style, but the old saying 'never trust a guy who doesn't drink' sprang to mind. Three orange juices were about my limit anyway.

'Beer. S'il vous plaît.'

'Heineken, monsieur?'

'Oui, Heineken. Merci.'

Lambert had a young, fresh-faced look about him – amplified by his pock-marked skin and angular limbs. Although the keen eyes, confident manner, and set of his face indicated someone older and more experienced than I might be giving him credit for. I glanced towards the pool and Manny acknowledged his awareness with a nod.

The ghost of a thought manifested itself, along with a growing unease. Admittedly we'd both appeared to recognise the other in similar fashion, but I'd guessed his identity by virtue of him scanning the restaurant patrons just when I expected someone to be looking for me. Had I stood out so much purely by dint of being a white guy sat alone? Or had he known who I was? If so, how?

Surveillance would be the paranoid answer, if not necessarily the wrong one. Before jumping to conclusions, I ought to check that Cal hadn't provided a happy snap of my smiling mug. I'd be pissed if he had.

Lambert hunched forward with his sharp elbows on the table and fingers interlaced. 'I'm told you want to buy diamonds.'

So much for no business talk. My eyes swept across to observe the waiter leaving the bar with our drinks order on a tray. I flicked them left and right to the adjacent tables while considering how best to answer.

'Perhaps.'

'Either you want to buy or you don't.'

The waiter deposited our drinks and removed my half-finished orange juice with a stony look.

'Salut,' said Lambert, lifting his glass.

I tipped the bottle towards him. 'Cheers.'

We both took a swig of our drinks before I set my beer down.

'My people want to buy, but it depends what you have to sell.'

A smile slowly spread across his face. A smile with little warmth. He twisted the glass in his hand and studied it, the remaining light brown liquid translucent under the nearby soft lighting. 'D'accord.' *Of course.*

I didn't want to get into a detailed discussion in public. 'Do you want to eat? Manger? I'm starving.'

'Yes.' He looked around and nodded appreciatively. 'I like it here and the whisky is good. American.'

'Okay. Let me call my colleague over.' I raised my hand to catch Manny's attention. After two or three seconds he turned my way, stood up, and walked towards us.

Lambert scrunched his nose and gave it a curious rub between his thumb and forefinger. As Manny joined us and greeted Lambert, a squat, bulky gentleman whose shirt buttons were fighting to contain his pot belly materialized by the table. Physically he was the opposite of Lambert in nearly every respect, apart from the similarly shaved head. His yellowy eyes had a bulbous quality that gave his round, stern face a malevolent edge.

Lambert's bony fingers had dropped from his face and now rolled open to reveal his palm. 'And *my* colleague, Sadou.'

Touché.

This evening everything on the restaurant menu was available, and I made the mistake of ordering a gristly and flavourless steak. From what animal I had no idea. Should have stuck with the barracuda. The conversation around the table was polite if limited. Much of it in French as Manny took it upon himself to probe our new friends.

Manny and I scrubbed up pretty well compared to Lambert and Sadou. We might not have radiated film star zing, but those two would be waiting a long time for anyone to swipe right unless they were a dab hand with Photoshop. Each had taken a hit from the ugly stick, especially Sadou, and both had the style of low-life gangsters. The swagger of men who considered themselves at the top of the food chain compared to the law-abiding masses.

And Sadou's face was familiar. That might explain how Lambert recognised me. I tried to recall where I'd seen it before. Sadou looked up and caught me studying him from across the table. I focused back on my uninspiring meal and thought about my counter-surveillance efforts to date. Not impressive. I needed to up my game.

'…de demander à Monsieur John.'

I turned to Manny on my right. 'You'll need to ask me what?'

Manny indicated Lambert. 'He's asking us to go with him to another place.'

I looked from one to the other as I answered. 'I've got work to do. And it's been a long day.'

'But you like music? Live music,' said Lambert.

'Yes, but we've had some issues with our car today as well.'

The major issue being we didn't have one without either Condé or the general's men on hand.

'I have the car here, outside,' said Manny.

Thanks a lot, Manny – that sabotaged my excuse. He must have driven Condé's Mercedes.

Lambert took his answer as a signal we'd agreed to join him. 'Good. You won't see la Guinée from the hotel.'

I snorted a laugh. 'Don't worry, mate. I've encountered more than enough local culture today.'

He fixed me with a neutral look. 'We should know each other better before we do business tomorrow.'

Irritation flared. He must know something I didn't. 'Tomorrow?'

'Yes. Simon has arranged it.'

'Has he now? Simon. Who's Simon?' I knew exactly who he

meant of course. But it didn't hurt to try and ruffle his composure.

Lambert's eyebrows clamped together. 'Mister Simon. Your Mister Simon.'

I paused for effect.

'Simmons. You mean Cal Simmons. That would be about right. I don't have all the details for tomorrow yet. What have you been told?'

'You bring the gemmologue tomorrow for inspecting the stones.'

'Gemmologue?'

'Gemmologist,' interjected Manny.

'We'll see. I need to speak with him before we take a final decision.'

Who was I kidding? Cal must have conjured up a gemmologist from somewhere and made arrangements for the next day without waiting for my report from this meeting. A good reason to stay here and check my emails; a better reason to go with these two jokers and try to find out more about them.

I issued a theatrical wave. 'What the hell. Let's go get ourselves some local culture.'

CHAPTER 23

We followed the gangsta twins' SUV until it pulled off the road into a busy car park. Lambert nosed into a double space and Manny reversed the red Mercedes alongside. Colourful signs, garish illumination, and bedraggled bunting announced the two-storey structure as an entertainment venue. The attempted hint at glamour aided by the drabness of the surrounding buildings. The foliage wrapped around the exterior balcony provided additional character, although it also offered an unnecessary hidden approach route for the local wildlife. I hadn't encountered any nasty critters yet but remained wary of anywhere they could be lurking.

Our popular new friends led us through clusters of people chatting and smoking amongst the cars, exchanging fist bumps and greetings along the way. The pungent aroma of marijuana hung in the air. A throbbing beat leaked from open windows, suggesting this wouldn't be a quiet drink. Close to the door, a handful of soldiers loitered around two military trucks. The red berets of the presidential guard: les Beret Rouge.

'That'll be the VIP area cordoned off then,' I said to Manny.

His answer was lost in the blast of music as the door opened ahead of us.

Unlike London clubs, the dress code was unlikely to provide a barrier to entry. If anything, Manny and I were overdressed compared to the jeans, trainers, and jazzy short sleeve shirts of our two companions.

After passing a disinterested bouncer, the heat from the crowd inside chipped at my enthusiasm for the excursion. I was already sweating from the humid night outside. Jammed inside a wooden box with half the city wasn't going to be comfortable.

We pushed through the mass of young men besieging the fewer young women and found welcome space away from the bar. Many of the clubbers wore sharp outfits and there was a lot of flesh on display, the same as nightclubs everywhere. Here it felt like an after-hours antidote to the dreary city outside. I hadn't seen another white face yet.

Manny leant close. 'It gets crowded later.'

'We won't be staying long. Keep your wits about you. I'm not sure what to expect with these guys. And see who the VIP might be.'

Manny nodded in response.

Lambert had strutted over to a table a few yards away. As we neared my heart sank. He was talking to the two men I'd tangled with at breakfast in the Novotel a few days earlier. The guys I suspected were Russians. The mouthy one raised his face in my direction before getting up and making his way over.

He intruded into my personal space and initiated a handshake with a fierce grip. Tosser. I gripped back and tried to manoeuvre my thumb onto a pressure point.

'Englishman. You know Lambert. You drink with us?' A heavy accent with a dubious level of bonhomie.

Not the evening I'd envisaged, and I did nothing to hide my reluctance. But he probably put it down to his show of strength crushing my hand.

'Whisky?' he added.

He finally released the handshake and gave his wrist a subtle rub. That provided some satisfaction as I ignored my own aching fingers.

'I thought you'd be drinking vodka. You're Russian, yes?'

'Yes, but you taste the godawful stuff they serve here? At least the whisky is the real thing. Ever tried Russian vodka?'

'In Moscow once or twice.'

His eyebrows shot up and he cocked his head to one side. 'I'm Sergei. And this is Peter.'

His big friend at the table acknowledged my glance with a lacklustre wave.

'John. And my colleague here is Manny.'

'Another Englishman, or maybe not?'

'Kind of. And I'm a Kiwi. New Zealander. But brought up in England.' A lie, but no one liked the English. We don't like each other much either.

'You've been to Russia, huh. Only Moscow?'

'And Kiev.' I couldn't help smiling as his face darkened.

'Kiev is Ukraine. Not Russia. No Soviet Union any longer.'

I opened my hands, fingers of the right still throbbing, and shrugged my shoulders. His scowl remained.

'What is an English Kiwi doing in Russia and Guinea?'

Sergei leaned away and barked something in Spanish to an olive-skinned chap with shoulder length hair sitting next to Peter. Then he laughed unconvincingly. 'Maybe you've been to Columbia as well?'

I played it straight. Time to ratchet down the implied suspicion. 'No. Never been to South America. Work takes you where it takes you. And here we are.'

The background music dropped and a burst of whooping and cheering interrupted the conversation at a convenient point. The band were on stage.

Feedback howled through the sound system before an enthusiastic male voice introduced the group. A surge of bodies flooded from the bar area towards the stage and blocked my view of everything except a colourful light show flashing over the top half of the animated compère.

Unseen drums exploded into a pounding tempo and a myriad of rhythm instruments kicked off an African sound with a bluesy feel. The evening was looking up. My foot began a spontaneous tap with the beat and the energy of the rapturous crowd reminded me of clubs and gigs from too many years ago.

I checked whether our enlarged group were joining in. No, they weren't. Manny had commandeered the briefly empty table next to the Russian party. He pointed at a glass filled with dark liquid on the tabletop in front of him, then lifted a can of Coke to his lips. Hadn't I asked for a beer?

I plonked myself down opposite Manny. Next to him, Sadou stared at me as I took in Lambert's slim frame wedged between his bulk and that of Sergei. Lambert and the Russian were engaged in a conversation drowned out by the boisterous atmosphere.

I braced myself as I lifted the glass, nodded a thanks to Sergei that caused his eyes to flick to mine while he continued speaking to Lambert, and hoped it was decent whisky and not some local gut rot. My eyes watered when I threw the large, neat measure down my neck, even as I gave a silent thank you that it tasted like Jim Beam and not moonshine. Manny's eyebrows tilted as he watched me place the empty glass down.

Half an hour of this and we'd make our excuses and leave. I wouldn't learn much in this environment, other than the type of music currently popular with the youth of Conakry. Although knowing Lambert might be a 'face' around town meant it had already been a useful exercise. I'd be advising Cal that we must apply caution dealing with this guy and his cohorts.

An hour and four drinks later, I stood to stretch my legs and take a closer look at the instruments being played by the band. The crowd had thickened in places, but in other spots space opened around young women as they gyrated in uninhibited, hypnotic, sensual dance.

'She's pretty, no? You like the local girls?' Sergei shuffled to my right, leering in the same direction I faced.

'Actually, I was looking at the guy over there with the beret.'

Unless it was a patron attempting the Che Guevara look, the Beret Rouge had wandered in and joined the party.

Without looking, Sergei flicked his hand in the same direction and sneered. 'With us. You like this girl or not?'

He pointed to an eye-catching young woman wearing a yellow dress that looked as though it had been sprayed on – and without needing much paint.

'She certainly knows how to move. Very nice, yes. What do you mean "with us"?'

But Sergei had turned and was shouting and gesturing towards Che Guevara. As the tall soldier came towards us, a splash of white light revealed the red of his beret. Another brawny soldier emerged behind him. Sergei spoke to the men and pointed towards the dancing girl with the yellow dress, five metres to our left.

They swaggered over and one of them caught the girl's arm as she waved it in the air in mid twirl. She stopped dead and her head flashed round to face him. As she tried unsuccessfully to pull her arm from the soldier's grip, a man stepped out of the crowd and the other soldier squared up to him.

'What's happening?' I asked Sergei.

'You wait.'

Nearby faces turned in our direction as one of the soldiers spoke with the man who had challenged him. The woman in the yellow dress followed the eyeline of the Beret Rouge holding her arm and looked at us. At me.

The soldier escorted her over. As they closed, lights danced over her features to reveal an attractive face. Beautiful even. And young. The same age or younger than my eldest daughter, Natalie, who had recently turned twenty.

'For you,' said Sergei.

'What? No.'

The girl lifted her eyes, the brows knotting together.

'No, I mean she's very pretty, but I'm not looking for a woman. I'm married.'

'But her man, he says you can have her. It's agreed.' Sergei spoke with the soldier in rapid French. 'Yes, it's all agreed.'

'Sergei, I don't care. I'm here on business. This isn't going to happen.'

'John, is everything okay?' Manny's voice cut through the throng behind me.

I continued with Sergei. 'You need to tell her I'm sorry, she's very pretty, but she should go back to her boyfriend or husband, whoever.'

I turned to Manny. 'Let's go mate. They've served me up this girl. Out of nowhere. Come on, we're out of here.'

A commotion kicked off near the second soldier as I held up a hand in Lambert's direction and caught the tail end of an insult from Sergei that questioned my manhood.

'Yeah, whatever mate. This is bullshit,' I fired back.

We swept out through the door into a haze of sickly light and energetic insects. You could almost chew on the soupy air, although it was fresh compared to inside the club.

'Her man isn't happy,' said Manny.

'I'm not surprised. Christ, forcing a girl to do that. It's rape.'

'No, he's not happy because you turned her down. You refused his woman after he gave her to you.'

'What? Are you serious?'

We passed the soldiers outside and trudged over to Condé's Mercedes. I shook my head. 'This place is fucked up.'

We reached the car as a ruckus emerged from the club entrance. A posse of angry locals began arguing with the soldiers now stood-to around their vehicles and shouts reached out to us. I could see the yellow dress in amongst them and hear a high-pitched voice giving as good as the others. It sounded like I'd upset everyone with my highfalutin moral standards. I was no stranger to the odd cultural faux pas, but this was in a league of its own.

'We need to get out of here,' said Manny. He held the key up. 'I hope this thing starts.' He plunged it into the ignition and twisted. The engine sputtered into life.

'Yesss.' He grinned at me, threw the car into gear, and slammed his foot on the gas. The tyres screeched as we hit the road at speed and swerved to avoid a gaping pothole.

I sat back with a sigh and swept a persistent mozzie off my knuckle. 'I've ticked enough culture boxes today. Let's try for a quieter day tomorrow.'

CHAPTER 24

THE FOLLOWING MORNING

After an early breakfast, I waited in the lobby for the business centre to open. Concerns about the previous day's checkpoint fracas played on my mind, and I still had no idea what had been arranged with Lambert. When I'd tried to ring Cal the previous night for a heads up, the satellites wouldn't play ball. After five minutes as mosquito bait in the gardens, I submitted and went to bed. Now I needed to catch up on the latest email correspondence and send a warning about Lambert and his cronies.

The dull hum behind my eyes hadn't been alleviated by orange juice, coffee, and carbohydrates. A good reason I never drank spirits. Not counting the odd bottle of spiced rum shared with an ex-bootneck oppo when we occasionally met up to swing the lamp. I sucked at a bottle of water and considered the day ahead.

We were due to meet with Édouard at 10.00 a.m. to report on our field trip, provided he hadn't bumped us off his diary again. Unless I introduced something new, there wouldn't be much of note to discuss – I'd be leaving out any mention of the excitement on the return journey. But with any luck, Cal had already sent the draft agreement by email, along with updated instructions for the Pinnacle negotiating position. That would allow me to begin steering this deal towards a satisfactory conclusion. Until that side was agreed, we might all be wasting our time.

After Édouard, I hoped to fit in a visit to the bank before whatever had been planned with Lambert and his people, whenever and wherever that might take place.

I was first through the door when the business centre opened and wasted no time setting up my laptop in a secluded corner. Another expat scooted in and had a coughing fit behind me while my machine booted up. Out of the corner of my eye I watched him drop into a chair at the other end of the room, pleased he wouldn't be launching an invisible cloud of Christ knows what lurgy into my immediate vicinity.

I intended to be nice and quick, and not just to avoid catching some honking disease. This was the best time of the day for sending and receiving emails and attachments, especially from behind a temperamental VPN. The centre's shared signal would soon slow to a crawl with the morning rush and I wanted to be done and dusted before then.

Along with a smattering of spam, two emails from Cal downloaded into my inbox. The newest message, sent the night before, had two documents attached. I checked the smaller, earlier email first; sent the previous afternoon while we'd been enjoying the eventful return drive from the field trip.

From: CS
To: JP

Subject: Inspection

1. Things have moved faster than expected at this end. Two Geos are inbound and will arrive today. Booked into the Cameyenne. Will supply names and contact details asap. They're hired help only – keep them safe but share no info with them. They're coming in to do the appraisal only.

2. Meeting with seller to inspect stones arranged for 1700 tomorrow. You will have met with their rep by now. He will collect you from the hotel at 1630.

3. NO PRICE NEGOTIATION during this meeting. Let the Geos do the inspection and we'll review the results. Provide a full report

of the meeting asap on completion. As much detail as possible re the seller and the stones origin. Include photos if possible.

Note: Provenance of the stones is unclear.

Rgds,
CS

So much for my plan to advise Cal to take things slowly with Lambert and the sellers he represented. The diamond deal seemed to be moving full steam ahead, although the request to report after today's meeting showed I might still exert some influence.

A rasp of wet coughing from the other side of the room cut through my scepticism. I instinctively swallowed as though clearing mucus from my own throat and remembered I needed a resupply of hand sanitiser.

A quick check revealed two more workstations were now occupied. The users had their heads down, probably trying like me to get done before the rush, and before they caught whatever laughing boy at the back had picked up.

I moved on to the second, subsequent email.

From: CS
To: JP

Subject: Revised Draft

1. You'll see the attached draft has been prepared in French (& English for you only). Get it to the lawyer for review before you submit to E.
2. Meanwhile, you should introduce the outline of the new proposal at the next meeting with E. to warm him up. New Co to be incorporated as per previous comms.

Main points of the accompanying agreement:

- Sapro to place the licenses for all six concessions into the new co.
- Pinnacle will provide sufficient funding to complete survey and valuation of all 6 concessions within 12 months. No specific amount will be agreed in advance or paid to third parties.
- The board for the new co to comprise 2 directors from Pinnacle, 2 directors from Sapro & chairman from Pinnacle.
- Shareholdings: 51% Pinnacle 49% Sapro.
- Shareholder agreement to provide for 50-50 profit share.
- In-country funds to be controlled by the Project Manager to be appointed by the board.
- Accounts to be audited prior to any profit extraction by recognised, international chartered accountant firm, as selected by the board.

They'll kick back at first, but the strong assessment here is they will agree. Get the terms into their heads. Make it clear you have no authority to negotiate alterations to any of the above points. Follow up with the French draft once approved by F. Tell them you have instructions to return to London in 3 days unless a deal is agreed. Let's get this deal signed and a green light to mobilise.

3. I've had confirmation the geos have arrived in-country and checked in to your hotel. Timings for the inspection tomorrow unchanged. Lead geo is David +33 7 42 28 02 31 – no local number provided. He'll be expecting your call in the morning. Any alterations your end – let me know asap.
4. Call me when you get this message (via sat).

Rgds,
CS

After downloading the attachments, I reread the email. 'Return to London in 3 days' met with my approval. Claire would be happy with that as well. The Skype icon showed missed messages and calls. I'd try to get hold of her later with the good news.

As for the rest of Cal's message, Pinnacle was going in bold, trying to dictate the terms along with the change of structure. I didn't imagine Édouard and the backers of Sapro would be pleased with Pinnacle wanting to seize control. We'd soon see if this tactic overstepped the mark.

My watch showed 08:20. I had to get the French draft to Fozzie – another appointment to add to today's schedule. Rather than risk printing it here in public, on a printer that might retain the document in its memory, his minions could arrange that in the downtown 'Parisian' office. I logged off, shut down, and packed up. No point replying by email when I was about to ring Cal on the sat phone.

The Thuraya displayed the ready signal as I walked through the garden past the empty pool and bar and towards the low wall separating the hotel property from the Atlantic. Next to the rocks, a small patch of dark sand had been revealed by the low tide.

I breathed in the salty air. The ocean breeze could hardly be described as refreshing, but it did take the edge off the start to another scorcher. And the beachside view wasn't a bad outlook with which to begin a working day. The lack of insect attention helped brighten my mood, plus the fuzzy edges around my thoughts had cleared.

I dialled Cal's Thuraya in the UK. He answered on the second ring.

'About time John. I've been trying to get hold of you since yesterday evening. Did you get the emails? And did the meeting go okay with the seller's people?'

I ignored the barbed greeting. 'Yes mate, I've got them.'

'And last night went as planned?'

'To be honest with you, I don't like the guy, Lambert. Or his sidekick. And they know everybody here. Russians, locals, and even Colombians, I think. I'd be careful with these guys.'

Cal had begun talking over me. '...not a popularity contest. You don't need to like them. Just need to get the business done.'

I closed my eyes as the throb behind them resurfaced. Then pinched my forehead in a vain attempt to expunge the self-inflicted discomfort. I blew out a long breath, partly to disrupt something droning near my mouth and partly to control my annoyance.

'I know that mate. I'm not trying to fucking date the guy. I'm just telling you that I don't trust him or any of the other fuckers in this shithole.'

'Alright John, sorry. Didn't mean it to come out like that. Pressure is on here to get this deal done. That's why the geos have been flown in already. I tried to get them to wait until after the meet last night. Oh, and don't worry about Lambert. He's just the local contact. The real sellers are much bigger fish.'

I didn't believe he'd tried very hard, if at all.

I removed my finger and thumb and opened my eyes. The bright light made me blink for a second, but the throb had gone — for now. 'Your email says no price negotiation. That might be tough.'

'This deal is big. Potentially very big. They're claiming to have twenty-five thousand carats for sale. Just for starters. You're only going to see a sample today and we need to confirm what the quality is like before we can begin to talk prices.'

'That does sound big.'

'It's huge, mate. Profit on a deal that size could be a thousand dollars a carat if the quality is as they say, and we play this right. We've got buyers waiting if they're the real deal. And remember, you've got a piece of the action.'

Very true. Five per cent if I remembered correctly: up to an unlikely $1.25 million based on Cal's projection. There were a hatful of 'ifs' and 'buts' to overcome before any of us would see a dollar of this doubtful windfall.

'Okay, that's the diamonds. I'll report in full after the inspection. Talking of which, that's a French number you've given me for David. What's the story with those guys?'

'Just as I said in the email. Hired experts. Israelis, not French. Based out of Paris. Get them in there to do their thing and onto the plane tomorrow. They're coming straight here to London to brief the board, unless it's a total write-off.'

'Are they on French passports or Israeli?'

'I'm not sure. It won't matter. With diamonds, no one will care or be surprised by Israelis. Probably be more credible if anything.'

Perhaps. Working in the Middle East I had always been sensitive to Arab-Israeli tensions. More than once in the early days in Iraq, I found myself under suspicion of links to Israel purely due to my being a Westerner, albeit operating in an unconventional manner. Islam was Guinea's primary religion and I'd be surprised if none of that tension and suspicion reached this far.

My research had confirmed significant Jewish involvement in all the major diamond bourses, so maybe Cal was right: an Israeli or Jewish element might even be beneficial to enhance our credibility. Maybe. To be on the safe side, I'd be watching for any sign of a problem.

I switched focus to the Sapro-Pinnacle negotiation. 'I don't think Édouard and his people are going to be chuffed with Pinnacle taking control. He told me the fifty-fifty split wasn't up for negotiation the other day. What makes you think they'll agree?'

Cal's voice fired back a strident answer through the static. 'What choice do they have? They still get fifty per cent of the profits and we still make all the investment. This agreement will ensure the project funds get spent where they're needed and not pissed away at the hands of the locals like an open ATM. And Édouard wants his monthly fee. He gets fuck all if this doesn't get signed. They'll come around.'

'I'm not so sure. Three days won't be enough time for them to accept the idea and review the contract. Let alone fight us on every clause.'

The sat phone hissed and crackled. I'd paced across the garden towards the pool. Cal had a Thuraya desktop docking station, linked to an external, rooftop aerial. Assuming he was using it now, the signal problem probably originated from my end. I strode the few metres across to where my daysack leant against the low wall and faced the same direction as when I'd begun the call.

Cal's voice wavered and stabilised. '…there mate? I've lost you.'

'Yes, still here. I said three days won't be enough to get the deal signed off.'

'Don't worry about that. We'll bring you back here for a few days to let them stew on it, then you can fly back in. If the diamond deal is a go, that will also give us the time to arrange the funding and figure out the logistics to make sure we don't get screwed.'

That wouldn't fit in with my family holiday plans, but it wasn't a conversation for now – with Cal or Claire.

'I'm definitely flying out in three days then?'

'That's the plan. Let's see what happens with today's meetings. Try not to get in any more fights.'

'I hope that's all been swept under the carpet. No one's said anything yet.'

'Good. Make sure to get the French draft to Fozzie as soon as.'

'I'm on it, mate.'

Manny was sat in front of a stacked breakfast plate by the time I re-entered the restaurant. I grabbed myself another coffee and orange juice and joined him at the table.

'Condé still out fishing?'

'Mmm.' He gave an affirmative nod as he chewed a mouthful of scran.

'Did you get a lift from Baldé and Demba?'

'Mm mm.' This time a shake of the head as he chewed faster, then swallowed.

'Sorry…' He coughed. 'Sorry, no. I've tried lots of times, but I couldn't get hold of Baldé. I drove the Mercedes here. They left so quick last night we didn't make any arrangements.'

'We're still meeting with Édouard at ten?'

'As far as I know. I'll call him.' He looked down at his plate. 'After this?'

'Eat your breakfast, mate. We've got plenty of time. It's only twenty to nine.'

While Manny demolished the food on his plate, I sipped my strong coffee and thought again about the incident the previous afternoon. I wouldn't blame the two locals for being pissed off about it. A surprise that Baldé wasn't answering his phone though. If we couldn't reach him, then we'd just have to make our own way to Édouard's gaff.

I popped up to my room to grab the last of my hand sanitiser while Manny attempted to call Édouard to check the meeting time remained unchanged. His usual smile was missing when I arrived in the foyer.

'We meet with Édouard later.'

'For fuck's sake. What time?'

'I don't know yet. We must go to another appointment first. Camp Alpha.'

'Camp Alpha? The military base?' I'd driven past it but, as far as I knew, all military installations were off limits to foreigners

'Yes.' Manny sighed heavily. 'It's because of yesterday.'

'Fuck.' I needed another strong coffee and a piss.

As he walked through the main door at 08:55, the set look on Baldé's face told me he already knew about the change of plan. On reaching us, he merely nodded without saying a word. Our own faces must have told him the same story.

For the first time since meeting him, Baldé's uniform had a crumpled look and sweat stains were visible around his armpits. He hadn't shaved either. I hoped it was a sign of unfortunate plumbing and laundry issues and not a fundamental switch in attitude due to my actions the previous day.

CHAPTER 25

The muted conversation in the car ratcheted up a few notches once Manny translated Baldé's revelation.

'What do you mean he told them? For Christ's sake. I thought we went through this yesterday and he understood.'

Demba guided the Land Cruiser through the traffic, while I digested the news that Baldé had informed his commanders about the incident at the checkpoint. By the book, he'd done the right thing, but this was a can of worms I'd hoped we could avoid.

'He says it's his duty. He had to report it.'

'Yeah, I get that mate. But…' I shook my head and felt the legacy of last night's whisky still present. My exasperation deflated, replaced instead by numerous permutations flashing through my head of how this might play out – none of them good.

'Okay. Okay. What did he tell them? And does he know who we're seeing at Camp Alpha?'

'Last night, he told them an incident had occurred at the checkpoint. The commander firing the shot and, only after that, your reaction. Our reaction. He and Demba have been held in the headquarters since then and had to answer a lot of questions. All night they've been held.'

Manny asked a question in French and Baldé turned to answer, looking at me as he did so. This close, the bloodshot eyes, stubble, and unfamiliar slump in the shoulders reflected his weariness. His left eye showed evidence of a recent blow.

'Answering questions' in this country might be accompanied by other 'persuasive' measures. A mix of anger and guilt exploded at that image. Plus, an uncharitable thought: *Now you know why I told you not to say anything.*

Before I could respond, Manny continued. 'This morning they have been answering more questions until General Ndidi arrived. Then they were sent to collect us. He thinks they won't have to answer any more. But the commanders want to question you. Us.'

'But what exactly did he say…did they say?' I swung a pointed finger at both front seats.

'Mr John demande ce que vous avez dit, exactement?'

Baldé turned again from the front seat. My eyes were drawn to his left temple, slightly above his eye. I couldn't be sure if there was a swelling or not.

'Je leur ai dit exactement ce qui s'est passé. Rien d'autre.'

I understood even before Manny translated. 'He told them exactly what happened. Nothing else.'

'Et vous, Demba ?' I asked.

'Oui, moi aussi. Le même.' *Yes, me also. The same.*

'Thanks guys. Thanks to both of you. I'm sorry for this and for whatever you had to go through last night. I hope they treated you well and not as…suspects or prisoners.'

Manny translated and both local men answered with an unconvincing 'merci' and a glance at each other.

The news that General Ndidi was now involved lifted some of my apprehension. The risk in these scenarios was usually if you got stuck with 'enthusiastic' first responders. Once the big guns took over, things ought to calm down. Especially as the general and I were old pals. A bit late for our two shattered escorts, but me and Manny should be granted a more civilised reception.

The vehicle slowed as we approached the gate of the military base, wedged in the middle of the city to the north of the airport. Above the sunshade-style entrance, the white-panelled front of the canopy was emblazoned with 'Camp Alpha Yaya Diallo' in thick black lettering under a unit crest. A bulky soldier in camouflage uniform topped with a red beret spoke with Baldé, then glared at me before waving us through.

'Presidential guard on the gate?' I asked.

'No,' said Manny. 'Not all soldiers with red berets are presidential guard. There's BATA, who are the airborne guys, and others as well.'

'Airborne? Does Guinea have much of an air force?'

'A couple of helicopters and old fighter planes. Russian models. Not much more than that.'

We drove around a marching squad of soldiers wearing black berets. Other pockets of troops hovered near the myriad buildings and eyed us warily as we passed. Demba drove without instruction from Baldé, who remained silent.

We pulled up outside a four-storey building. Two life-size grey statues of soldiers on plinths guarded the steps leading to the entrance. The bottom line of a busy sign proclaimed it belonged to the 'Bataillon Special de Conakry'. Either side of a central door, coloured windows protruded up to the top floor in a semi-circular design, giving it the appearance of an office block. A headquarters building.

Baldé opened the door and stepped out. 'Attends ici.' *Wait here*

After Baldé entered the building, more than one passing officer scrutinised us. They had to manoeuvre around the car because we were nestled close to the entrance steps.

A tall, uniformed figure marched briskly towards the steps, then veered to the driver's window after giving us a second look. As he demanded to know why Demba was parked in this spot, Baldé reappeared from the building with General Ndidi behind him. The general called out and Demba's cross-examination ceased as quickly as it had started. His interrogator instead executed a crisp salute to the senior officer before continuing into the headquarters.

General Ndidi walked towards my door, causing Baldé to scoot ahead of him and open it. The general's eyes swept over me and on to Manny.

'Emmanuel, please come here to wait for my return.' He pointed down at the ground beside him.

I turned to face Manny. His eyes met mine before he nodded gently. 'Of course, Général.' He opened his door and stepped out of the car.

'Et vous,' the big man continued, pointing at our escort pairing. 'Caporal, Demba et toi attendez ici aussi mon retour.' *Corporal, Demba and you will also wait here for my return.'*

'Oui, Général,' Baldé and Demba fired back in unison.

The general squeezed his large frame behind the wheel and cursed as he fiddled with the seat controls. Demba jumped back to the car and reached in from a crouched position to help make the adjustment. I shuffled across to where Manny had been sitting to make it easier for the general and I to talk – and to ensure plenty of leg room.

'Voilà,' the general exclaimed as his seat crunched backwards to its furthest extent. A potential kneecapping experience for an unwary passenger.

The door slammed shut and we glided away. Even though the general didn't appear angry, I anticipated the West African equivalent of an 'interview without coffee'.

We locked eyes in the rear-view mirror for a second before the big man spoke.

'I have tried to prevent yesterday's incident from running out of control.' He paused with a heavy sigh. 'But your actions were very serious.'

The dryness in my mouth made me reach for a bottle of water and take a glug. The action generated an instant flush of perspiration. My eyes flicked back to meet his via the mirror.

His tone gained a steely edge. 'Assaulting soldiers at their duty and threatening others with stolen firearms is unacceptable. In any country. In London, you would be in a cell already.'

We were driving at ten miles per hour. Passing nondescript buildings and inert troops. I spotted occasional parked vehicles, but the camp road was empty of traffic. General Ndidi pulled the car over and stopped, then turned to face me through the gap between the front seats.

His sudden, seething intensity took me by surprise. 'I have spent many hours preventing you from being taken to a dark place where you would soon regret your actions.'

He took a breath and his features softened.

'I'm sure you did what you thought was right. And those soldiers involved will face…' – for a moment he looked away and searched for the right words – '…questions of their own. As have my two men.'

The last comment said with a note of regret as his eyes drilled into mine.

I opened my mouth to answer, but he cut me off, the steel back in his voice.

'Unacceptable, dangerous, and very, very unfortunate.'

'I'm sorry, General. It *was* an unfortunate misunderstanding. I can only apologise to you, to the men at the checkpoint, and to Baldé and Demba for putting them in a difficult position. I hope they were treated well for acting so professionally in reporting it on their return.'

'I'm a cultured man, Mr Pierce, and I have good eyes and ears. I know how some of our troops act and make no excuse for them. However, these soldiers you assaulted – disrespected. That disrespect extends to the army of la Guinée.'

'It was never my intention to—'

He raised his hand to silence me. 'The place I am taking you to, the man you will see, he does not have an international outlook like myself. He is not tolerant of disrespect. The reason I am talking to you like this – here, now – is to warn you. Be very careful with this man. He has the power to make things very difficult for you. Very difficult and nasty.'

That introduction prompted another gulp of water. 'I understand. Who is this man I have to see?'

The general turned to his front and released the handbrake. We crept forward. 'He is another general. With a security portfolio. General Sylla. I have argued your case already, but he demands to see you himself. Be careful what you tell him and how you say it. He is not involved in your business.'

The car sped up.

'His section is in those buildings ahead. I will drop you there and send my men to pick you up afterwards.'

'Does he speak English?'

'Yes, he is well educated. Even if he professes not to, he will understand all of what you say. Assume that.'

We pulled up outside a clutch of small, low buildings dotted around a central, larger, two-storey affair. The peeling paint on a wooden sign on the roadside matched the tired look of its surroundings. I couldn't translate the word puzzle fast enough to make sense of it as we passed.

General Ndidi turned to face me again.

'La Guinée is going through troubling times. The whole world knows of the violence of recent weeks and months. Do not underestimate General Sylla or rely on any idea of help from outside. I've done what I can for you. Act correctly with the general and you will be able to continue your business.'

'Thank you.'

I tried to remain calm as my mind screamed *fuck*. I opened my door and stepped into the morning heat. General Ndidi pointed at the two-storey building. 'He's waiting for you. And you're on time. A good start.' The accompanying smile revealed his teeth as he indicated for me to close the car door.

I glanced at my daysack containing the sat phone, laptop, and other gear, jammed behind the big man's seat. Was there time to ring Cal and warn him about my new appointment? No, acquiring the satellites took too long. Hanging around here in the open would only attract attention and suspicion. And what could Cal do anyway?

'I'll leave my rucksack in the car.'

The general leant round to look at it. 'Perhaps that is for the best. It will be safe there.'

After I slammed the door shut, he performed a smooth one-eighty turn and accelerated back the way we'd come.

CHAPTER 26

The front door opened as I approached the building. Butterflies fluttered in my stomach, while the whine of bugs had me brushing a futile hand past both ears in quick succession. I wasn't perspiring any more, I was sweating. Partly from the heat and mainly with apprehension. The quicker I got in there, planted my heels in General Sylla's office, and got this bollocking over with, the better.

After the bright sunlight, it took a second or two to adjust to the gloom of the interior. A uniformed soldier sat behind a desk next to the stairwell. No surprise registered on his face that a foreigner had entered the building. My first *Ah, Mr Bond, we've been expecting you* moment.

The door slammed shut behind me and I caught a flash of white in my peripheral vision. The soldier by the door wore a white belt and white sash indicative of military police. That made sense given the reason I was here, although the clerk behind the desk was in regular rig.

'John Pierce to see General Sylla.' I spoke confidently as though reporting for a regular meeting. To my surprise, it prompted a sense of calm. General Ndidi's pep talk had at least indicated I should come through this unscathed.

The clerk studied me for a moment. He didn't open the A4 sized book in front of him or lift the adjacent pen. Instead, a hand snaked towards an old-fashioned, black, rotary dial telephone on the desk, and he dialled a single number, staring at me as he spoke.

'Monsieur Pierce est ici pour voir le général.' *Mr Pierce is here to see the general*

Two nods as he acknowledged the reply from the other end. 'Oui. Oui.'

He replaced the handset without taking his eyes off me. I looked down at the pen, expecting to be asked to sign in, but the clerk clasped his hands together and remained silent.

A door slammed upstairs, followed by a rising, familiar sound that could only be parade boots clacking along a hard floor. That took me back. A figure in dress uniform appeared on the landing and beckoned me to join him. 'Monsieur, viens avec moi.' *Sir, come with me*

I made my way up. At the top of the stairs, there was a swish of green, a resumption of heel strikes, and the words 'suis moi' trailing in the wake of my escort. *Follow me,* I assumed.

He led the way along a dingy corridor past a handful of closed doors. Weak light spilled from three open doorways at the far end.

Once at the brighter end, I could see into three rooms. A soldier sat at a busy desk through the doorway on my right. Another cluttered desk featured through the one on my left, the seat empty. Both illuminated only by the daylight that penetrated grimy windows.

The usual hum of office equipment was absent, and the only sign of modern IT was a closed laptop. My escort had stopped before crossing the threshold into the middle room.

'Attends ici,' he ordered. *Wait here.*

The deep pile carpet, elegant bookcase, and comparative cleanliness in what I could see of the larger, central room had all the hallmarks of a commander's office. Here, the sunlight streamed through the windows in healthy abundance. A wall unit blocked my view to the right where I assumed General Sylla lay in wait.

'Viens,' barked a new, deeper voice. *Come*

The general sat behind a polished executive desk. It had seen better days but, if anything, the wear and tear accentuated its character.

A big man, he didn't lift his head from the document he studied.

Either his uniform was made-to-measure, or he had lucked out with a perfect fit from the stores. I now knew his red beret didn't necessarily signify presidential guard, but his physique struck me as that of a man of action rather than a desk-bound bean counter. The two stars on his form-fitting, starched uniform indicated the rank of brigadier general. The same as General Ndidi.

He laid the papers on the desk and looked up, scrutinising me from head to toe as he tapped his lips with a finger. There was an aura of intelligence about his features and a spark of danger in his eyes. I imagined he was a hit with the ladies.

His eyes dropped back to the file in front of him.

'John Pierce. Born June 1968. British soldier. Here in Guinea for business. A mining project. Unarmed, ambushes five armed personnel on duty at a checkpoint and comes out on top. Who are you really, Mister Pierce?

'A former soldier, General.'

'What?'

'I'm a former soldier. It's in my past.'

'And yet you behave like a redcoat from the British Empire.'

'I'm sorry about the incident yesterday. It was a misunder–'

The general raised his voice to speak over me. 'You travel in Iraq, Russia, here in Africa. You meet with people at the heart of business in our country. You negotiate about strategic resources. You discuss political concerns. I ask again, who are you really and what are you doing in la Guinée?'

'General, I can assure you that I'm here on business. Purely business. I am responsible for assessing risk. All risk.'

'Assessing risk,' he said with slow and deliberate emphasis on each word.

I considered explaining further but recalled the earlier advice to assume everything would be understood.

He turned his head to the orderly, standing at attention next to the desk. 'Laisse nous.' *Leave us*

'Oui, Général.' The orderly saluted and marched past me.

The general ignored the salute. 'Ferme la porte derrière toi.' *Close the door behind you*

Once alone, he stood, circled the desk, and perched on the front edge, arms folded. A couple of inches taller than me, his eyeline still broadly matched mine. His eyes narrowed and he glared at me from only six feet away.

I wasn't one of his soldiers and wanted nothing more than to tell him to go fuck himself, but I needed to play the game and accept this bullshit without stirring up more trouble.

'Why am I only hearing about this project now?'

I opened my hands. 'I have no idea.'

'You are talking with other generals but not me.'

'These are contacts from before my involvement.' My open hands now raised in exaggerated supplication.

'Tell me about your project.' He spat the words at me.

'Six mining exploration concessions in different parts of the country. You need to speak with Sapro. With Édouard.'

He sneered as he answered. 'I'm not speaking with them; I'm speaking with you. There will be no business for you here without my involvement.'

Previously unregistered tension left my neck and shoulders as I relaxed.

That's what all this was really about: the guy was making a play for a share in the deal.

If he was a big swinging dick in town, then that could be a good move all round – and help to draw a line under yesterday's tête-à-tête at the checkpoint.

'I'm sure there will be room for an agreement. Liaison with the security forces and influential officials will be vital to ensure success.'

I might have thought we were on the same page, but General Sylla still wasn't giving off a warm and fuzzy vibe.

'I don't trust this project. I can smell there is something more to it. If there is, then I *will* find out. And I will be watching you carefully, Redcoat. Don't give me reason to bring you here like this again.'

I shrugged off his aggressive manner and implied threats. 'We will need additional military assistance in the future. I'll be happy to include some figures in our forecasts.'

The general shook his head. 'You will make no mention of this talk between us to anyone else.'

That would make things complicated.

'Then how are we to proceed?' I motioned between us with my hand.

'I need more time to review your activities. Get me a summary of the project.'

'I'm sure I can pull something together. But you need to know that I won't have control of the funds. Keeping your involvement quiet will be difficult.'

For the first time he smiled. A thin smile. 'You will find a way. I will send someone to your hotel at seven a.m. tomorrow to collect the documents. Include the forecasts.'

I didn't have much choice but to play along – for now at least. 'Okay, I'm staying at the–'

'I know where you are staying and which room. Have it ready when they come.'

CHAPTER 27

CAMEYENNE HOTEL – THREE HOURS LATER

By the time we'd returned to the hotel for lunch, I was already knackered. Last night's whisky might have been a factor but the mental pummelling from the morning meetings had taken its toll. I needed a decent plate of scran to recharge the batteries before facing the afternoon, which would include the next phase of the diamond deal. A deal that could soon be sucked into the mayhem engulfing the mining project negotiations if we weren't careful.

In the last twenty-four hours, every development – every incident, meeting, and subtle or not so subtle signal – had blared out warnings I couldn't afford to ignore. We couldn't afford to ignore.

I'd left a worried Manny flopped in a chair in the foyer while I sent an encrypted report to Cal in London from the empty business centre. Our shattered escorts, Baldé and Demba, had both been dismissed for the rest of the day. The ease with which General Ndidi accepted that request reflected my fall in grace after yesterday's fun and games.

The first inkling of my diminished status had been leaving General Sylla's lair to find no sign of the promised car waiting outside. Although I hoped it might simply be due to the anticipated grilling finishing sooner than expected after comprising a warning rather than a robust inquisition.

After traipsing back to the Battailon Special headquarters and arriving sweaty and irritable, I'd been reunited with my phones and other gear. Despite the accompanying relief, and a sense I'd escaped my Camp Alpha experience lightly, an uncomfortable silence settled on the car for the rest of the morning as we drove around Conakry ticking off tasks on the to-do list.

Against Manny's advice, we'd door-stepped Édouard. I didn't have the time or the inclination to piss around today and we reached his place by 10:15, only fifteen minutes later than the original scheduled appointment.

That cancellation must have been due to our sojourn to Camp Alpha rather than any pressing business on his part, because Édouard was home and appeared to be doing the square route of fuck all. He wasn't pleased to see us at the door and the meeting went downhill from there.

Perhaps I was blunter than strictly necessary, but there was no easy way to announce that Pinnacle wanted to rip up the existing agreement and introduce a new structure and methodology. *Oh, and by the way, we'll have control of the project – not you.*

The stream of rapid and angry French from Édouard after I revealed this new development hadn't needed translating, even if Manny could have kept up. He didn't exactly throw us out, but we didn't have time to enjoy cold drinks in the garden before we were back on the street outside.

It wasn't as though Édouard's reaction was unexpected, although even he appeared shocked by the venom of his own initial ranting before he calmed down in the face of my dispassionate scrutiny. His loss of face had been about the highlight of my morning.

To be fair, my apparent intransigence was aided by my distracted focus on the earlier encounter with General Sylla. Nearly every aspect concerned me. His demands for secret involvement; his knowledge of my movements and activity; and the unspecified threats if we didn't bow to his demands. The only thing he didn't seem to know about was the diamond deal. And how long could that last?

There hadn't been a chance to discuss any of it with Manny yet, but with our escorts now dismissed for much-needed rest after their long night, we should get some privacy. I planned to run through it with him after completing my report to Cal.

The lawyer, Fozzie, had fitted us into his busy schedule and arranged for the draft agreement to be printed. He carved out ten minutes between meetings and put his best guy to work on it right away. He promised to review it in depth himself by the end of the day or, more accurately, by the end of his late evening catch up.

We ran out of time to visit the bank to discuss opening the business account. Once we'd eaten lunch, I'd review whether we could fit that in during the afternoon.

For now, I was trying to log on through the VPN and getting exactly nowhere. With no one else in the business centre, you'd have thought the Internet would be flying along. After rebooting my machine for the second time and then sneaking up to the router and switching it off and back on with zero improvement, I finally gave up.

Patrons dotted around the pool and restaurant meant little privacy at the bottom of the gardens. I mooched along the border hedge and rang Cal on the satphone.

'Cal it's me.'

'Everything okay?'

'We have a bit of a problem. I can't get online to send a secure message, but I wanted to give you a heads up.'

Cal adopted a slower, cautious tone. 'Okay. Go on.'

'I was called into a meeting with another general at Camp Alpha. He wasn't a happy bear. He's obviously had me under surveillance or accessed my records. Passport, hotel check-in, everything.'

'Hang on, which general? Is this because of yesterday? For fuck's sake.'

'Calm down, mate. Just wait till I've finished.'

Cal's voice rose and distorted through the static, although I could still make out his words.

'Don't tell me to calm down. I've been working on this project for over twelve months and you've thrown your weight around just as we're ready to sign off on everything.'

That prompted a flush of anger. 'That's bullshit and you know it. This fucking general wants in on the deal. Doesn't want anyone else to know. And according to your friendly general, this dude is a real fucking player. A nasty bastard. And don't get me started on Édouard and Sapro. He went fucking apeshit when I gave him the good news about the revised deal.'

'Christ.' Cal sighed at the other end and we both took a breather.

Before continuing, I checked my immediate vicinity for anyone who might be in earshot. 'Fozzie has the French draft and will look at it by the end of tonight.'

Cal's voice matched the calmness of my own. 'Right. We expected Édouard to take it badly, but he'll come around.'

'Yeah. This general is a problem though. He wants in on the mining project and he'll be all over the diamond deal if he finds out about it.'

'Just make sure he doesn't then.'

I gave a dismissive laugh. 'As easy as that, eh? I tell you one thing, if I detect surveillance on the way to this inspection today, then I'll be aborting.'

'Now hang on, John. This deal is important. For all of us. You're the man on the ground and it's your call, but I'm sure you'll be able to deal with any local interference. Don't be hasty to abort. This could be our only shot at it.'

'I don't like it, Cal. That general knows about me, where I'm staying, which room I'm in. He might have sussed my travel in Russia and Iraq from my passport or he's got ears and spies everywhere. Either way, if he can get hold of all that info, we should assume he's got access to everything.'

'What did you say his name was, this general?'

'General Sylla. Security, intelligence, military police, I'm not sure exactly which. Maybe all three.'

'Sylla.' He paused. 'Let's finish there and link up by secure means after the inspection.' And with that, Cal hung up.

I looked at the damp handset and had half a mind to take a run up and throw it into the sea. *Thanks for nothing, Cal.* One mention of Sylla's name and he'd fucked off sharpish. Meanwhile I had to try and keep this dubious side deal with a bunch of local not-rights secret while looking after a pair of Israeli gemmologists and getting them to this inspection and out of the country without anyone cottoning on. Especially General *bloody* Sylla.

That reminded me. I pulled out my local phone, selected the most recent added contact, and pressed call. The dial tone sounded more distant than that of the satellite phone.

'Hello.'

'It's John. Come to the bar next to the pool in the garden, now. Both of you.'

'Okay.'

I hung up. Time to get eyes on the gemmologists.

I wandered across the garden, taking apparent interests in the trees and shrubs. After three minutes I changed course and headed at a casual pace towards the door to the hotel. When two men with dark hair and healthy Mediterranean tans approached the door from inside, I lengthened my stride. Both wore sandy coloured cargo trousers and safari shirts.

'David?' I called out from ten feet away.

The taller man smiled and began to reach out a hand. I shook my head and slowed as I approached on a trajectory to pass them. He retracted his hand.

At six feet away I said, 'Your room number?'

'Three-seventeen,' David answered. He seemed to understand my intention for a brush contact, but the shorter, dumpier guy's brows were clamped together in confusion.

'See you there at sixteen hundred.'

I passed them and continued into the hotel on a new mission to get a coffee and some scran from the restaurant.

CHAPTER 28

16:00 – CAMEYENNE HOTEL

I knocked on the door of room 317 and cast my eyes down the silent corridor to an abandoned cleaning trolley. We hadn't encountered any guests or staff since ascending from the ground floor as the hotel slumbered through another humid afternoon. The door jerked open, and the taller guy from the garden stepped to one side without a word.

The two gemmologists each sat on a bed, Manny commandeered the desk chair, and I remained standing next to the television.

'I'm John and this is my colleague Manny.' I pointed at the taller man sitting next to an open case crammed full of inspection equipment. 'So, you're David?'

'Yes. And this is Shimon.'

The shorter man held up a hand and turned from me to Manny. 'Hi.'

Manny lifted a reciprocal hand while I cracked on. 'I'm not going to sugar coat this; I'm sure you two have been around a bit. Have you travelled on Israeli passports?'

David stiffened. 'Yes, why?'

'Okay, no problem. I just wanted to establish that from the start. It's sensitive times here in Conakry. Brits, Israelis, Americans, we're all used to being scrutinised when we're off the beaten track. That's why I've decided we shouldn't be seen together.'

Both men returned blank looks.

'The situation is that we need to keep this deal, and therefore this inspection, under the radar. We're not sure exactly who from yet, but it would be better for all of us if we got this concluded without the authorities knowing about it. Interference from corrupt officials or military officers could cause complications.'

David's eyebrows raised. Possible complications might not have featured in the job briefing. I didn't bother about Shimon. My focus stayed on the senior man.

'We're going to take precautions today because we're not a hundred per cent sure about the seller either. In fifteen minutes, you need to go down to the front of the hotel where you'll see Manny waiting outside making a phone call. He will signal for a taxi driven by another colleague to pull forward and pick you up. You'll be driven to a house ten minutes away where another man will join you there for extra security. What are their names, Manny?'

'The driver is Alain. Security guy is Samuel.'

The flat monotone of Manny's answer generated a flash of anger reflected in the daggers I fired in his direction. He met my eyes and lowered his head again quickly. I wasn't happy about this afternoon either but here and now wasn't the time to sulk about it.

'Right, Alain and Samuel. Manny knows them well and they are good guys.'

Manny responded with a lukewarm smile and accompanying nod.

'The taxi will remain static until we are at the inspection location and happy with the situation. We'll then call you forward. Okay?'

David looked at Shimon and rolled his shoulders in a 'so–so' gesture as his head bobbed in unison and his nose wrinkled with the rest of his face. Tough crowd. Manny's attitude probably hadn't helped.

'You'll remain in the car and wait with the team for our instruction to proceed. Okay?'

This time, David's reticent posture morphed into a begrudging nod. 'Okay.'

'Good. We'll stay flexible for the return journey, but the taxi will probably drop you straight back to the hotel. Once we're all complete, I'll come here and check in with you.'

'How are you traveling to the inspection? And can we have your number?' asked David.

'Yep, I'm just about to give you our details. Only to be used if we have a problem. I suggest we all turn off our international phones and use local cell phones.'

'We don't have a local phone.'

'It's alright, we've got an unregistered spare for you.' I indicated to Manny, who pulled a basic Nokia model out of his pocket. After a couple of minutes faffing about, we had exchanged contact details and switched off our other phones.

'The seller's people are coming to the hotel at half-four. We're expecting two guys, Lambert and Sadou, who we only met yesterday. They don't know it yet, but we're going to be following them in a red Mercedes saloon, not traveling in their vehicle. We don't know the location for the inspection, which is why we're setting it up this way. It might seem like unnecessary bullshit, but better safe than sorry.'

A smile finally broke out on David's face, although Shimon still didn't look convinced. One out of two wasn't bad.

Back in the corridor I grabbed Manny's arm. 'Mate, as far as the geos are concerned, we need to be on top of this today.'

'I'm sorry,' he replied. 'This general you met earlier…' His voice trailed off and his attention fixed on something over my shoulder. I looked round to see a cleaner pushing the trolley.

'Get down the front and get these two away in the taxi. We'll talk afterwards out in the bar while we're waiting for Lambert.'

While Manny made his way to the front of the hotel to coordinate the pick-up, I headed down to our favourite garden hangout to wait for Lambert and Sadou. The place was empty. Even so, I tucked myself away at a rear table.

The barman wandered over. 'Bière, monsieur?'

'Non. Jus d'orange, si'l vous plaît.' An orange juice should help perk me up.

After lunch we had squeezed in a tedious meeting at the nearest branch of Societe Generale bank. The manager had become disinterested once he realised we didn't possess the necessary documentation to open an account there and then, or a big chunk of change to deposit. I should have cracked a siesta instead.

Manny had then dropped me back at the hotel while he disappeared to scratch together the extra vehicle and manpower. I hadn't met Alain the driver or Samuel the extra muscle, but trusted Manny to source capable people, despite the limited time available.

I shook my head as I recalled the events of the last twenty-four hours. What the hell was I going to give General Sylla's early morning callers at 7.00 a.m.? I'd focus on that once we'd got the inspection completed. One issue at a time.

Manny strode past the restaurant bar and took a seat opposite. 'This general you met earlier, he's serious trouble.'

'Tell me about it. He wants in on the deal.'

'I asked around this afternoon. They call him *Momba*.'

'Momba? What does that mean?'

'You know, the deadly snake.'

'Mamba?'

'Yes, Mamba. It's said different in French. He's a powerful man with eyes everywhere. You were lucky but this is getting dangerous. They say he earned that name many times.'

Movement caught my attention. Lambert and Sadou had arrived. They ignored the barman's offer of a drink and skirted the bar.

I watched them approach and murmured, 'The geos got away okay?'

Manny followed my eyeline to the approaching fashion disasters. 'Yeah. Alain will take them to Condé's place, link up with Samuel, and wait for my call. Shall I come that side?'

'No, stay there.'

'Ça va?' said a smirking Lambert as he pulled out the chair next to Manny and diagonally opposite me. His bright shirt would have won a prize at a Hawaiian-rig run ashore. Sadou's outfit was muted in comparison – it was the manky green and red mix of his ensemble that let him down. He dumped himself next to me and flashed a yellow-toothed grin that matched his oppo's top.

I downed the last two inches of my orange juice and interrupted Lambert as he began to ask Manny a question in French. 'Where's the meeting?'

Lambert glowered at me; his annoying smile now absent. 'Downtown. Where are the experts?'

'They go separately. This is the way it's going to happen. You show us on the map exactly where the meeting is taking place and tell us who will be there. We'll make our way in our own vehicle and bring the experts with us.'

Lambert was already shaking his head. 'That's not what has been agreed.'

'I don't care. That's the way it happens, or we cancel. People are taking an interest and we don't want to attract attention. Now where's the meeting?'

'What people?' Lambert frowned and glanced at Sadou.

'We don't know exactly but if we want to keep this deal under wraps, then we all need to play this afternoon carefully. So, where's the meeting being held?'

Lambert held my gaze for two or three seconds, then his eyes flicked to Sadou for a moment before returning my way. He looked at his watch and took a deep breath.

'A room at the Novotel. Cinq heures.' *Five o'clock*

'Fucking hell, you're joking. That goldfish bowl.'

He seemed comically affronted by my outburst. 'We have three rooms on the fourth floor. Private. No one will know.'

'Maybe private in the room. But everyone will see us arrive. We need to get in and out separately.'

Wrinkles erupted on Lambert's face as he considered my point. He cursed in French under his breath. I found it satisfying to see his arrogance punctured, despite the underlying cause also giving me plenty to worry about.

My watch showed 16:25. We'd be lucky to make the meeting on time. 'We'll be at the lifts on the fourth floor at five o'clock, or as near as dammit if we get held up.'

Then I jabbed a finger at the two of them. 'You wait for us there and take us straight into the meeting. That way we can all pass through the main public areas separately, rather than hanging around like a school beano to Blackpool.'

Lambert turned to Manny. 'Qu'a t'il dit?' *What did he say?*

As soon as Manny finished translating, I continued. 'You need to go now, and we'll follow a few minutes behind. One last thing, who will be at the meeting?'

'The seller and one other. And sécurité.' Lambert's answer was measured, cautious.

'Security in the two rooms either side?'

'Oui.'

'We don't have money with us today. This is an inspection only, by our experts. Everyone understands that?'

Lambert nodded. 'Yes. It is the agreement.'

I leaned back in my chair and flicked a dismissive hand. 'Right, off you go then. Best you thin out to the Novotel and square everything away.'

They got up to leave, faces uncertain. Probably wondering how come it was me dishing out the instructions all of a sudden.

'And Lambert…'

He looked down and met my best steely glare. 'Yes?'

'If there's a problem, then make sure you call us before we get there.'

CHAPTER 29

I'd kept my eyes peeled for signs of surveillance all day, particularly around the hotel. The difficulty was the number of potential candidates. Uniformed hotel staff, cleaners taking it easy, guests lounging around the lobby – take your pick.

On the road it wasn't much better. The torrent of motorbikes and cars in the slow-moving traffic had me seeing watchers everywhere. Or nowhere. The rest of the day it hadn't mattered. Now it was showtime.

Manny juggled the phone and the steering wheel with practised ease. No one cared here; they were all at it. I doubt even the police knew if it was technically illegal or not. The call was important enough that I didn't complain with my usual vigour. We'd set off a few minutes behind Lambert and Sadou, and now we needed to apprise our other team of a change of plan.

'Alain? Alain? You have Samuel in the car? Good. Go now to the Novotel.' Manny listened for a second before continuing. 'Yes, we're on our way there. We'll reach it before you. Pass the phone to David.' A pause. 'The taller one.'

Manny handed me the phone.

'David?'

'Yes.'

'When you get to the hotel, take the lift to the fourth floor. I'll be waiting.'

'Okay.'

I cut the call and deliberately slipped the handset onto the shelf in the central console. Manny looked at its new home, gave me a sideways glance, and then focused on the road ahead.

We travelled in silence through the late afternoon jams while I scanned the mirrors and saw potential followers in every direction.

Once we'd crossed the causeway to reach downtown, I grabbed the map to check our route options and pointed ahead to an upcoming junction.

'Take a right in two hundred metres, another right one hundred later, then a left after one-fifty.'

Manny's head turned. 'What? But we'll be late.'

'We need to flush out any dickers. It'll only add a couple of minutes. If anyone shows out, you need to be ready to pull some moves.'

I could feel his eyes on me.

'I'll pay any fines, okay. We just need to lose them if they're on our tail.'

'Condé won't forgive me if I scratch his car.'

'Well don't then. Keep your concentration and it'll be fine. I doubt we'll see anything anyway. Here, mate. Turn here. And step on the gas.'

Manny bullied his way across one more lane with little room to spare before the turn. In the lighter traffic he put his foot down and jinked past slower vehicles. Thrown around in my seat, observing the cars that followed us off the main artery became a struggle.

'Next right.'

'Got it.'

We swung into the corner at speed to a chorus of shouts from a gaggle of pedestrians forced to take evading action.

I watched the scene in my wing mirror. 'Come on. Pick it up. Second left.'

Angry faces turned in our direction from the group shaking themselves down in the middle of the road. They bomb-burst as a black car shot around the corner with a motorbike in tow, two up.

'Shit. We've got company. Floor it, but don't miss the next left.'

Manny cursed as I felt the car jerk left then right around a hazard. My attention remained on the mirror, so I didn't know how close it had been. More shouts from somewhere behind and more muttering from my left.

Ahead, the left turn was snarled with traffic and a stream of oncoming vehicles didn't help. 'Cancel the left. Right, right, right, seventy-five metres.'

The old Mercedes accelerated with a satisfying growl, helped in part by a dodgy exhaust.

A car and a box van swept out of a street we'd already passed on our right. I couldn't tell if the pursuing black car hit one, both, or neither, but everything in my mirror ground to a halt – apart from the motorbike, which wobbled around the rear of the van before straightening up and following in our wake.

We tore into the next right and almost took out an oncoming taxi in the middle of the road. Our tyres screeched as they bit into the tarmac and a jiggle of weightlessness accompanied Manny's commentary. 'Fuck.'

I was so surprised by the real swear word and his wonderous tone that I began laughing.

'Well done, mate. Left, left, left at the end here.'

We hit eighty miles per hour before Manny went heavy on the brakes for the next left. The moto hadn't followed us into this street. From my restricted viewpoint I hadn't seen it go past the junction either.

I checked front. The left turn had emerged as a ripe candidate for a demolition derby.

'Cancel left. Right, right, right.'

'What the fuck, John.' Manny went off then back on the brakes as he threw the wheel to make the turn. I grabbed hold of the door handle as we slew to the right.

We narrowly avoided a street seller and his cart crossing the road and righted ourselves out of the skid.

'What are we doing?' Manny's maniacal shriek cut through the road noise.

Ahead of us, the traffic we'd left earlier on Route Niger crossed our path; behind us no sign of pursuit.

'Punch through. Will this take us to the coast road? I'm sure it does.'

After a second, Manny answered with an animated, 'Yes'.

'Go, go, go.'

As we both settled down after the excitement, thoughts turned to the plan at the Novotel. No surveillance vehicles had shown out as we motored down the coast road and past the beachcomber bar. Manny was shaking his head and muttering again under his breath, although he couldn't hide the twitch at the corner of his mouth.

'Don't tell me you didn't enjoy that.'

His face cracked open to betray the truth in my words, even as he shook his head.

'When we get into the car park, drop me off then keep a look out for our guys. When Alain arrives, get Samuel to stay with the cars. I'll make my way up to the fourth floor. You follow behind David and Shimon. Jump into their lift with them. If you miss it for some reason, then take the stairs.'

'The stairs?'

'You might be there all day waiting for another lift, or for theirs to come back down. Get up the stairs a bit lively and you might even beat them up.'

I'd almost forgotten the last important point. 'Oh, and if anyone else tries to get in their lift, stop them.'

'What? How?'

'I don't care. Just interfere the best way you can if you see anyone following them.'

Manny's smile had been replaced with a frown. 'No one behind us?' he asked.

'Not that I can tell, mate. But you never know.'

CHAPTER 30

THE NOVOTEL

I acknowledged the indifferent hotel manager as I strolled through the hotel lobby with my daysack slung over one shoulder. Leaving it in the car had been an option but, after consideration, keeping it close won the day.

I took the stairs to the fourth floor rather than chancing the lifts. From the RV point, I rang David's new number from my local phone.

'Hello.'

'It's John. I'm here, waiting.'

'Okay. We'll be…' – he had a quick conflab with the driver in the background – 'we'll be there in less than ten minutes.'

Rapid footsteps sounded along the corridor and the fashion twins appeared, eyes darting around. Not as laid back as when rocking up to our previous meetings.

'See you then. Manny will be behind you downstairs and follow you up. Don't acknowledge him.' I put the phone back in my pocket.

'Where are the experts?' Lambert made no attempt to hide the concern in his question.

'On the way.' We'd made good time: 16:55 by my watch. I lifted my hand to placate the dynamic duo. 'A few more minutes.'

Lambert's face creased in annoyance. 'They should be here with you.'

I ignored his harsh tone. 'Don't worry. We're being careful, for security. No problems here?'

'Non, rien. Everything calm.'

During the next ten minutes, I had to fend off repeated questions from Lambert about where the experts had got to. Several times the lifts stopped at our floor and either disgorged occupants or opened to reveal annoyed faces before resuming their arbitrary journeys to the sound of buttons being hammered. All that did was spark him up again.

In the end, I had to tell him in no uncertain terms to stop flapping. Other figures mooched around in the corridor. Apparently, they were from the seller's security detail.

By the time the lift doors opened to reveal David carrying his Peli Case, with Shimon and Manny stood either side, I'd been tempted to call again to check they hadn't swanned off somewhere else. Lambert shepherded them along the corridor, a relieved look on his face.

I monitored for any sign of watchers as the group passed, catching Manny's eye as he brought up the rear. 'Any issues?'

'Nothing I could see.'

'Good. When we leave, me and you will head down first to check it's clear with Alain and make sure the cars are ready. Samuel keeping an eye on ours?'

'Yes. Just like you asked.'

'Sorry, mate. Just checking.'

It wasn't that I didn't trust Manny to follow instructions, it was just that we'd had plenty going on during the journey here. Easy to miss something.

Before I could enter the hotel suite, Sadou and then Lambert pushed their way out. From their matching dark expressions, I assumed they'd been dismissed by the boss. I'd have slung them out as well – for dress code violations.

Inside the room the temperature was stifling. The air conditioning couldn't handle eight of us crammed in. The single beds had been shifted to the sides of the room to enable a pair of pushed-together tables and a smattering of chairs to occupy the centre.

Our experts were already taking their seats at the table, on which rested a closed silver briefcase. Two smartly dressed, bearded men sat behind the table. One older guy with a well-fed, confident look and the other younger, skinnier and wearing prescription glasses.

A couple of beefy chaps with similar short beards and slightly scruffier dress sense preened behind them on either side. They stood with chests pushed out and hands clasped by their waists – a typical security stance.

Spare chairs were available, set back from the table. But I had stopped in my tracks at the scene. I couldn't hide my surprise that all four men from the seller's side appeared to be Arabs.

The two men at the table stood up and our gemmologists bounced back to their feet as though they'd sat on burning coals. The older chap walked around the table, ignoring David and Shimon, and offered his hand. 'Welcome. You are Pierce, I assume?'

We shook hands. A gentlemanly handshake. On closer inspection, subtle gold lines in his white shirt became apparent and oozed designer quality.

'Yes, John Pierce. And you must be the owner of the stones.'

'Abu Nizam.' His gaze shifted to my right.

'This is my colleague, Manny.'

'Hello, sir,' said Manny.

Abu Nizam gave a brief nod and turned to David and Shimon. 'Your experts have all the equipment they need?'

'I believe so.'

'Yes, we are ready,' said David.

Abu Nizam faced me again. 'Ishaq will answer any questions and provide any assistance you require. As salaam alaikum, Mister Pierce.'

He walked past me to the door where another broad-shouldered Arab had appeared.

'Alaikum as salaam,' I said to his retreating figure.

No sooner had he disappeared than Lambert and Sadou cruised in, the door shutting behind them. By now David had sat back down and pulled his black Peli Case onto the table. Shimon and Ishaq spoke quietly as the two goons at the back looked on.

'What do you reckon?' I murmured to Manny.

'Lebanese.'

'Is that normal?'

'I don't know. Probably. There's a lot of Lebanese in West Africa.'

Lambert and Sadou squeezed past us. Lambert took Abu Nizam's chair at the table and puffed himself up. Sadou parked his fat arse on one of the single beds. There were now nine of us in the room. Cosy.

I settled into the nearest chair as the first prickles of perspiration arrived, my focus on the two big lads. Manny followed suit after half turning his chair towards the closed door.

At first, I could only see the lids of the open cases through the limbs and torsos moving around the table; David and Shimon readying their inspection equipment and Ishaq arranging the goods.

Then I caught a glimpse of a diamond. Now I'd bought a few stones in rings and necklaces for Claire in my time, and even a few emeralds to match her green eyes, but this wasn't a stone – this was a fucking rock. It literally took my breath away.

On a technical level, I wouldn't know a diamond from a chunk of glass, but I just knew this was the real thing. I lifted out of my seat to get a better look. One of the goons flinched as I moved forward. I shot him a questioning glare and he rolled back on his heels.

Ishaq had already placed five beautiful, mesmerising rocks on a tray with his gloved hand. When David shone a powerful light on them, the diamonds sparkled like an image from a fairy tale.

'Jeez,' I said under my breath before checking Manny's reaction.

His eyes widened and he craned his neck for a better view. He let out a slow whistle. 'Wow.'

The next five stones produced by Ishaq were smaller and the last five smaller again. Still big mind you; the first lot had all been the size of kids' marbles. Fifteen glittering gems that David and Shimon now processed one at a time.

Ishaq and the Israeli experts maintained a quiet, professional dialogue throughout the next forty-five minutes as the diamonds were assessed and photographed using callipers, magnifying scopes, a high-res camera, and plenty of beeping kit I'd never seen before.

I had to hold one.

The moment their activity waned I popped the question. After donning a white glove, I selected the largest stone and held it up. A shiver of excitement, lust, greed, longing, envy – pretty much a cocktail of deadly sins – enveloped me.

Fucking hell. If these were the real deal, then I was going to be rich. Manny frowned and asked, 'What's wrong?'

'What do you mean?'

'Your face. Looks odd.'

My facial muscles instantly relaxed and turned off the bizarre leer I must have been displaying. Shit – this stuff could screw with your head. I shook off my embarrassment and focused on the stone in my hand without the previous emotion. It wasn't easy to stop it returning.

After the inspection was completed and all the equipment and treasure packed away, there was no further sign of Abu Nizam. He'd either already left the building or wasn't a fan of emotional goodbyes. And the diamonds spoke for themselves. And the appreciative nods and comments from David indicated they spoke volumes – volumes of potential profit for all involved.

We left the seller's men on the fourth floor and headed to the cars in pairs. Manny and I went down first as planned, followed by David and Shimon once we'd located and positioned the vehicles for a swift getaway.

We detected no signs of watchers but that didn't mean they weren't there. It was more accurate to say that the presence of anyone we clocked as questionable could be otherwise explained.

Alain and Samuel drove the Israelis back to the Cameyenne, with Manny setting us off a few minutes behind. I kept a watch on the mirrors during our quiet journey. Quiet in the car and quiet on the streets as far as added excitement was concerned. Just the usual road mayhem.

CHAPTER 31

Nothing appeared amiss as Manny dropped me off outside the Cameyenne, but the story was different inside. Two thickset locals in sober white shirts and grey slacks stiffened as I strolled through. They looked at each other before studiously avoiding eye contact with me.

I felt kind of relieved. If this was the standard of tradecraft, then it was doubtful we'd been followed or pinged at the Novotel. The normally chatty young receptionist also looked away as I approached. Not such a good sign.

'Evening,' I said to her. 'Ça va?'

She turned to me, glanced at the two jokers pretending not to be there, and ventured a nervous smile. 'Bon soir.'

Her eyes flicked back to the new lobby additions. 'Ça va bien,' she said quietly, her long lashes blinking rapidly as she delivered a shy smile.

I winked and she laughed. A hand immediately shot to her mouth as she looked at my new shadows again. Not good at all.

I snubbed the lifts and bimbled to the door leading to the stairs. Once through, I sprinted up the flights on the balls of my feet, cushioning the impact to make as little sound as possible. Who needed the gym?

Up at room 317, David confirmed the diamonds had been high quality. Possibly too high, so he said. Apparently, the large flawless stones would be so expensive they might be tricky to sell. Better value could often be found with less perfect diamonds, which had a lower price tag but would still appear impeccable to all but the most skilled examiners.

Neither man had spotted anything suspicious during the afternoon's operation and there was a distinct whiff of scepticism in the room when I warned them to stay vigilant for undefined and unseen threats. David confirmed they had reservations for the next day's Air France flight to Paris and would print them off in the business centre.

I told them to remain cautious and not leave the hotel until Alain's taxi arrived in the morning. Manny would coordinate again, just like today, and only swipe our local phone back from them at the last minute.

The corridor was empty as I scuttled out of their room after a final reminder not to acknowledge me if we bumped into each other in the public areas of the hotel.

My room appeared untouched, not that it contained anything other than clothes and bits of non-essential gear. I bolted the door, took off my shoes and sank on to the bed. Time for a power nap to recharge the batteries.

It took a lengthy shower and the last sachet of coffee before I began to recover my wits after forty minutes of blissful nothingness. The USB stick for Mamba still needed to be prepared. Probably best I didn't know how General Sylla had earned his nickname.

Before dealing with the USB, I decided to give Cal another shout. With the diamond inspection completed, Sapro thoroughly pissed off, and surveillance goons in my face, now seemed like a good time to push hard to Foxtrot Oscar the hell out of here.

I had my sleeves rolled down and trailed a fresh squirt of eau de DEET on my way into the garden. No point making it easy for the mozzies. I had spied one pair of stationary grey slacks out of the corner of my eye when I'd made the swift right turn in the lobby. No sign of my other fan, but I suspected he'd be lurking nearby.

I wandered over to the far side and slipped into a shroud of darkness where a row of garden lights were out. The phone locked on to the satellites and I checked for privacy as the dial tone sounded.

Jeez – a figure loomed less than five metres away. My night vision hadn't fully kicked in yet, although I could see that he or she held a rake. The stance and build suggested a man. A bit late for a spot of gardening whoever it was.

Cal's tinny voice came through the speaker. 'Hello, John.'

'Hang on a sec, Cal.' I clutched the phone to my chest and glared at the nearby figure.

'Excusez-moi s'il vous plaît.' No response. 'Aller, s'il vous plaît.'

He made no move to leave. I turned and stomped along the hedge towards the hotel. 'Sorry, mate. Things have got a bit…' – a pair of grey slacks caught my eye ahead. I looked up to see shadow number two.

'Are you there, John?'

A quick check revealed the mystery night-time gardener had followed me and stopped ten feet away.

'Cal, you need to book me a flight out of here asap. I'll send a secure message in the next hour. Be ready to reply on receipt.'

'Why, what's happening? I won't be able to pick it up straightaway.'

Grey slacks stared at me, now also only ten feet away.

'Just do it,' I said into the phone and ended the call.

After dropping the phone into my daysack, I opened my body and lowered my head to keep both men in view and be ready to react if they kicked off. Then I struck out across the grass towards the lights and other guests.

When I reached the business centre the sweat was flowing. The sudden feeling of vulnerability out in the garden had stirred me up. I'd been ready to take both men down, but more shenanigans like that and another run-in with Mamba would be on the cards.

The business centre was packed; the only free seat next to the blonde South African woman I'd bumped into before. Normally I'd have welcomed the chance to chat. Not tonight – I needed privacy.

My decision to leave and try again later was reversed when a chap wearing glasses and a weathered expression rose from a desk tucked in the corner. I made a beeline for it.

From: JP
To: CS

Subject: Sitrep/Request Return to UK

1. New proposal submitted to Sapro.
2. Hostile interest from Gen. Sylla (aka Mamba) in Sapro/PMC project. Anticipate specific financial demands to follow shortly in return for non–interference/patronage. Without a deal, this man could present a serious risk to the project.
3. Diamond assessment completed. Experts return to Europe tomorrow.
4. Most administrative tasks completed. Lawyer has new draft terms for review.
5. Heavy surveillance (overt) is now in place.
6. Advise immediate return to UK of JP. MI to SL.
7. Request you acknowledge receipt and make necessary arrangements asap. Seats available on tomorrow's flights via Paris, Brussels or Casablanca.

JP

The line about seat availability on tomorrow's flights had been an educated guess. The Skype tab flashed in the corner of the screen.

Claire: Are you there?
Claire: Ur showing online. Please answer if ur there.
Claire: The kids are out and I'm only wearing a towel...
John: Hey
John: V busy here.
Claire: Really!!!! You only answer when I offer a show??????
John: Place is packed, so can't even take you up on the offer.
Claire: In your dreams... ;) Need to ask you about the holiday dates. When are we going?? Work know ur away, but it's going to be difficult to book the time off if I don't do it now.

John: Just sent an email about coming home very soon. Next couple of days. If they don't book the seats, then I will. Choose the dates you want from next week and we'll find something on lastminute.com. Story of our lives!

Claire: Ok will do. Got time to chat?

John: Not really. Maybe later though x

Claire: Ok. I'll be here xxx

John: xxx

'John.'

I kept my head pointed at the screen and swept my eyes from left to right, searching for the owner of the heavy whisper.

'John.' Louder this time.

The figure at the printer waved. Shimon. Our eyes met.

'I need to print the tickets and they're not coming out. Do you know how to work it?' He pointed at the large printer and shrugged his shoulders.

Which part of 'don't acknowledge each other' did this clown not understand?

Through the glass I could see a pair of grey slacks on the sofa, legs crossed with a white sock exposed above a swinging black shoe. Very 1980s school uniform.

'I don't know. You'll need to ask.'

Of course, the service desk was empty. I shut down my own machine as Shimon walked past me on the way to his seat, empty handed.

'Can you help me? he asked. Now stopped right by my shoulder and leaning in.

Pointless trying to pretend I didn't know him.

'Give me a minute.'

I stowed my laptop and went to apply my rudimentary IT knowledge to his problem. How some people got by when they couldn't sort shit out themselves was beyond me.

★

By the time I had eaten another plate of spicy fish at the restaurant under blatant observation from you know who, I'd decided enough was enough. If Cal didn't book me a ticket by tomorrow morning, then I would do it myself. Get a flight out of here and send Manny back to Freetown. Too risky for him to remain here alone once I'd gone.

Up in my room I prepared a USB stick for General Sylla containing an outline of the project and the financial forecast highlights from the latest business plan. With that completed, I considered how the 7.00 a.m. meeting might pan out. I didn't want to take the chance that whoever came knocking might seize my laptop and other documents.

Five minutes of checking for potential cache locations and I couldn't do better than the false ceiling. A quick test showed a half-full daysack would fit without bulging. I then had to wipe the giveaway finger marks from around the panel. Then embark on a cleaning spree around most of the surrounding panels to avoid leaving other tell-tale signs. Half an hour of balancing on chairs later and it passed my careful inspection.

I returned to the business centre at 9.45 p.m. to check for an email reply from Cal. Nothing. The watchers watched as I ignored a new Skype messages from Claire.

Alertness following a late-night shower dissipated fast and my eyelids drooped soon after my head hit the pillow. The phone alarm was set for 6.00 a.m.

When the ringing phone roused me, it felt like I'd hardly slept. 2.15 a.m. – I hadn't. It was an inbound call. I unplugged the charging cable and answered. 'Hello.'

'John, it's Manny. Get out of the hotel. Soldiers are coming.'

CHAPTER 32

My revival was instant. 'When? Now?'

'It's what we've been told. Condé is home and his friend at Camp Alpha just called to warn us you are being arrested.'

'Fuck. How long have I've got?'

'They're on their way. Not long.'

My mind raced with the logistics of escape. 'We need an RV. Can't be here. Too much risk of getting caught. I need to get out and meet you some other place. Far away enough you won't get pinged.'

I dropped my hand and looked at the phone. We had to assume our calls were being monitored.

'Get to the first property we visited three days ago. When we checked a few places out.'

After a brief silence, Manny said, 'I know where you mean. But how will you get there?'

'I don't know. I'll find a way. Might be from the back.'

'From the back? Really?' Another pause while he digested my consideration to approach the Vatican Embassy from the beach side. 'We'll go there but call if you need us somewhere else.'

'Thanks, mate. Give me a couple of hours at least. Be careful yourself. Both of you. And get the lawyer ready if they pick me up.'

'Understood. Good luck. See you soon.'

By the meagre light of the phone torch, I threw on the rig already laid out for the morning and stuffed extra kit into my daysack. Once I'd located my mini-Maglite, I flipped the red filter over the lens and used that instead. The Ka-Bar knife went to one side.

A peek out the window into the gardens revealed no unusual nocturnal activity. I checked the room one last time. It annoyed me to be leaving clothes and gear behind. Fat chance of an appropriate tick box on the insurance claim form.

I tightened the shoulder straps on the rucksack, gripped the Ka-Bar so the blade ran hidden up the inside of my forearm, and gently opened the door. The empty corridor was a good sign: no stack of armed troops lined up outside the door. I headed for the stairs rather than the lifts.

As the stairwell door closed behind me, the lift pinged. Time to assume the worst. I bolted down the stairs in the dark, trying both to cushion my footfall and avoid tripping arse over tit. One day I'd take this route like a normal person.

While I strove to mask my movements, there was the distinct sound of footsteps below. Plodding footsteps rather than someone on their toes and closing fast. I stopped and peered down into the gloom. A vague outline of a white sleeve moved in stop-start fashion along the stair rail two flights down. Only one person. Laboured breathing. Good.

I crouched against the metal rail, stowed the Ka-Bar, and prepared to launch myself at whichever grey-trousered goon had drawn the short straw. He was about to have an uncomfortable end to a long day.

The condemned man stomped and wheezed closer with no change in pace. On cue, a white shirt emerged fifteen feet away at the bottom of my flight of stairs. After a deep breath, I sprang up and pushed off into mid-air, leading with a right foot kick that was less roundhouse and more Geoff Hurst.

A flash of pain as my boot connected with the guy's head; nothing compared to what he must have felt. A crunch as I landed on my back, the daysack softening the blow until the back of my head met concrete. Fuck. A downside to the attack plan that I'd overlooked.

The figure in front of me was an unmoving heap. If he'd made any noise, it hadn't registered during my crude performance. However, the sound of something metal clattered down the stairs far below.

I felt the back of my head for signs of blood, like a football player after a glancing collision. Unlikely, but nice to be reassured nothing was leaking out. Back on my feet, I gave the inert heap a token kick before taking off down the stairs.

The cavalry would likely arrive soon, so there was no time for anything more than a rudimentary scan for the dropped weapon. I wrapped on that pretty fast to focus on getting clear of the hotel asap.

The reception area might have been quiet, but outside the main door headlights, slamming doors, and shouting meant *right turn Clyde*. The male receptionist stared open mouthed.

'You haven't seen me, okay.' I didn't recognise him but it was worth a shot.

Out in the garden I gravitated towards the darker right-hand side. Fingers crossed a midnight swim wasn't on the agenda because the clothes and gear in my rucksack weren't waterproofed. All the times I had bothered in past years and when I needed it most my two dry bags were packed away upstairs.

The whistles and shouts behind me weren't going to encourage five-star reviews from the other guests. Fortunately, none of the new arrivals had reached the gardens yet.

I charged towards the rocky beach and recalled what lay to the right side: a lot more rocks. Left side: sand. Better go left, although wrong direction. I'd have to double back – OOF! Winded and flat on my back again, the rucksack having absorbed the worst of another crash landing.

A figure had erupted from the treeline and tackled me to the ground. Knocked the stuffing right out of me. I rolled left and began to rise until someone dragged me backwards by the backpack and threw me to the floor.

A third man – the gardener from earlier? Bollocks. I'd forgotten about him.

On my hands and knees, a boot swung at my face. It caught my upper arm and grazed my cheek. I snatched at it and twisted my body round, bringing the foot and the rest of the assailant along for the ride. A shouted curse rang out as his legs gave way and he landed heavily on his arse. His other foot shot out and caught me on the nose as he also kicked to free the one in my grip. Ignoring the intense stab of pain, I dived forward on top of him, still holding one foot and opening up a juicy target. My knee landed right between his legs with all my weight behind it, resulting in a satisfying, animalistic howl of pain.

Pressing the advantage home with my knee, I lifted my body before bringing my elbow down with sickening force into his face. Then I rose and hammered it down again for good measure. Something gave way with a crunch and a splash decorated my forearm.

A shouted order from above pierced my brutal focus. 'Arrête. Ça suffit.' *Stop. That's enough.*

The unmistakable clatter of running soldiers preceded several pairs of unpolished black boots encroaching into my eyeline.

When I raised my head, it was into blinding torchlight before a sharp blow struck my temple. I turned away as it landed to lessen the impact and tried to stand. That prompted another strike, this time across the side of my head with something hard and heavy.

CHAPTER 33

My head pounded. All over. A painful throb pumped behind my eyes, mixed with a dull ache spreading from the back, and the side of my face was on fire. An attempt to work my jaw from side to side proved ill-advised.

Opening my eyes took an effort.

The blinding glare of lights above. Laid out on a bed. What happened?

Hazy memories; images of violence; the chase; surrounded; a struggle. Captured?

I blinked and generated more pain. If it hurt to blink, then I hated to think what… *Christ,* my hands were tied to the bed. And my legs.

My blurred vision began to clear. I lifted my head and instantly regretted it. Fuck. Dropped it back sharply. Double fuck.

A recollection – hitting the stairs with my swede while making like Jackie Chan.

A uniformed figure entered my line of sight. General Sylla. Mamba. His leering smile as our eyes met didn't contain any warmth.

To his left, a tall man in a white coat. A doctor?

The pain now registering from my back, limbs, and extremities suggested he would be a busy man. My balls ached and prompted memory of another man who'd have a similar problem. Retribution must have been immediate.

The general spoke as his eyes roamed across my face and body. 'Fais vite.' *Make it quick*

'Oui, Général.'

The doctor's bedside manner wouldn't have passed muster at BUPA. He poked and prodded body parts that hurt and left them hurting even more. A handheld beam shone into one eye then the other. A rough spatula held my tongue while fat latex fingers filled my mouth. Other fingers gripped my head. I gasped as they aggravated painful spots.

'Fuck.'

'A sign you are back with us,' said the general as the doctor continued testing the limits of the hypocratic oath.

'Where am I?'

My recently violated mouth throbbed and clicked when I spoke, as if long-lasting damage might have been inflicted. My tongue didn't detect any missing teeth or newly jagged edges; the pain emanated from the surrounding bones.

'You're mine,' replied the general. 'I warned you last time we met. And now we have you and your partners and all the time in the world.'

If my mouth hadn't already been parched, then that welcome would have done the trick. An attempt to moisten my dry, irritated lips with my tongue failed and trying to generate some saliva only highlighted my ravenous thirst and scratchy throat.

Behind the doctor, anatomical posters on faded white walls and the silver sink unit suggested a dedicated treatment room.

'Water, please. S'il vous plaît.'

'Il va bien,' said the doctor, ignoring my request. 'Mais attention à ne pas se cogner à nouveau la tête.' *He's fine. But be careful not to hit his head again.*

The general waved his hand and previously unseen figures approached from behind my head. Rough hands clutched at my limbs and undid straps.

'Which partners? Where are they? Hey, careful. Fuck. Watch it. What's happening?'

The general turned away and disappeared through a far door without answering my questions.

'Where are you taking me?'

I concentrated to keep my voice low and authoritative even as panic threatened to take over. Not easy when four soldiers hauled me upright, aggravating the injuries I knew about and sparking pain in new places. The doctor watched impassively. Somewhere along the line I'd taken a right pasting.

Strong arms gripped each arm and shoulder as the troops bundled me out of the room. Shafts of sunlight revealed dust dancing in the corridor and the temperature jumped compared to the cool, windowless treatment room.

Daylight indicated I'd lost at least a few hours. Where had my watch gone? And come to think of it, what about my rucksack with all my gear?

The dingy corridor and peeling paint reminded me of General Sylla's headquarters in Camp Alpha. Although this particular place didn't ring any bells.

One of the soldiers opened a door and I was turned sharply out into the blinding sunshine. Without any warning of the steps I tripped, forcing my handlers to grip harder to prevent a fall. Bolts of pain erupted through both sides of my body from hip to shoulder. My head jerked and the resulting sear of agony caused automatic tears to blur my already blinking vision.

We approached a military ambulance and several SUVs parked outside. When we passed the cars, I began to fear this rough forced march could inflict more, unnecessary damage. Safe to say, I considered my status should be *not fit to be moved* – unless to a hospital.

The surrounding squat, rundown buildings did not look inviting. After an agonising mile that was probably less than two hundred metres, my limbs had begun to loosen up and even my head had begun to clear. Maybe this was all part of a radical new holistic treatment plan: one soldier in front, ordering me to speed up, two gripping and shoving me despite my injuries, and a fourth behind me, giving an occasional shove and French reprimand.

A guard detail, not a medical escort. Which made me a prisoner.

Outside a two-storey stone building, two soldiers loitered with their weapons held loose. Presumably, my 'partners' – Manny and Condé – would already be inside. I hoped they had been treated better but feared for their welfare.

As we reached them, the two guards both glared and one spat at me, hitting my stained and muddy trousers with a disgusting splatter of phlegm.

'Connard,' the other growled. That meant *bastard*. Not a fan then.

I dug my heels in ready to respond and received a fist in the kidneys from behind as a reward. An indication I enjoyed a universal poor standing with the troops. At a guess, my reputation preceded me. Another unfortunate consequence of my use of force at the military checkpoint.

Tweedle Dee and Tweedle Dum dragged me through a double door opened by the detail leader. His scowl made me rear away from an expected accompanying strike although nothing followed. Instead, he bared his teeth and laughed. The humiliation worse than a physical blow.

Inside the foyer, the gloom took some adjusting to. There were signs of activity: a desk, papers, a radio, and a collection of charging batteries. If those items hadn't been present, the place could have passed for derelict. A couple of insipid yellow lights provided meagre illumination that failed to reach the distant corners.

We passed the desk and skittered left like contestants in a three-legged race. An adult version with me as the duty punchbag in the middle. Seemingly emboldened by the blanket of shadows, I received an escalating number of blows and kicks from all directions, each accompanied with a muttered curse.

Behind each door loomed a worsening prognosis. The one being held open by a new face, perhaps the desk-jockey from this forbidding establishment, led into a narrow corridor that didn't need a signpost. The open door was rusted metal and had a tell-tale metal grille at head height.

The cloying, damp atmosphere in the corridor came out of the rough stone walls. Walls blackened with moisture, rot, blood – who knew? A person's imagination would be their worst enemy in a place like this. A prison. Along the cheerless corridor, the doors had similar barred openings: cell doors.

I lost my footing and stumbled; concentration lost at the realisation of my vulnerability. My helplessness.

A cuff round the head, directly on my injured temple, had me seeing stars. When I staggered after the unexpected strike, a knee in my thigh ignited the large muscle.

'For fuck's sake.'

The punch to the same temple that followed left me dazed and I slipped. That was a mistake. Hands released my arms and I fell to the floor. A flurry of kicks slammed into my body and one connected with my balls and made me yelp. The violence abated as quickly as it had begun.

'Se lever. Se lever,' a mouth screamed inches from my face. *Get up. Get up.*

They manhandled me back to my feet and we were off again down the corridor. Through another door into a grim ablutions block. The boys increased the pace before throwing me to the floor using the increased momentum. I landed in a snotty heap. No judo rolls and bouncing up to take on the enemy. I lay in the middle of a communal shower cubicle, breathing hard and hurting. I was too old for this shit.

The stained and crumbling porcelain cubicle measured twenty feet by ten feet and had a drainage hole currently blocked by my elbow. I pulled my knees up to protect my core – and my balls – but made no effort to rise. The allure of laying down and being left alone trumped everything at that moment. It couldn't last of course.

Footsteps and voices from my increasingly hostile escorts preceded a continuous blast of water straight into my face. A sharp blast that hurt almost as much as the earlier punch. Lukewarm rather than the freezing water from distant memories of similar training. Not that it helped much when the flow was this powerful. I turned my head away to try and escape the jet that was being directed at my face from a thick hose held by one of the gang.

'Se lever. Se deshabiller.'

Get up and do something. I started to rise but the water knocked me over. Those rough hands reappeared and wrestled me onto my knees before tearing at my shirt. With my arms flailing under the assault and all kinds of pain spasms reverberating across my body, they ripped the shirt off and began to pull at my trousers.

Rape. Fuck that.

I needed to summon every ounce of strength and willpower to take these bastards on.

Grappled by three of the men while the other kept the hose pointed away, I had no chance right now. The moment I was free, I'd have to improvise something.

My trousers, underwear, and socks were removed and thrown into the corner. Once I was naked, the three men lifted me to my feet and stood back. The force of the water hit me again as French jeers rang out. Derogatory comments about my tackle, no doubt.

I planted my feet to provide a sturdy platform and closed my fists. The four men stood at the edge of the cubicle, the nearest no more than six feet away. My chances of taking them all down were slim, but I had to try.

'Lavez-vous.' *Wash yourself*

A bar of soap hit me in the midriff and bounced to the floor.

I eyed the four threats, loath to bend and recover the soap in case it prompted an overpowering assault.

'Ramasser. Lavez-vous.' *Pick it up. Wash yourself.*

None of the men made any move to approach. The soap could be a weapon. Dig it under my nails and get those fingers jabbed into eyes; throw the bar itself as a distraction to allow me to close and attack.

I reached down with trepidation, but they didn't move. The hose was even switched off as I scooped up the soap and then began to tentatively lather my body and face. The only sound – the gargling of water into the central drainage hole.

No sooner had I finished, than the hose was switched back on and sprayed up and down to blast off the soap suds.

'Tourney autour.' *Turn around*

The moment of truth.

I turned and braced myself for attack, prepared to fight back; to target eyes and throats with rips and gouges, elbows, fists, and fingers. My clawed hands kept the soap accumulated under the nails from being washed away. *Come on then. Let's fucking go.*

No sound of approach, no cries of bloodlust, no attack.

Ten seconds later, an order to turn and face front again.

Four pairs of eyes set in hard faces. Each with matching sneers of contempt. But no move to overwhelm, overpower, dominate, and humiliate in the worst way.

When the hose was again switched off, the detail commander threw me a dirty orange boiler suit. 'Mettez-le.' *Put it on*

Orange boiler suit. The favoured imitation of Guantanamo Bay inmates by regimes worldwide. I was simply grateful they weren't dressing me in a short skirt and high heels to soften the unappealing vista of my hairy arse before they all ploughed through me. My wry smile elicited a frown from the commander.

No sooner had I donned the boiler suit than the four of them rushed me and hostilities were resumed. The commander leaned in and spat a few words I didn't catch apart from 'smile'.

My new, undersized outfit stuck to my wet body and chafed in unfortunate places as they bludgeoned me into the squalid corridor and dumped me in the first cell.

While I lay catching my breath and letting the pain neurons settle, one of the guards snapped a leg iron into place on my right calf. I waited for the door to slam shut behind him before checking out his handiwork. Cutting through the short, thick chain linking it to a bracket on the wall would need some serious hardware. And then what?

Right now, all I wanted was water. My stomach rumbled. And something to eat. I needed to keep my strength up if I was going to get through this and find a way out. What about disease? That thought prompted a wave of fear. It was black as a witch's tit in the cell and silent. Or was that the clicking of cockroaches. Or the scuttle of a rat.

My cheek scraped against the gritty, damp floor as I lifted myself up. If the beatings didn't kill me, some gopping disease just might. Opening more wounds by sliding and bouncing around my new home wouldn't help.

My heart raced as I sat and waited for my night vision to adjust to the surroundings. The leg iron already dug into my calf muscle and the top of my foot. It wouldn't take long for sores to open. Using the leg of the boiler suit, I wedged the metal cuff into place to prevent it moving. A small victory.

Once my eyesight had adjusted, I could make out a bucket in the corner and a warped metal bed fixed into the wall. No sprung mattress or Egyptian cotton sheets.

I tottered onto the bed and lay down. Hurting, damp, chafed, and scared. But every moment they left me alone was a chance to regain strength: mental and physical. I closed my eyes and thought of home.

The door crashed open just as sleep beckoned. Figures swarmed in, shouting and screaming. If the intent was to scare the shit out of me, it worked. Powerful grips tried to drag me towards the door as the chain tightened and drove the leg iron hard into my foot. Now I was the one screaming.

A heated squabble ensued before someone found the key and released my damaged foot. The dampness might have been water or blood. Whatever the case, it hurt like fuck. A glancing punch to the side of my head indicated someone blamed me for the fiasco. The doctor's instruction about no more head shots clearly hadn't been taken on board.

They applied a slimy, stinking rag as a blindfold. Calloused fingers strayed close to my mouth and I considered biting into one. No, any fight back would have to wait for the right moment, the right opportunity.

As they hauled me out and to the left, we'd be passing the other cell doors. In all the commotion and yelling, I shouted, 'Manny. Manny.'

The only response was a savage blow to the solar plexus that sent my pain receptors into overdrive. I coughed and retched as a second blow struck my side above the hip. Tears joined the moisture in the manky rag.

My knees took a bashing as we ascended a flight of stairs after passing through the door into the foyer and moving further into the recesses of the building. Token blows continued to land on my head and body, but nothing that competed with the burning void left by the earlier gut punch.

My shoulder banged into a doorframe as I received a hard push from behind into a brighter room, the improved light reaching through the blindfold.

A chair hit the back of my knees and hands pulled me into a seated position. Footsteps retreated and a door closed.

My breaths were shallow and rapid. The shock of capture and its implications dominated a kaleidoscope of thoughts. Rape, torture, disease, escape, Manny, Claire, Cal, help.

My breathing slowed and I became hyper aware. My hands were free. Was I alone? Should I remove the blindfold. Fuck it – worth a try. I lifted my hands to the rag and braced for impact. Someone moved behind me, but no strike was forthcoming.

The minging blindfold left a trail of slimy shite as I pulled it off my head. I squinted in the bright light. General Sylla sat motionless, staring at me from behind a desk much less impressive than the one in his last office.

Although this didn't look much like an office. A simple, central table; chairs either side; a neat pile of papers next to an A4 image of yours truly; and a mean fucker staring at me with malice. I'd sat in interrogation rooms before.

'Remain seated. Do not attempt to stand up or you will be punished.'

The general's eyes flicked up and passed a message to whoever stood above and behind me.

'As an enemy of the state you have no rights. Don't think about the Geneva convention or your British military training. Listen to my questions and answer them truthfully. Then I will decide what to do with you.'

Today, the general wore combat fatigues rather than his dress rig. I couldn't recall if he'd changed since leaving the doctor's room.

We hadn't exactly enjoyed friendly repartee during our last meeting, but his aggressive tone suggested that I'd already seen his good side. Say hello to Mamba.

'Understood,' I croaked. 'Water, please.'

'Later. If you answer the questions to my satisfaction.'

He leant down and lifted my daysack onto the table. My empty daysack.

'Before we start, I warn you: do not make the mistake of lying to me. I have an expert searching your laptop and phones for evidence. Now, tell me the real reason you are here in la Guinée.'

'I prepared the documents you requested. I'm here for Sapro to negotiate the final contract for the six concessions with…'

Mamba hurled himself around the table fast for a big man. The baton in his hand that I hadn't noticed before whipped down onto my left elbow with lightning speed. Excruciating pain shot through my arm and I pulled it away in reflex as I cried out.

Something bony crunched as I moved, causing me to yell again. 'Motherfucker.'

The baton landed again, this time smashing into my right shoulder on the collar bone. Something else gave way and I moaned in agony.

'Don't lie to me, Redcoat,' he screamed into my face. Mamba. Now I understood.

'You are plotting a coup against the president. We know all about it. We have your co-conspirators and they have talked. Tell me who else is involved and who is paying you.'

A pain-induced tear leaked down my left cheek as I tried to make sense of his questions.

'But…no. It's a deal with the president.'

He rapped the side of my head with the baton. Hard enough to aggravate my existing injuries but not so much as to cause new ones.

'Do. Not. Lie. To. Me,' he said, tapping the baton on the top of my skull in time with the words. 'We know about the diamonds to finance the coup.'

I held both arms across my lap to prevent any movement initiating sparks of pain from my left elbow and right clavicle. Wrong I hoped, but both felt shattered. Almost as though I could hear and feel the crunching bones. No way to use either arm now. I feared how this would end.

'The diamonds…' I half retched, half coughed. Flecks of bright red blood spattered my wrist. 'The diamonds are something else. Another deal. For people in London. Nothing to do with the president.'

He raised the baton high and brought it down fast. Then everything went dark.

CHAPTER 34

Darkness. Water. Gagging. Drowning. Dreaming? No, drowning –
fucking drowning.

Water filled my mouth. Panic exploded in my head. My arms
flailed and burning pain lanced up from my elbow, eclipsing the sparks
from my collar bone. I couldn't lift my head out of the water. It was
held in place by strong hands as I bucked my upper body every which
way to get free. A ledge pressed hard against my chest.

I couldn't see through the water. Something sucked against my
face. A hood? A death mask? Being murdered.

Someone fucking help me.

Someone. Anyone.

Water cascaded into my throat. I'm dying and it's shit. I thought
drowning was meant to be peaceful. Liars.

Not like this. Don't let it end like this.

Don't give up. Keep fighting. Ignore the pain – must keep fighting.

Wretching, throat filled with water, eyes closed, strength going,
slipping away.

Claire, I love you. Girls. My girls. I'm so sorry.

CHAPTER 35

I vomited water while a soldier knelt over me, pushing double handed at my sternum. His face a mask of concentration, mouth set in a snarl, as he forced my body to breathe. Saving my life. Probably one of the bastards that had tried to kill me.

That's enough. I'm awake now, mate.

I tried to speak and gagged instead. My throat raw and aching. My elbow on fire with pain. My head a mess. What the hell were these psychos trying to do?

My saviour glanced at my face and heaving chest and stopped the compressions. 'Général, il respire.' *He's breathing*

My body ached everywhere that didn't already quiver with pain. On the inside now as well.

A tall figure blocked out the flickering light. Mamba. Bastard. Motherfucker. Killer.

The hatred multiplied inside me until I thought the devil would burst out of my chest and kill every fucking one of these godforsaken cunts.

But I was broken. Helpless. Vulnerable.

Fuck.

'Mettez-le.'

What the hell?

Hands grabbed me, hauled me into a sitting position.

A glimpse of a filled bathtub behind the chair.

Someone howled as my left arm was bent down by my side. An animal scream. Me. Screaming, howling, hurting – the fucking pain.

Hands pressing on either side of my battered face. More agony. Jesus help me. Darkness as the hood went back on. Soaked. No Oxygen. I began to hyperventilate. Some air getting through but not enough. Now what?

Head forced back. Rough, saturated material pressed against my nose and mouth. Suffocating. Fucking stop. Stop.

'Tell me about the coup,' said Mamba, his voice soft and near my ear. 'Tell me and this will stop. Everyone breaks in the end.'

I could hardly speak. Breathing fast. Don't drown me.

'I don't know anything about a coup. You've got it wrong.'

Water poured through the material over my nose and mouth. My head was gripped tight. I tried to lift my arms. The pain flashed. Agony. Now drowning. Again. Please no.

Do it. Fucking do it. If you don't kill me, I swear I will come back and destroy you. Mamba. Motherfucker.

Breathing again, fast. The hood still stuck against my face.

'Just answer my questions and I will let the doctor take a look at your injuries. When will the attacks take place? How many attacks and where? Who are the traitors? Who is their leader? General Ndidi perhaps?'

To answer, to deny, would be of no use. I remained silent and continued trying to drag air into my lungs through the sodden cloth.

'Answer my questions.' His voice rising to a shout. Angry. Evil.

Situation hopeless. A FUBAR to trump them all. There was no way out of this. Nothing I could say. Might as well bring it on. 'I don't know anything about a fucking coup.'

The blow could have come from any angle, from any fist, knee, foot, elbow, baton. Whatever struck the side of my head, the result was me hitting the deck and a return to the welcome embrace of unconsciousness. Away from the despair.

CHAPTER 36

My eyes opened, not that it made much difference. The darkness hid my surroundings. Instead, my senses went into overdrive and the aches and pains reported in. Most everywhere felt tighter, stiffer, swollen, tender. My head and face especially.

I sat up carefully and groaned with the effort. A tentative feel around my elbow revealed little swelling. But an ominous numbness had settled in above and below the joint. I held the arm across my body and reviewed my options.

Although my right collarbone felt mashed up, that arm worked okay. The injury couldn't be as bad as I'd feared. Lumps, abrasions, and cuts adorned my head. Probably a good job I didn't have a mirror to reveal my captors' handiwork in all its glory.

I'd woken on a bed, in the same cell as last time I assumed. No one had installed mood lighting since my last visit, although as my vision adjusted, I caught sight of a bucket in the corner like before. It prompted an instant gurgling in my guts. A spasm of muscles seeking to eject whatever was left inside my digestive system out through my arse. The fetid air in the cell pressed down as a wave of sweaty, burning, feverish nausea swept through my body from deep inside.

I clawed at the jump suit, using one arm to undo the press-stud fasteners down my chest in a race against the burbling in my lower intestine. I rolled the top half down and stood up. For a moment, the raw area on my scrotum eclipsed all other flashpoints.

I shuffled to the bucket and leant back against the damp wall. Something bit me as I rolled the bottom half down and attempted to position my arse over the bucket for a bomb drop – my legs bent at a ninety-degree angle and my back against the wall. A self-inflicted stress-position.

A rush of air and shit exploded out of my arse and covered the bucket, my legs, the jumpsuit, and the floor. Weakness gripped my soul as a further wave of liquid shit fired out, this time getting a direct hit into the bucket. Too late, the damage was done. No way I could wear the shit-covered overalls anymore.

Stepping out of the legs, I used the least worst smelling section to wipe myself down. Another bite on my arm. The stress position had left me drained of energy and I began to shake uncontrollably as I mopped at my legs. Unable to see in the darkness, it felt as though I was only smearing shit everywhere.

I dropped the clothes and staggered back to the bed. My balls were on fire. If shit had got into that wound, I'd be in trouble. Yet another mozzie or other flying bastard bit my back. I had no idea how long I'd been here and no idea how long the doxycycline would protect me from Malaria and other diseases.

I lay down on my back, holding my left arm against my chest. For someone who'd been practically drowned I had a raging thirst. And having just shit my insides out, the growls of hunger from my stomach were a poor joke.

Without a window, there was no indication if it was day or night. At a guess I'd been here less than twenty-four hours. Less than one day. I tried to be positive, but how long could anyone endure this without losing their mind?

In Vietnam, Americans had been held for years. Prisoners in both Gulf Wars, hostages in Lebanon – all those guys had faced worse hardship and come out the other side. I'd just have to hold on, somehow. Hope that someone was working to get me out. Cal. Claire. My girls.

Exhaustion pulled me into inanimate bliss.

CHAPTER 37

Shouting yanked me back to consciousness. Blinding torchlights danced across my face and into the carnage by the bucket. Coughs and shouts from the three soldiers all holding their hands to their noses. Safe to assume the place stank. Christ, it did. I did.

A torch scanned the length of my body and the diarrhoea camouflage pattern decorating my legs. Someone screamed into my face. Maybe they thought I was laying here battered, bitten, and stinking out of some mastermind strategy to escape. Fucking idiots. What did they think would happen given how they'd treated me so far?

They stood over me and deliberated how best to take me out of the cell. I crossed my right arm over my left and gripped my left shoulder to protect that limb as best I could. I thought they'd understood from my body language until one of them tried to lift me by the fucking left elbow. Even the numbness couldn't shield my nervous system from that, and I emitted a piercing scream that needed little enhancement to get the point across.

Powerful hands on both shoulders lifted me vice-like and propelled me into the corridor. A corridor I recognised. We turned right into the ablutions.

I spotted the chair and bathtub from my earlier questioning and a breath caught in my throat. I shivered despite the heat. My automatic body systems went into panic mode and adrenaline flashed through my bloodstream. Before the terror took hold, they guided me into the cubicle on the left and retreated.

As I stood catching my breath and trying to control wild emotions, a hose appeared in the hands of one of the guards and a blast of water drenched my legs. The brown residue of the earlier battle with the bucket washed down the drainage hole.

After a thorough hosing down, one of them returned with a grey jumpsuit, similar to the previous orange version. When I put it on, I was almost elated to find it was larger than the first offering and provided my nutsack room to breathe.

Rather than try to force my left arm into the appropriate armhole, I pulled the flapping arm of the jumpsuit around my neck and tied it round my wrist in a makeshift sling. The guards shouted and gesticulated as I worked but didn't stop me. Another small victory.

It didn't last. Once I was finished, they mobbed me and slipped the soaking hood over my head. A renewed frenzy left me bound to a chair facing the bath. I could hear panting and muttering behind me.

After a wait that felt like an hour, I'd almost fallen asleep in the sitting position when heels dug into the floor and marched crisply towards me.

'Do you think anyone is coming for you?' whispered Mamba from close to my right ear. 'Do you think the British government will try to save you?'

Footsteps crossed from my right to my left, a leg banging into my own as he passed.

He spoke into my left ear. A whisp of a voice, almost lyrical, sensual, breathless. 'There is no Geneva convention here. There is only my questions, and you must answer them.'

The terror had left me. Maybe my adrenaline was depleted. Either that or I'd subconsciously accepted my fate. It's not like I had a choice in what they did.

I considered admitting to involvement in this supposed coup. And say what? Implicate my friends and other innocent people? I could hardly stay awake let alone conjure up a convincing pack of lies about some bullshit coup attempt. Fuck it. Do your worst.

'I can't tell you what I don't know. If there is a coup, it's nothing to do with me or the people I work with. I'm just here for business. Mining business. And to look at some diamonds. With the president, not against him.'

'Redcoat, you disappoint me.' Mamba's voice sounded from directly above and in front of me. 'I thought you were an intelligent man. You must know what is going to happen next.'

His tone contained a hint of regret.

'You have until the end of today to provide me the information I need. I take no pleasure in your pain. Not anymore. Just give me what I want, and we can end this.'

My mind emptied the feelings of discomfort and pain. Even my breathing under the hood had regulated itself. A sense of total calm entered the silence.

'I don't know anything about your fucking coup.'

★

The next hours were a blur of waterboarding and returning to the putrid cell. When I got caught out by another, smaller burst of diarrhoea, it flowed down the legs of my jumpsuit and caked my arse. That was a side issue. It was a case of when they'd kill me, not if. And probably by accident rather than design.

When a soldier revived me for a second time, I wondered why he'd bothered. *Just a do us all a fucking favour.*

And then I woke in brightness. I couldn't be dead because my throat burned from vomiting and every part of my body still screamed for medical attention. Two men wearing white coats fussed over me. The medical room. The layout the same as I remembered.

A proper sling held my left arm in place and one of the men dabbed at my forehead with a clean-looking cloth that emerged spattered with dark blood. Maybe I'd told Mamba something he believed, or maybe they'd given up.

'Water,' I whispered. Ignored.

'Water, please.'

The medic from my last visit filled a plastic cup from a water bottle out of the fridge. Together with his oppo, they lifted and supported my upper back before he tipped the cup to my lips. I sucked at the beautiful, cold liquid like a desperate animal, spluttering half of it over my chest, until the plastic crunched empty and I laid my head back down, exhausted.

Sharp scratches on either arm and I began to drift into visceral dreams so real I couldn't tell afterwards where reality stopped and my imagination started.

Images like a half-forgotten movie of a bandage wrapped around my head, covering my eyes. No one noticing when I adjusted it for comfort and found I could see underneath with my right eye.

A stretcher, a car journey, a wooden platform, the lapping of the sea, a boat trip – so vivid, like an actual memory. Euphoria at the sun on my face, the swell of the ocean, the salt in the air. Freedom. Life. Escape from hell.

But I hadn't escaped, not completely.

I had been moved to a new home, a new cell in another place. Cleaner and brighter, with a high window. Different medical staff attended to my wounds. And as the hours rolled by without any sign of Him, Mamba, I permitted myself to feel hope.

When the drugs wore off, the pain returned, although nowhere near as bad as before. It registered as discomfort rather than agony. Food, water, assisted showers, silent guards who didn't reek of violence – something had changed. I hardly dared allow hope to rise, but a full night's sleep rejuvenated my spirits as much as my physical strength.

My confidence grew that I had been transferred to a safe environment; that the threat to my life had evaporated as quickly as it had appeared and come to dominate my world. My head was clear, and I wanted to ask questions of my own. Discover where I was being held and when I would be released. If I would be released.

Dark thoughts of lengthy imprisonment in this half-life swept over me regularly to challenge my burgeoning optimism but couldn't quash it. I tried talking to the medics and guards in faltering French without any response to my questions.

I estimated it was early afternoon on day two in my new abode when I heard murmuring outside the cell door and the peep hole slid back. A shiver of fear rippled through me on hearing a voice I recognised.

Not Mamba, not now. Please.

CHAPTER 38

The door opened and General Ndidi walked into the cell, shooing away a guard who attempted to accompany him. His fierce expression softened as he stood and cast his eyes over the injuries to my face and the sling supporting my left arm. He sighed and shook his head. Unlike the first day we met, there was no laughter. Even so, my hopes rose.

'General, are you here to collect me? Am I being released?'

He looked through me as though I hadn't spoken. 'It is regrettable that things have turned out like this.'

The ensuing silence stretched for an eternity.

'Am I being released?' I repeated. Then a thought slammed into me. 'You're not a prisoner as well, are you?'

He shook himself out of his reverie. 'Moi? No, no, no. And yes, you are to be released. That is why I am here.'

'Thank you. I can't tell you how grateful I am. I will never forget this.'

He let out a dismissive grunt. 'I am here simply for protocol. To be humiliated by my association with you.'

His weary, bloodshot eyes bore into mine. 'It is not me you should thank. Emmanuel has saved you from…this.'

He looked around the cell.

'And worse places of course. But then you know those places now.'

'Manny is here? Is he okay?'

'Yes, he is waiting at the front with the lawyer. You are a lucky man, Mr Pierce.'

He spun on his heels and marched out with me hobbling in tow. He barked at the guards skulking outside, first to make way and then to assist me. We passed through a series of open doors manned by nervous soldiers into gradually brighter corridors. I assumed the general had swept through spitting fire and no one dared close the doors to obstruct his return journey. I tried to protect my elbow and other sore areas while the guards did their best to frogmarch me to keep up with him.

Sweat poured off me while I winced and grunted through the painful jostling. I lost sight of the general but could hear his footsteps leading us out. We crashed into a pair of closing double doors with a final jolt and emerged into a crowded reception area. Sunlight streamed in through the windows and the air smelled sweeter – to me at least. The scent of freedom.

Manny, holding my trail shoes in one hand, and Fozzie, suit sharp and brogues shining, both stood as we approached.

General Ndidi leaned in to say a few words to Manny, then made as though to speak to me. But he must have thought better of interrupting my wobbly attempt to don the shoes without falling over, because he turned away and marched out of the building to his waiting car. It was impossible to see whether Baldé and Demba escorted him.

A big, fat smile broke out on my face and hurt where my eyes crinkled. Manny nodded at someone over my shoulder and guided me out through the main door into the sunshine. I followed him and Fozzie to a Land Cruiser in a silent procession. They clearly wanted to be well out of earshot before we spoke.

Once at the car, I scoured Manny's face for injuries but there was nothing obvious. 'Thank you, mate. Are you okay? Did they take you as well?'

'No, I'm fine. We tried to find you and the others, but no one knew where you'd been taken. Two days ago, we discovered you were on Kassa Island. Mr Leclair won the fight for your release.'

The solicitor wore a satisfied smile when I turned to address him. 'Thank you. Thank you so much.'

Before I could say anything else, the energy drained out of me and I sagged. Manny grabbed my midriff and apologised at the resulting grimace.

I flipped a gasp into a question. 'Which others?'

My mind had caught up. If Manny and Condé hadn't been arrested, then who else did they mean?

'The Israelis,' said Manny.

I glanced back at the doors. 'Are they being released as well?'

'They already flew out. Yesterday. It's one reason Condé's contacts discovered you were at Kassa Island.'

'So why…' I stopped and tried to wade through the brain fog to understand. 'So why wasn't I released with them?'

Manny looked at Fozzie.

The lawyer answered in a matter-of-fact voice. 'Our understanding is the initial arrests were made on spurious reports that you were part of a coup plot against the president. When it was quickly established those reports were false, the two Israeli gentlemen were released.'

He scratched his chin and fixed his eyes on mine.

'Unfortunately, the authorities retained you for further questioning. Perhaps related to business and other recent activities.'

His last comment had sounded almost like a question.

'The Sapro deal?'

Fozzie pushed his glasses up his nose. 'Yes, and your recent interactions with the security forces have left a number of soldiers requiring medical attention.'

I leant back against the car. Too knackered to process this information and figure out the whys and wherefores. 'So, what now?'

Manny pointed behind me. 'The guy in that car is from the British Embassy. He's taking you straight to the airport. Cal has arranged the tickets for you to fly home.'

A car I hadn't noticed sat adjacent to ours. A white face stared in our direction from the passenger seat. I turned back to Manny, thoughts tumbling on top of each other 'What about you? And what about my gear?'

'I'm heading for Freetown shortly. Maybe I'll see you in London again soon. Your gear is in the back. We picked it up from the hotel and they' – he pointed towards the prison block – 'gave us your rucksack, shoes, and some clothes half an hour ago.'

The white guy had exited his vehicle and now stood with hands on hips. His thinning hair, reddened pate, and cream linen suit had Foreign Office written all over it. He had a determined look on his face.

I shook hands with Fozzie and then embraced Manny with my one working arm. 'Thank you, mate. I owe you.'

He shook his head. 'It was Condé and Mr Leclair who did the real work.'

Then he gestured towards the rear of the SUV. 'Check your bags before you go. If anything is missing, Condé will get it back. Maybe you should do it now. That guy doesn't look happy.'

He nodded towards the embassy bloke and we both laughed. It felt like a lifetime since I'd last done that.

At the rear of the immaculate Land Cruiser – Fozzie's car, I assumed – I made a half-hearted effort at a one-handed check through my bags. My electronics had all been returned apart from the local phone. The scuffs on the laptop and a hairline crack on my UK cell phone hinted at an insurance claim after all. The lucky eyeball had survived – fat lot of help that had been. I rummaged through the main bag, looking for a fresh set of clothes.

'We need to get moving,' said a well-bred British voice from behind. The flight leaves in less than ninety minutes. They'll hold it for us, but we can only push it so far.'

'Just getting some clean rig. I can't fly anywhere in this get up. Not unless you're taking me in handcuffs.'

Still leant over my bag and without looking up, I swung my working arm across my body and up to the left. 'John Pierce. Although you'll know that already.'

'Yes, and I recognise you from the picture in our files.'

He gave my hand a light shake. Folded up like a piece of origami,

I couldn't tell if it had been a Masonic handshake or not. Having only dabbled in the craft, I was no expert.

'Alan Gough, commercial attaché at the British Embassy. No handcuffs, but I must ensure you make that flight. The Guinea government is keen that you leave as soon as possible. No charges, just leave.'

I located my wash kit, stuffed it alongside a set of crumpled, clean rig and the damaged electronics, and hoisted the light rucksack onto my shoulder. With only one good arm and a plethora of aches and pains, the larger, heavier grip required an able assistant.

'Can you do the honours?'

Gough let out an exasperated sigh before grabbing my bag and leading off to his car. When I glanced back to the other SUV, Manny stood outside the passenger door and lifted a hand in goodbye. I reciprocated with a shoulder-height signal as I fought to keep the daysack from pressing on my injured collar bone. Fozzie already sat in the driving seat, ready to whizz off and help the next client.

The embassy man had a similar white Land Cruiser model with a beefy engine and a driver at the helm. Inside was clean enough, but the worn, scratched interior suggested 'pool car'. I edged my way into the rear seat.

'I'm honking. I need a dhobi and to get fresh rig on.'

Gough slid into the rear seat from the other side. 'It will have to be at the airport. There's no time to divert to the embassy.'

The driver keyed the ignition while Gough pulled a handful of papers out of his inside pocket. 'These are your tickets and boarding passes.'

He reached into his other pocket. 'And your passport.'

So much for my kit check.

He continued as I flicked through the documents. 'You'll see that your employer has provided business class tickets on Air France. It means you can use the lounge when we get to the airport to clean yourself up and get changed.'

I reached a white envelope with *Mr J Pierce* handwritten on the front and my passport number underneath.

'That's a message from your employers. They've been in regular contact over recent days since your arrest. Bit late mind you. Would have been better for all of us if we'd been aware of your presence and your activities before all this blew up.'

I ignored the jibe and opened the sealed envelope. The message inside read:

John,

Well done for coming through this misunderstanding with the authorities. All the Pinnacle board and I are grateful for your efforts during these difficult negotiations.

I am pleased to report that, despite the recent hiccups, we have now reached agreement with Sapro for the terms of the project. Thank you for your hard work and we all wish you a speedy recovery so you can return to Guinea and oversee the project mobilisation.

It has been agreed that you should receive a $10,000 bonus for steering the negotiations to a successful conclusion.

I look forward to sitting down with you in London on your return.

Warm regards,
Cal

Gough let me read in silence, speaking only when I lay the sheet of paper in my lap and raised my head. 'There's water, energy drinks, and some chocolate in the fridge here.'

He opened the lid of the central console between the front seats and selected a Lucozade Sport and a KitKat, which I took. Then he produced a packet of pills. 'Some painkillers from the embassy dispensary. Stronger than over-the-counter stuff. Two at a time, at least four hours apart, I believe. But check the instructions.'

'Thanks.' I popped four out of blister pack without checking the dosage details and swallowed them with a glug of the orange-flavoured electrolyte drink. That might deal with the headache that had returned with a vengeance.

The statues outside the Camp Alpha headquarters building flashed by and confirmed where I'd been held since my vaguely remembered transfer from the Kassa Island hellhole.

'You've read the message from Cal, then. And my file, no doubt.'

'Yes. Interesting, on both counts.'

'And does the commercial attaché usually roll out to escort released prisoners? Not that I'm complaining.'

'Everyone is very keen to make sure you get on that plane. These are precarious times here and a diplomatic spat is in no one's interest.'

After a brief pause, he got down to business, just as I'd expected he would. 'We only have maybe thirty minutes at the most. I need you to tell me everything you recall about who you have been dealing with since you arrived in Guinea, where you were held, officials who oversaw your treatment. And any other prisoners you encountered. I strongly suspect we already know more than you do, so it's pointless trying to withhold anything.'

He followed my glance at the driver and a predatory smile touched his lips. 'Jenkins is one of us. In fact, his clearance is probably higher than mine. You can speak freely amongst friends here.'

Gough made no attempt to conceal the recording device as I began describing an abridged version of the last couple of weeks. He scrunched his face in obvious disdain at the mention of the coup allegations. As though he would have known in the unlikely event I'd been involved in that kind of skulduggery. I left out any hints of bribery and corruption. The diamonds didn't get a mention either.

When I finished, he made a show of stopping the dictaphone and fixed me with a stony glare. 'Bullshit. I told you not to withhold anything. We know there's more to it than that.'

'Speak to Cal Simmons then. I'm sure you're already well acquainted. I'm just the fall guy sent in to get fucked up while the fat cats reap the big rewards.'

Our hostile stand-off in the back was interrupted by Jenkins. 'Boss, approaching the airport.'

We each broke eye contact to check outside our respective windows.

'Bloody Cal Simmons,' muttered Gough.

Jenkins parked in a reserved area right outside the terminal. A local army major and two soldiers watched Gough and I exit the car. Gough spoke to the major privately and then handed my bag to one of the soldiers.

'Your welcoming party,' said Gough as he led the way into departures. 'Welcoming you to leave the country and not come back.'

He'd got that about right. Cold stares from the major and his men implied they'd relish carting my jump-suited arse back off to Kassa Island if my chaperone wasn't there.

Gough carried on. 'Your employers mention you overseeing the project mobilisation but if you take my advice, you won't come back to Conakry. Find a job in the back office in London or elsewhere. This whole business has left a bad taste in a lot of people's mouths. You're lucky those local contacts of yours stepped up. Otherwise, well, you don't need me to tell you.'

I stopped my uncomfortable shuffle to give my patched-up balls some relief from the renewed rubbing caused by the day's activity and to adjust the position of the daysack on my aching shoulder. Gough halted alongside me and our eyes met.

'Don't worry. It will be a cold day in hell before I set foot back in this place.'

CHAPTER 39

THREE DAYS LATER

VETERINARY SURGERY, EPSOM, UK

I stroked Taz's head as she lay at my feet under the plastic waiting room chair. In a few short days, my life had been turned on its head. Anger fought with regret and sorrow as I tried to make sense of it all.

The consequences of my incarceration and associated injuries continued to reverberate following my return to the UK. Our family holiday plans had been shelved, much to the disappointment of Claire and the girls. Not that Daisy understood what had happened, being only two and a half. Becky took to calling me 'silly daddy' and shaking her head, just like she had after the last time I'd returned home with facial injuries – from Iraq three years before.

Claire was shocked at my condition and frustrated by my refusal to discuss what had happened in any detail. She didn't disguise her upset at our ruined holiday plans either. But it was all eclipsed by a far greater adversity that had struck our family.

While I had been beaten and tortured in an African prison, my running partner and our beloved family dog, Taz, had fallen seriously ill. Claire and our eldest, Natalie, had rushed her to the vet and tumours had been found. Clear evidence of internal bleeding resulted in crushing news the previous day from the vet. Our faithful friend was dying and it was time to say goodbye.

Tears flowed from all of us. Claire and the girls had said their farewells and now I sat in the waiting room with Taz's chin resting on my foot as we waited for the final appointment. I stroked her greying head with my good hand.

Both of us were broken, but the doctors could fix me up. The following day I had my own appointment for day surgery to have the broken radial head on my left elbow screwed back into place.

Taz looked up at me with heavy eyes. The lump in my throat expanded as I comforted her. 'I'm sorry, old girl. I'm sorry.'

The young, friendly vet who had imparted the unwelcome news the previous day put her head around the door and softly called out 'Taz Pierce'. Her sad smile changed to a concerned look as both of us struggled to our feet. Taz stumbled alongside me as we crossed the reception area to the treatment room. I hardly fared better.

A fleeting snicker escaped the chokehold developing in my throat. *At this rate, neither of us will be coming out of that room.*

The vet and her assisting nurse provided a balance of gentle explanation, professionalism, and warmth as the procedure was outlined and the preparations made.

I had never considered how difficult it must be to help owners of much-loved pets make the heart-breaking decision to relieve suffering and end a dear friend's life. And then, once the decision had been reached, to witness at first hand the anguish. A tear rolled down my cheek.

Sarah, the vet, stroked Taz and comforted her. Taz herself panted following the exertion – mainly involving the two women due to my knackered arm – of lifting her on to the treatment table. The solitary tear lingered on my grazed chin.

'You're going to stay with her?' Sarah asked, nodding encouragement as she spoke.

'Yes, of course.' I rubbed Taz's head and she laid it down. Her breaths came fast and shallow.

'Good.' Then sadness washed over her face. 'They look for you, the owner, when it's time and they're scared. Like they know.'

A second tear followed the trail of the first as I made an effort at conveying my thanks with a mixed nod and smile. The quiet, petite assistant handed a syringe to the vet.

'Ready?'

I looked down at Taz and continued to stroke her head. 'Yeah, ready.'

The sharp needle pierced the dog's skin. As the vet pushed the plunger that would release the deadly drug, Taz's life flashed before me. Our puppy, my running partner. Christmases, birthdays, births, and deaths. And now hers.

The panting stopped. Death's macabre stillness took its place.

Bye old friend.

PART III
AMBUSH

CHAPTER 40

TWO YEARS LATER, JUNE 2010

EPSOM DOWNS, UK

The sun had yet to sweep away the chill left by the clear night sky as I reached the top of Epsom Downs. It left a refreshing bite in the air to cool the sweat generated from the initial, uphill miles of my early morning run.

Thoughts of Taz surfaced when I spotted the galloping horses from one of the nearby racing stables through the trees. Usually it would only be a fleeting recollection but today the images lingered. Last night's phone from Cal Simmons had resurrected a heap of buried memories. I preferred to focus on Taz than the dark alternatives.

We hadn't spoken much since I'd returned from Guinea two summers earlier. After being patched up, my recovery had been slow. A ghostly throb in my elbow ignited as I ran. Psychological of course, like much of the residual effects. I stretched out and flexed my left arm to prove it, the two-inch operation scar acting as a reference point for the imaginary discomfort.

The initial prognosis that I'd never again bend that arm past ninety degrees had proved as overly pessimistic as it sounded. Beasting myself with the weights was no longer an option, but full range of movement had returned after months of careful physio.

The mining project in Guinea had joined me as a casualty. The 2008 banking crisis took down Fortis Bank and with it the funding for the whole deal. Pinnacle tried to find alternative finance without success.

Fortunately, the project's demise didn't occur until well after everyone had been paid in full. I even received the promised $10,000 bonus. Not that ten grand was enough to compensate for my apparent use as a bargaining chip in the negotiations between Sapro and Pinnacle. Bastards.

I slowed the pace and sucked in deep breaths. My continuing bitterness hurt no one but myself.

London shimmered in the distance. A spectacular view that made this my favourite running route. Not that I'd been here too often recently.

Once I'd recovered from my African nightmare, it had been back to Baghdad and a management role with my American buddies in the Green Zone. That contract had finished before Easter. After a fantastic family holiday in Florida, extended by a week thanks to a volcanic eruption in Iceland, I'd been on the hunt for another position, preferably closer to home for once.

Cal had popped up like the proverbial bad penny soon after my job hunt began in earnest. We met for a drink and a bite to eat at his club in Central London and evaded the contentious issues. It didn't leave much to talk about.

Of course, he'd had an ulterior motive, that was a given. Vague descriptions of projects in various far-flung locations. Initial talk of Somalia, Afghanistan, and Iraq gave way to hints of possibilities in South America and then finally the crosshairs settled on Africa.

Africa.

As our conversation expanded, my suspicions grew that it had always been the real destination for our discussion. The reason for us meeting. Cal sounding me out, seeing if I was really broken beyond repair or ready to bounce up and crack on.

Then came the wrecking ball, smashing the pretence of old friends just meeting for a catch up.

'Pinnacle is still active. Opportunities continue to arise in West Africa, even in Guinea.'

'No fucking way.'

'Hear me out, John. I understand your reservations.'

That did it. Flash to bang. Two years-worth of built-up resentment unleashed. 'Fucking reservations. They tortured me. Half fucking killed me.'

Cal's hands shot out from his sides and beckoned me to lower my voice. Confidentiality might have been a concern, but he was probably more worried about his standing at the posh private club. Aggrieved faces of other members had already turned our way.

'I know, I know, and everyone was appalled. And sorry it happened. It was unexpected.'

He offered a raised hand in the direction of the other occupied tables. Apologising for his uncouth guest in the opulent surroundings.

'I warned you. I fucking told you it was going south.' It came out in a venomous hiss as I attempted to rein in the anger and show a little decorum.

A waiter appeared by the table. 'Is everything okay, sir?' he asked, studiously ignoring me and angling his head towards Cal.

Rage surged through me as I imagined Cal and the Pinnacle board members feasting on exquisite dishes from the five-star menu and gorging on fine wines while I had been enduring hell. 'Why don't you f—'

Cal cut in sharply to prevent a scene, grasping my forearm and taking control with a firm voice. 'Fine. Yes, Antonio, everything is fine. My friend here has just received some shocking news.'

Both men surveyed for my reaction. I hesitated; the moment lost. Instead replaced with clarity. Clarity that I was behaving like an idiot. Embarrassment gripped me.

Cal had guided me back to civility. 'Are you ready to order, John?'

One advantage of a tough uphill start to a run is the easier downhill finish to take you home. We'd had to move house when our previous landlord sold up the year before. Now we lived in a private, gated road, paying eyewatering monthly rent for a large, detached property.

The end of the contract in Baghdad hadn't set off financial alarm bells. After all, we'd built up a cash reserve over the previous eighteen, well-paid months. But it was amazing how fast the balance had diminished with nothing coming in to keep it topped up. Those three weeks of memorable family fun in Florida hadn't come cheap either.

The outcome of our expensive lunch those few weeks ago had been nothing of substance in the end. The same as the rest of my job-hunting efforts. General talk rather than the attempted railroading I'd anticipated. We parted with a vague promise to meet again soon and a loose agreement on my part to consider projects in Africa – anywhere other than Guinea.

That's why Cal's phone call the previous night had rendered me speechless. He wanted us to meet later today at the club to discuss a new venture in Guinea. Brazen, unapologetic, matter of fact. A ludicrous satisfaction surfaced that my suspicions had proved correct.

He kept the conversation short and one-sided, providing as little opportunity as possible for me to go all postal over the airwaves. My refusal had been ignored, spoken over. The arrangements made to meet at two o'clock, even as my fury began to uncoil. Then he was gone and only the demons he'd released remained.

I pounded the pathways along leafy streets. My running fitness had returned quickly over recent weeks. Our villa in Baghdad's red zone hadn't been equipped with a treadmill but a small, clean swimming pool had enabled me to stay in shape.

Half a mile from home, the gardens of the cavernous houses either side of the road would contain a sprinkling of pools. I liked living here. The girls liked living here. Becky and Daisy's school sat only a few hundred yards from our front door.

Could I really consider, even for one moment, returning to Guinea? For the money? Hadn't fate already shot a bloody great warning across my bow about that place?

Once through the gated entrance to our road, I upped the pace for a sprint finish. Punishing myself for the stupidity of the path I might take – would take – if it was offered.

I knew myself. The fear and loathing for what I had endured was surpassed by the elicit thrill, the challenge, the opportunity to face down the demons. It was the same flaw in my character, or feature depending on your view, that propelled me to the military and then kept me returning to dangerous, shitty places year after year, project after project, warning after warning.

Back at the house I warmed down and stretched out in the back garden. The buzz of a hard run offsetting the disquieting thoughts about Cal, Africa, Taz, life, mortality.

Two years should be long enough. It's not as if I'd been sunning myself on a beach in the meantime. Iraq had offered direct threats that surpassed anything Africa should throw at me. And a brief sojourn to Afghanistan the year before had hardly been without risk.

But hard as I tried to be rational, *He* lurked at the edge of my reasoning, taunting me.

Mamba.

Could I really risk falling into his clutches again?

A pointless question. If the opportunity arose and the deal was right, there was no way I'd turn down the chance to test myself, to prove to no one and for no justifiable reason that I could do it – overcome the fear.

And under it all burned white hot hatred.

Maybe, just maybe, I'd have the chance for vengeance.

CHAPTER 41

LATER THAT DAY

CENTRAL LONDON

The long-standing president of Guinea had died in December 2008, three months after the Pinnacle mining project collapsed. The rumours of his poor health had been on the money after all. His death had sparked the instability to be expected when a strongman leader dies after twenty-four years in power. Within hours, a military coup announced the installation of a little-known junior officer as the new head of state.

I'd followed all this at the time with a detached interest, scouring the reports for any mention of figures I knew. Always expecting to discover that *He* had navigated his way to high political office and greater power.

But his name never appeared. Nor did that of General Ndidi. Not that the political machinations in French West Africa merited many headlines in the British press or online articles.

The new man lasted a year until an assassination attempt and forced exile saw power transferred to an interim leader. Now, six months later, a democratic presidential election campaign was underway.

'Did you say something?' Foster Cranshaw, the expensively tailored toff who had been summarising Guinea's recent political history, cocked his head and fixed me with an insincere smile. His coiffured dark hair probably cost more to maintain than Claire and the girls' annual salon trips combined. No way did anyone preen like that unless they were an obnoxious twat.

The rest of the table focused in my direction. To ensure confidentiality we occupied a cosy private room. All dark wood panels, large epic paintings, and stylish antique furniture. The assigned waiter had been shown the door once the main courses had been cleared away: my old mate, Antonio, unruffled by the demand. His only show of emotion today had been a rogue facial twitch on clocking my face amongst the private diners.

The fleshy face of gregarious Pinnacle managing director, Sir Jeremy St John – Sinjun to his friends – displayed a spark of interest unlike Cal's stony look. While Cal probably suspected another unpleasant scene might be about to scupper his next big payday, the two immaculate Pinnacle minions, Kevin and Melissa, matched their boss's curiosity with an eagerness that bordered on parody. Both leaned forward with their fingers interlaced as though expecting me to bestow some great wisdom.

I hadn't spoken. Foster's question had come in response to my unsubtle laugh at the suggestion of a democratic election.

'No, you just took me by surprise, that's all. I'm not sure how likely it is that these elections will be democratic. Not in the way we think.'

When it became clear that was my only offering, three heads returned their attention to the impossibly handsome Foster. He might have come across as a bit of a tosser, but he oozed a confidence borne of wealth and status. I suspected he drove a classy motor, lived in a top-notch pad, and socialised with a beautiful girl, or boy, on his arm while hobnobbing with A-listers.

All very well, *but can he yomp?* as we used to say in the Corps. Not that I was envious – much.

Only Cal maintained eye contact with me. He screwed his face into a fixed mask of a smile. *Don't fuck this up* seemed a likely interpretation. I shrugged my shoulders and responded with my best *Who, me?* look of innocence.

With his audience returned, Foster put his glass of water down after a quick sip and flicked an annoying strand of textured fringe out of his eyes. It annoyed me anyway.

'That's as maybe, but our assessment is that a new president will take power without any significant violence or protests. That will begin a five-year term that should see increased stability in the country. You have a different view?'

'No, that seems reasonable. My point was simply about the definition of democracy in the country and what it means for companies seeking to invest. That is what you're here for, I assume?'

Foster's triumphant sweep of his manicured hand, protruding from a chunky shirt cuff with a gold cufflink, would have been more at home in the Roman Senate. The measured seriousness now injected into his voice would also have been more suited to discussing important matters of state. *What a chopper.*

'The definition of democracy is irrelevant. Provided we have accurately gauged that Guinea is on a path to increased stability, then the immediate opportunities for Pinnacle are huge.'

True perhaps, but the room needed a reality check. 'They are, but those of us around the table who remember the difficulties encountered in 2008 understand all too well the risks. Before your time of course.'

Sir Jeremy cut in, facing me as he spoke. 'And let me reiterate how sorry we all were with what happened to you.'

'I didn't mean that, Sir Jeremy. Well, not specifically. Regardless of who's in power and how they got there, corrupt elements, significant corrupt elements within the corridors of power in Conakry, will take years to root out and eradicate. That's the reality of the country as it is now, in my opinion.'

Foster piped up again. 'But isn't your opinion sullied by your arrest in the country for assaulting military personnel? Isn't that what disrupted our negotiations with the government in 2008?'

His awareness of my previous escapades came as no surprise. Neither did the inaccurate narrative. Time to put the record straight.

'No.' My gaze swept around the table, ignoring Cal's panicked, silent plea, before returning to Foster's frowning grid. Overly dramatic but it felt right at the time.

'Military forces arrested me, and two others contracted by the company, on trumped up charges because corrupt senior officials demanded shares in the project, and Pinnacle tried to play hard ball. I was tortured and held as a pawn in the negotiations until agreement was reached.

'Do you really think some poxy election after two years of coups and instability is going to change all that? Do you think you're going to somehow avoid a similar thing happening again? Just because a vaguely fair process has produced a new incumbent from the same swamp as the old days.'

My turn to raise a triumphant glass and take a glug of expensive red wine.

Cal's eyes had dropped to the table and Sir Jeremy's friendly tone had been replaced with an iron glare. Kevin and Melissa blinked ten to the dozen as their heads bobbed like feeding budgies. I couldn't decipher Foster's expression. He regarded me intently with perhaps a hint of new respect. The files he'd read were unlikely to have included those snippets.

Much as I wanted to resent and dislike all of them, they were seeking to make the best decision from the information available. And willing to pay me handsomely to help them in that process. Even Foster ought to get the benefit of the doubt. He wouldn't have ever set foot in Guinea and therefore had to rely on the sober black and white information from desktop research, corporate assessments, and business speak. I needed to start thinking of these guys as the client and not the enemy.

Heads lifted in surprise as I continued after setting my glass back down. Cal's wide eyes suggested a fear I might still mention the diamonds, despite a specific earlier instruction from him not to.

'It doesn't mean Pinnacle shouldn't explore opportunities in Guinea. But it does mean that any assessment needs to be honest and objective. No sugar-coating the risks. Let's face it, the only reason the potential rewards are so high is because so are the risks.'

Sir Jeremy had continued to glare at me while I spoke. Now he switched his attention to Cal and dipped his head. No point trying to second–guess what that meant. I grabbed the chance to set some ground rules.

'It needs to be warts and all. Full and frank disclosure at all times. If that's agreed, then I'm willing to get involved again and lead the field operation. Just understand from the outset that I'm not a yes man. I'll call it as I see it.'

'Thank you, John,' said Sir Jeremy. 'I can assure you that we all wish to heed the lessons from 2008 if we are to return to Guinea.'

'Are you resurrecting the old project? The six concessions.'

'No, this is a totally different investment. Did Cal not give you an outline?'

'No, Sir Jeremy,' said Cal from across the table. 'I thought it best to wait until today. Allow us to have a frank exchange of views and ideas.'

I prevented another laugh from escaping and concentrated on maintaining a straight face. Prior to the meeting, Cal had stressed that a 'frank exchange of views and ideas' was the last thing he wanted. I'd been ordered to either be on my best behaviour or turn around and go home.

Sir Jeremy grunted his approval. 'In that case, Foster, cut to the chase and give us the highlights. Let John know our objectives and what needs to be done on the ground over there.'

He turned to me. 'I want to hear what you think, warts and all.'

Foster, Kevin, and Melissa rose from their seats. Young Kevin went to the windows and dealt with the blinds, darkening the room but leaving enough ambient light to work by. Melissa unpacked and efficiently assembled a robust stand from a box I hadn't noticed in the corner. Into it she fixed a thirty-inch-plus display screen, juggling it with confident ease and ignoring Kevin's offer of assistance.

Meanwhile, Foster produced a silver laptop, positioned it on the table, and booted it up. He and Melissa exchanged whispers, which resulted in her completing the set up with a cable connection between laptop and monitor. After a silent, rueful appeal from Foster, her fingers then danced over the keys in a final flourish before she returned to her seat.

A vivid map of West Africa appeared on the large screen behind Foster. I took another swig of wine.

'To orientate everyone, Guinea is here.' Foster scrolled the mouse pointer in a loose arc around the land borders with Guinea Bissau, Mali, Ivory Coast, Liberia, and Sierra Leone.

'The capital, Conakry, here.' The arrow hovered just offshore, on top of the Îles de Los and Kassa Island. Almost certainly a coincidence. My fingers brushed through my short hair as I looked away. Forgetting what happened in 2008 would be essential for this to work with me involved. Time to get a grip.

The map zoomed in to focus on Guinea and a chunk of Sierra Leone that pushed against its southern underbelly.

'And the gold concessions are up here, five hundred kilometres or so to the northeast, near the town of Siguiri. Just outside the town is the large AngloGold Ashanti gold mine. Eighty kilometres further east is the Leifa gold mine. Between them they produce over fifteen tons of gold per annum. And this area in between is our area of interest.'

The mouse arrow circled within an empty green and brown area to the north of a winding river and the N30 road. Much as I fought to contain them, the first flickers of interest and excitement began to stir.

A new map appeared, showing the northeast of the country and the reference points Foster had indicated: Siguiri and the two nearby gold mines.

'I don't think the business details are relevant here.' Foster looked for guidance towards Sir Jeremy who shook his head.

'Right, so our intention is to send an experienced mining engineer and a geologist to confirm the results of the 2005 survey by Scottish geologist Freddie Barker. They will need to be escorted for the duration of their visit by you, John, and whatever support team is necessary.'

I nodded even while I jotted *Business Details??* into my notebook.

Foster pressed a key on his laptop and four semi-transparent, rectangular shapes appeared on the map. They sat in the eighty-kilometre gap between the Siguiri gold mine to the east, and the Leifa gold mine to the west.

'The Barker report identifies specific sample sites by lat/long coordinates and description. John, I've got a copy you can take with you.

'These sites are spread over two gold exploration blocks. Block A is near the village of Fifa, marked there to the south on the N30, and contains twelve high grade sample results. Very high.

'Block B, over here, is of lesser importance because the results were much lower grade. Plus, Barker describes the block as lying on a marshy flood plain. The recent start of the rainy season could make access difficult to much of that area. We may need to leave Block B until another time.

'The minimum objective is to obtain confirmation samples from the twelve high grade gold sample sites in Block A and at least three random samples from Block B.'

I pointed a finger at the screen. 'What about the other two areas to the north and northeast, marked C and D?'

'Yes, I was coming to those.' Foster said sharply. 'We don't have any previous sample data from Blocks C and D, but they are very much of interest. Our experts anticipate similar high-grade results to those found during the Barker expedition. Samples from these two northern blocks are the secondary objective once the fifteen or more samples have been collected from A and B.'

'That all seems straightforward,' I said. 'Anything else?'

'Not as far as the purpose of this trip is concerned, apart from seeking to establish a good working relationship with both the CPDM and local officials in the operating area.'

'CPDM is the Ministry of Mining?'

'Yes, pretty much. In order to collect samples from Blocks A and B, you'll need to obtain a license from their main Conakry office.'

'What about C and D?'

Foster's eyes darted to Sir Jeremy and then to Cal. The first hint everything might not be as simple as suggested. After a pause for another drink of water he continued.

'Blocks A and B are part of a potential tie-up with another foreign company that already holds the exploration rights. C and D on the other hand, are still available to Pinnacle directly. It also means that, strictly speaking, we shouldn't be taking samples from those two blocks because we don't have an exploration license.'

In the middle of the jungle, who would know? From my point of view, that development was welcome. It gave me justification to pump up the budget. You wouldn't have known it by the way I sucked in a breath, shook my head, and scribbled in my notebook.

Loose Cordon. Counter-surveillance. Team composition.

Cal interrupted my thoughts. 'No one will take any notice. This area contains scattered villages with no government presence. And the country will be busy. All attention focused on the upcoming presidential election.'

I waved my pen in his direction. 'I'll come back to the objectives in a minute. My first question is when are you intending this mission to take place? The election is due at the end of this month. Are you trying to squeeze it in before that or wait until the dust settles?'

Sir Jeremy answered my question. 'We'd like you to prepare a plan to undertake it immediately. We want to get our feet firmly under the table before the election and steel a march on any competitors who might have similar plans.'

'That doesn't give us much time. What date is the vote?'

'Sunday the twenty-seventh of June,' said Cal. 'Though you should probably leave Guinea by the twenty-third. Give yourself three clear days before voting in case they shut the airspace or there is widespread civil unrest. That's exactly two weeks from today.'

The date was Wednesday 9th June. I used a calendar in my notebook to make some calculations regarding movements, logistics, and admin.

'Realistically, that means we need to get all our visas and permissions in the next two days and fly out over the weekend. Where are your two experts based?'

Foster piped up quickly, before either Cal or Sir Jeremy could answer. 'One in London, the mining engineer, and the geologist is in Paris.'

'Okay, that's good. You need to instruct the geologist to fly to London today, ready to visit the Guinea Embassy with us tomorrow. I assume you've already been in touch with them?'

The conversation flipped back to Cal.

'Yes, we've been dealing with the commercial attaché in London who's been arranging things at the Conakry end. I'll make a call when we finish to ensure they're expecting you tomorrow.'

'I'll need money. A cash float and money up front for the team and expenses. We need to have at least one other expat on the team, preferably two. It's very short notice, so I don't know who will be available until I get on the phone.'

'You think it can be done before the election?' asked Sir Jeremy.

'If the embassy issues the visas and you give me the resources I need, then yes we can do it. I'll have to work on a plan overnight, but we should be on the ground in Guinea by the start of next week.

'But I want to be clear now, the logistics involved mean I can't guarantee we can achieve all the objectives in such a tight timeframe. Even if we're in Guinea by Sunday night, we're going to need admin days in Conakry before and after the mission, plus a travel day in each direction between Conakry and Siguiri. Getting out by the twenty-third means we may only get – and this is back of a fag packet calculation only – five, maybe six days on the ground in the concession areas.'

Sir Jeremy placed his hands face down on the table and threw out a question. 'Is that enough time?'

He studied the faces around the table.

'It's tight,' said Cal. 'But our only other choice is to wait until after the election.'

Foster steepled his fingers and faced Sir Jeremy. 'If no candidate wins a majority, then the leading pair will face a run-off vote no earlier than July, probably later. That's the most likely scenario. In either event, it's impossible to say whether we would still get permission to conduct the trip in the near future. It could result in a delay of months.

'We have a window to get in there now and establish whether a new gold mine is an attractive option. It could also be expected to enhance our chances of securing permission for further trips even during the political upheaval and change. If we want first-mover advantage, then we need to move now.'

'John?' asked Sir Jeremy.

'Give me what I ask for and we can do it now. I'll start mobilising the team immediately. I've sketched out some numbers and you're looking at fifteen thousand pounds by bank transfer to my account asap and fifteen thousand dollars in cash.'

'Seriously, John? said Cal. 'You'll need to cost that out in a proposal.'

Sir Jeremy cut him off with a raised hand and a firm, 'Cal.' He then pivoted to face me. 'That's fine. The bank payment will be made today, and the US dollars will be ready to collect from the office tomorrow. Is there anything else that you need?'

I focused towards Cal. 'We've heard the political situation, What about the military? Are you talking to anyone in Conakry? Full disclosure. Are the same officers still in power and what is my status if I go back?'

Cal's tongue ran over his bottom lip as he paused before answering. 'Honestly? We just don't know. All our contact has been via the commercial sections at the embassies in London and Paris rather than direct to Conakry. The situation with the coup and then the new interim government means no one is sure who remains and who has the real power. As Foster outlined, the one commonly agreed certainty is that the interim president intends to honor his pledge for transition to civilian rule through this upcoming election.'

'Is General Ndidi still in post?'

'We don't know. We think so.'

'And General Sylla, Mamba?'

'That we don't know at all. I've tried, John, but I just can't find out anything about him. The temporary guy is nicknamed "El Tigre", but there's no sign of "Mamba" according to my contacts.'

'Spooks?'

'I have been speaking with some government contacts,' Cal said in a measured tone.

A silence descended on the room. All eyes were on me.

'Do they know it'll be me that's coming?'

Cal shook his head. 'No. Not unless it's relayed back from the visa application tomorrow. The country's in a mess and about to get its third administration since you were there in 2008. They've got more important things to be concerned with.'

I studied his face as he spoke and didn't detect any obvious signs he was being economical with the truth. His answers struck me as honest sounding for a change. It wasn't often that Cal Simmons admitted he didn't know anything.

'Okay, if you want me to mobilise the op, then let's do it. Just understand that I'll abort at the first sign of serious trouble. My decision. I won't do it lightly, but if it's coming down heavy on top then I'll exfil everyone out of there. None of us can afford a repeat of 2008.'

Sir Jeremy smiled and leaned forward. 'That's understood, John, thank you. Well everyone, we have work to do. Let's all provide John with whatever he needs to complete this phase of our new project.'

Then he pointed at Foster. 'Call Luke in Paris now and tell him to fly to London tonight. You can arrange his hotel and airport pickup.'

As the minions dismantled the equipment and reopened the blinds, Cal buttonholed me. 'Swap whatever info you need to with Foster. When you're done, we need to talk.'

CHAPTER 42

CHEZ PIERCE

EPSOM, UK

Cal had tried to trim a big chunk off my numbers. That wasn't happening. Thirty grand was the minimum I needed at my disposal. He stopped pushing when he realised I really would walk away if they didn't provide the budget.

A costed proposal would follow as I developed the plan and all monies spent would be backed by invoices and receipts where possible. What more did he want? He'd got me on board, which was more than either of us would have expected twenty-four hours earlier.

I suspected my discussion of the numbers with Sir Jeremy left no room for him to make a few quid. What's the betting that if I relented and agreed to reduce the budget, news of the reduction would make it about as far as Cal's pocket. Tough luck this time, old boy.

Once home I'd snuck into my upstairs office and shut the door. Claire and the girls were home, and I didn't want anyone overhearing something they shouldn't. I needed to choose the right time to tell Claire about the job. Little chance she'd be happy with the thought of me careering off to Guinea on another mining project. Meanwhile, my first, urgent priority was to assemble the team.

After a series of clicks and pauses, a hiss of static preceded an uneven ringing tone.

'Hello.'

'Manny, it's John. How are you?'

'John, good to hear from you again.'

His friendly voice prompted an instant smile. 'Remember what I said a few weeks back, about possible new projects in Africa? We have one.'

Now his voice flattened. 'I thought you might call soon.'

'Really. How come?'

'After you rang last time, I heard from Cal. Then he called again last week asking about Guinea. Lots of questions about the situation and the election. Now you have a project. Are you really going back?'

'Yeah. Yeah I am.'

I paused to reflect on the reality that I'd made my decision before even speaking to any contacts on the ground in Africa.

'I want you on this with me, mate. Condé too if he's available. I'm taking a pair of mining experts into Conakry on Sunday for ten days. Could you be there on Saturday to get things squared away and prepare for a convoy to Siguiri?'

A joyless laugh through the static. 'So it is Cal. He asked about Siguiri and the mines.'

'Yes, he's involved. But I've met the Pinnacle MD today and I'm satisfied I have control this time. If things get dicey, we'll extract immediately. Are you in?'

'Of course I'm in. I can't let you do this alone. I should be able to reach Conakry by Saturday. Maybe even Friday.'

'Thanks, mate. I'll have cash with me. Three thousand dollars for you. That sound okay?'

'Cool, but don't bring mine with you. I'll give you an account to pay into in UK.'

'Sure, no problem. What do you know about the military situation? Are our friends and enemies still in town?'

'Condé says General Ndidi is retiring soon. He stayed out of the politics.' After a static-filled pause he continued. 'Nobody is sure about General Sylla. Things are messy in Conakry this last year.'

I released the breath I'd been unintentionally holding. 'Understood. Ask him to keep his ear to the ground and let us know if he does hear anything.'

We knocked a few planning ideas back and forth before I rang off with a promise to call the following day once I'd firmed up the deployment details.

The tension in my neck and shoulders seeped away now the most important team member had signed up. Hopefully I'd be as lucky with my next calls.

My next effort went to voicemail. *'Please leave a message after the tone.'*

'Ryan, it's John. I've got a ten-day overseas task starting this weekend. If you're available, I want you onside. Four hundred dollars a day. Get back to me as soon as you can. Cheers.'

In case Ryan couldn't deploy, I'd earmarked another excellent French speaker in my little black book: a former Foreign Legion combat engineer I'd recently worked with in Baghdad. The distorted tones rang out until I cut the call. At a guess, he was currently deployed in the back of beyond rather than sitting at home in Sheffield.

I made a note to follow up with an email and moved to the names on my notepad listed under *Medics.* A pair of names from the convoy days in Iraq topped the list.

Mike's phone went straight to voicemail. I left him the same message as Ryan.

Jamie's phone didn't even connect.

Although not a medic, my old convoy ops manager, Hutch, sprang to mind. One more effort before I took a break and said hello to the girls.

A woman's voice answered brightly on the third ring. 'Hello, Graham's phone.'

'Liz isn't it? It's John. John Pierce. We met in London a couple of years ago. I was with my better half, Claire. Is Hutch around?'

The initial warmth in the answering voice disappeared. 'John from Iraq. And Africa?'

'That's right.'

'What do you want him for? He's got a proper job now. He doesn't go to those places anymore.'

'Okay, I just want to speak to him, Liz. It is Liz, isn't it?'

'Yes, and I remember your lovely wife. You should stop this before you get hurt. Again. Or don't come home at all. Graham told me what happened in Africa.'

'This is nothing like that. Is he there? I just want a quick word.'

Her voice lowered to a whisper as a door slammed in the background. 'Please don't try and take him away again.'

Then Hutch's distant voice. 'Who is it love?

'It's John. From Iraq.' Her tone flat.

Knocks, scrapes, and whispers suggested an unwilling handover of the phone before Hutch spoke. 'Hello, mate. Are you back in Baghdad?'

'No, I'm in London. Your missus doesn't seem to like me for some reason.'

'Must be that natural bootneck charm.'

'Yeah, or it's those wily female senses. She knew I was calling about a job. I hear you've got something settled though.'

'That's right. Logistics manager with a local engineering company. A bit of travel to Europe now and then. Paid on time and get to see the wife and kids nearly every night.' He paused. 'How about you? Still on that gig in-country?'

'No, it finished before Easter. Now I've picked up a short task. Need to recruit a small team by this weekend. I'm assuming you're not available.'

'No, I really can't. Hang on mate.'

After an exchange between muffled voices, he came back on the line.

'Sorry about that. I promised Liz I wouldn't go back to the sandpit. She worries people like you will lure me back.' He laughed but it sounded forced.

'Fair enough, I don't blame her. Do you know what the lads from Taji are up to at the moment? I've tried Ryan, Mike, and Jamie without any luck so far.'

'I haven't spoken to Ryan or Mike since we met for a beer last Christmas. Lost track of Jamie altogether.'

'Oh well, worth a shot. I only need a couple of guys for a ten-day job in Africa. Nothing heavy. Ideally French speakers including a medic. Any ideas?'

'Africa. Not the same place again, surely?'

'Actually, yes mate. But things are different there now. And this is strictly an unarmed escort and logistics job.'

He gave me a couple of names and contact details: one a medic I vaguely remembered and the other a former oppo from the guards who he thought spoke French. We agreed to get together for a drink on my return. Maybe even with our wives, if Liz forgave me for trying to entice her husband away.

The two new names went on my reserve list. I'd only try them if my guys couldn't deploy or we hadn't established comms by close of play the following day.

The sound of girls arguing broke my train of thought. I burst out of the office door with my biggest monster roar to be greeted on the landing by screams from Becky and Daisy, and one of Becky's friends.

'Daddy, you mustn't do that. Mummy says we shouldn't make *her* jump,' said Becky as my fierce monster face transformed into an apologetic Dad face.

'Sorry. I didn't realise you had a friend round.'

I lifted a hand in the direction of the shocked-looking seven-year-old guest. 'Hi, Scarlett. Sorry about that. Although arguing outside a monster's door is asking for trouble. What's the problem?'

'They won't let me play with them,' said Daisy. Her crumpled face displayed the pain of being three years younger and excluded from the fun.

I put my arm around her shoulders while making eye contact with Becky. 'Why don't you let them play together for a while and then you can join in later? I'm sure Becky and Scarlett will be okay with that.'

'I suppose so,' said Becky. 'Come on, Scarlett.'

They whipped inside Becky's room and shut the door behind them faster than a pair of trapdoor spiders.

I dried the tears on Daisy's face. 'Come on. I need to go downstairs and see mummy. Why don't you go fetch a book we can read? How about *The Snail and the Whale?*'

'Again?' But a smile brightened her face before she raced off to her bedroom.

Later that evening, after choosing to read both girls other bedtime stories with a theme of going away on an adventure, Claire and I were finally alone. The only response to my earlier messages had been an SMS from Mike: *On task in the Caribbean. Maybe next time. Stay safe.*

'How was your meeting today?' asked Claire.

'It was good. I've got a job. A fastball starting this weekend.'

'Instead of the football? It must be good.'

England's first match in their World Cup group was scheduled for Saturday, which I hadn't forgotten.

'I'll be travelling on Sunday, so I'll catch the first game at least.'

'Where are you going and how long?' Her voice laced with trepidation.

'Ten days. Guinea again.'

She stared at me. 'Are you serious?'

'It'll be okay. Things are different there now and I'll have control.'

'No. You haven't even got over the last time and what they did to you. Don't do this. Not to us and not to yourself.'

Claire had tried to persuade me to go for counselling to stop the nightmares and the mood swings after my return from incarceration in Guinea. I'd refused and chosen to sort it out myself – bury it somewhere. Probably not a good decision, but I relived the torture most nights during the first few months and the last thing I needed was to spend my days analysing it with anyone, Claire included.

Two years later and the nightmares were a distant memory. The mood swings as well. Tricky ops in Baghdad in the meantime had focused my mind on more immediate enemies and risks.

'It's only ten days and the money is good. Five grand.'

'I don't care about the money.' Her face flushed a red warning that I ignored.

'Right. I assume you have an alternative plan to cover the two-and-a-half thousand pounds a month rent. Come on, I'd love to hear it.'

'You need to stop playing soldiers and get a regular job. I don't know what. Just something normal and closer to home.'

Her sharp reply took me by surprise and hit deep. I changed tack.

'It's not that easy. Picking up a sixty or seventy grand job around here just isn't going to happen. But this could lead to a long-term number with great money and a good rotation.'

'You've already decided, haven't you? It doesn't matter what I say, you always do whatever you want anyway. I'm going to bed.'

She bolted from the chair and stomped out of the room.

My efforts to call her back were interrupted by the silent-enabled phone rumbling on the coffee table. The buzzing stopped as I reached to grab it. Then an SMS landed – Ryan.

Count me in, boss. I'm around all night for a call. Cheers.

He answered on the second ring. 'Hey John, getting the old team back together?'

'Something like that. Although only you from the Taji crew so far. Mike can't make it, Hutch's wife nearly bit my head off just for calling, and nothing heard from Jamie.'

He laughed. 'Sounds like Hutch is a lost cause. I know Mike's on a CP task bronzing on a yacht in the Bahamas. Lucky bastard. Jamie was heading home to the US last I heard. End of this month, I think. Might see him in-country, assuming we're heading to Iraq.'

'No, mate. It's Africa. Guinea to be precise. You okay with that? Your French will be useful.'

His breath blew into the phone like a gust of wind. 'Right. Shit. Your missus okay with that, after last time?'

'Not really but it'll be fine. The situation down there is different now to when that happened. It is a bit unclear though. We've got a window to get in asap to escort a pair of engineers to collect rock samples. Probably means a bit of yomping through the jungle. It'll be unarmed, although I am arranging a military escort. I wanted Mike or Jamie as a third pair of hands and to provide medical support.'

'Can't we cover that between us?'

He had a point. 'Maybe.'

Ryan expanded on his thinking. 'For any of the strong stuff, you'll need a local with access to the pharmacies anyway. I'll have my regular med kit, same as you I'm sure. That should cover ninety per cent of what we might encounter.'

'Yeah, you're right. If Jamie doesn't get back to me then I'll try and recruit a local medic. Well, first aider at least. Get some supplies arranged and give us another pair of hands if there is an issue.'

After discussing the details of deployment dates, medical insurance, and kit requirements, Ryan gave me bank details for his MUF and agreed to fly from Aberdeen to London early the following day. With luck he'd make it in time for our visit to the Guinea consulate to obtain the visas. Digs were no problem; he could stay with his sister in Kilburn until we flew out on Sunday.

Meanwhile, we'd have plenty of opportunity to fine tune the plan. With only two expats rather than three, the costs would be reduced. Enough to enable me to pay him for the extra three days' work before we deployed.

CHAPTER 43

FOUR DAYS LATER

WEST AFRICA

The half empty Air France plane rolled to a halt at Conakry's Gbessia International Airport. From catching the first sight of the Conakry peninsula to taxiing off the runway, the view out of the windows had provided no surprises. Little appeared to have changed since my last arrival two years earlier.

As we exited the main door and stepped into the clammy night air, I spotted two pairs of headlights approaching from the direction of the terminal. By the time we reached the bottom of the steps, two white SUVs had nosed through the loose cordon of bored-looking soldiers and stopped a few metres to our left. The lead vehicle's lights flashed.

'John, over here,' shouted a familiar voice.

I turned left and beckoned Ryan and the two Pinnacle engineers to follow. 'This way, guys.'

Manny stood by the open passenger door with a big grin on his face. 'VIP service, sir.'

I laughed as we shook hands. 'That's more like it. No shake-down this time. Manny, this is Ryan. I've told him all about you. Maybe you even know each other from Freetown back in the day. And these are the important guys. Bob and Luke from Pinnacle.'

Ryan and Manny shook hands and fired questions at each other about Freetown circa 2000. During our planning sessions, I'd briefed

Ryan about everything that happened on the last trip and given him a summary of the main personalities: Manny, Condé, Baldé, General Ndidi, Édouard, and even General Sylla.

To the outside world Mamba might have disappeared, but I remained sceptical about his fate until my local guys confirmed otherwise. As for Édouard, he ought to be ancient history. In London, Foster Cranshaw had assured me that Sapro had no involvement in the project.

I directed Pinnacle's strapping Australian mining engineer, Bob, into the lead SUV. Ryan took the French-Canadian geologist, Luke, with him to the second vehicle.

With my arm around Manny's shoulder, I murmured, 'Well done for wangling this. No Baldé or Demba this time?'

'General Ndidi. He didn't seem happy earlier when I told him you were about to arrive, but he called twenty minutes ago to say you'd all be processed through the VIP lounge. Baldé and Demba are waiting outside. These drivers are from the airport.'

The big man really was still in post. Another good sign, even if it might take some sweet-talking to clear the air.

My increasingly cheerful mood earned Manny a slap on the back. 'The gang reunited. This time, no mistakes.'

Manny resumed his seat up front in the lead car, and I joined Bob in the back. As we drove away to the uncertain delights of the airport VIP lounge, I focused on the present task and dismissed thoughts of where 'mistakes' had led last time.

After the underwhelming VIP experience at the airport, the Novotel hotel seemed positively luxurious. On the surface little had changed from how I remembered it. Except I'd been in control of the hotel booking this time and we checked in without any hassle.

My questions regarding Internet accessibility and Wi-Fi coverage received the customary positive answers, which the sceptic in me found difficult to take at face value. It was a pleasant surprise to discover every room had the promised working signal.

Once our party had settled in a cluster of rooms on the fifth floor, I walked Manny down to the two SUVs we'd arrived in. With Bob in the car, there hadn't been an opportunity during the short journey to speak openly with Baldé and Demba or catch up with the familiar faces manning Ryan's vehicle: Condé and Alain.

The lateness of the hour kept our interaction short and sweet. Baldé expressed an apology over what happened to me at Kassa Island, which I waved away. In turn, I apologised for the events that led to him and Demba being detained.

Noticing the extra stripes on their arms, I congratulated Baldé on his promotion to sergeant, and Demba on becoming a corporal. The warmth in the greetings and the easy flow of conversation and laughter suggested a genuine camaraderie between us, despite the language barrier and past events.

Walking back up to my room I felt confident we had a good team. General Ndidi's support in providing our cars and two of his best men was a definite bonus. We hadn't seen him yet, but I'd try to thank him face-to-face before we left for Siguiri.

★

Most of the hotel guests at breakfast the following morning appeared to be election monitors or other UN and NGO workers deployed in the face of the upcoming presidential ballot. A pretty Swedish UN official told me it was a similar story in all the major hotels in Conakry. Normally, I would have kept to myself, but Aussie Bob made friends with everyone he met. His infectious sense of humour had charmed the pair of Nordic UN workers now sharing our table.

As Bob embarked on another story that involved huge crocs, naked swimming, and a close escape, Ryan and Luke walked into the restaurant. Ryan smirked as I rolled my eyes at Bob reaching the punchline and our table erupting in laughter. Not the low profile I preferred.

Bob was a seasoned professional though. He fended off questions about our presence in Guinea with vague references to 'traveling into the bush', before setting the scene for another outlandish story.

Guinea operated a regular Monday to Friday working week, which meant Monday mornings in Conakry were manic. It made sense to divide the day's tasks and split the team in two. Bob and I moved over to the table where Manny, Baldé, and Demba sat wolfing down an impressive breakfast spread. Together we would hit the CPDM department of the Ministry of Mining to get the paperwork authorising us to collect soil samples. I'd keep schtum about our intention to also investigate the two northern blocks.

Condé had already joined Ryan and Luke at their table. Alain remained outside keeping watch on our two vehicles – without any prompting from me. That all French-speaking team would procure supplies for the long trip up-country, and Ryan would inspect the third vehicle we needed for the trip and assess a local medical orderly recommended by Condé.

At 9.30 a.m. we all prepared to leave the hotel. Passing the other car, I leaned in through the open rear passenger door to speak to Ryan. 'I'll call you when we're done, and we can all grab lunch somewhere central. Give me a shout if you have any issues. Don't let them chin you off with a heap of junk. And if they claim it needs an oil change, ignore it. Same with any other supposed urgent maintenance or repairs. They will try it on.'

Ryan lifted his sunglasses and grinned. 'I've already told Condé that he'll get a bigger bonus the less we have to spend on the cars and kit. But I'll be on my guard. Be interesting to meet this medic later. Maybe we'll do that together this afternoon.'

'Yeah, I hope we're done at the CPDM by then. Catch you guys later.'

'John,' said Luke quietly, leaning around Ryan. 'Do we have any security? Is it Alain?'

'Yes, mate. He's from some plain-clothed paramilitary ninja unit. He's got a badge that trumps most around here and he's carrying a concealed Makarov. Okay?'

'Yes, good. I thought so. I'm not concerned. Just checking.'

Yeah right. Although the slim, curly-haired Canadian geologist didn't display any obvious signs of nervousness. We hadn't spoken much, but so far he struck me as an intelligent and serious guy.

'Condé is clued-in with plenty of the military and the people that count. To be honest, he'd probably be the one to sort out anything you might run into. Not that we should have any problems in the city today.'

I switched attention to Ryan.

'Same drills as normal. If crowds start to gather, for the election, a protest, or anything, then it's time to bug out. Listen to Condé and Alain. They'll get you back here or to another safe haven. Don't risk hanging around just for kit. We'll make do if we have to. It's this flaming authorisation paperwork that concerns me. Maybe I'll be pleasantly surprised by their speed and efficiency in providing it.'

★

By one o'clock I had an itchy mosquito bite on my wrist, sweat rolling between my shoulder blades, and a rising temper. What I didn't have was the authorisation papers.

Both junior officials encountered so far had tried to fob us off. As a result, we'd elected to occupy the small, stuffy first floor waiting room until we found someone with enough clout to overrule them.

When the wheezing air conditioning unit packed up at midday, even Bob ran out of jokes and small talk. His earlier comment about the rickety machine blowing hot air rather than cold hadn't been far off the mark, although we soon regretted its demise. Without the airflow, a squadron of elusive mosquitos homed in on exposed flesh with regular and unerring accuracy. The stagnant atmosphere and relentless insect attacks elicited an occasional profanity from Bob's direction and a darkening mood in mine.

Manny had disappeared into the heart of the building twenty minutes earlier in one last effort to find a decision-maker who could help. One o'clock had been my cut off time. As soon as he returned, we'd get out of there and try to RV with Ryan for lunch. Whether we'd return later was questionable. I had a good mind to forget about the authorisation and punch out the following day for Siguiri regardless.

Voices in the corridor proclaimed Manny's return, clearly not alone. The tall, bespectacled man who followed him into the room wore a smart dark suit, sober tie, and polished shoes.

'John Pierce meet Doctor Jeffrey Diallo,' said Manny with a theatrical sweep of his hand.

I kicked Bob's foot and disturbed his catnap. 'Bob, wake up.'

'Lunchtime?' he asked, without opening his eyes.

'Not yet. There is a dirty great mozzie on your forearm though.'

As Bob swore and slapped a shovel-sized hand at each arm in turn, I rose from my seat to great the smart new arrival. We shook hands. 'Doctor Diallo, you speak English?'

'Of course. Welcome to CPDM.'

'Thank you. Has Manny told you why we're here?'

Bob arrived at my shoulder still rubbing his forearm. 'G'day doctor. Bob Haskey, senior mining engineer from Pinnacle Mining.'

'It's a pleasure to meet you, Mr Haskey.'

As they shook hands, Dr Diallo addressed my question. 'Yes, I understand that you wish to collect samples from exploration blocks near Siguiri.'

'That's right. It's been organised through the embassies in London and Paris. I assume they've been talking with people here.'

He shook his head. 'Unfortunately, this is the first I have heard of it. It won't be possible to travel to Siguiri before the election.'

'Come on now,' said Bob. 'I'm sure there's a way we can do this. You have a mining engineer and a geologist flown in from Europe by a company ready to invest significant sums into your country. How about we take you to lunch and have a chat about it?'

With that, Bob wrapped a friendly arm around Dr Diallo's shoulders and enquired about local restaurants.

I shrugged at Manny when he pointed at Dr Diallo and mouthed, 'He's the boss'. We followed the newfound friends as they chatted and laughed together on their way out of the building.

The immaculate, bijou French café surprised me, as did the hefty bill. Ryan and co hadn't made it. Our chat on the phone was serenaded by the sounds of bedlam at his end. He needed to stay in the main market area to continue trying to source a handful of elusive items. Radios and jerrycans being two of the most important. When I described the cream cakes in the patisserie section of the café, Ryan rang off with a warning.

'Careful, you're only getting older and fatter.'

Cheeky git. I wished him *bon chance* with whatever culinary delights he'd be tucking into.

Dr Jeffrey made and received several calls through our light and expensive lunch. By the time we sipped coffee with the grey-haired French café owner, permission for our activity in Siguiri had been granted, subject to assignment of a CPDM geologist for government oversight. Taking advantage of the friendly atmosphere, I sought to circumvent that requirement.

Dr Jeffrey was adamant. 'I'm sorry but those are the rules. Don't worry, I have allocated a good man. He will be no bother for you.'

I had to concede. 'Okay, fair enough. But we need him to report early tomorrow morning. We want to try to reach Siguiri in daylight hours.'

'Come to my office at nine o'clock and he will be there along with your permit to work on the concession.'

'Thank you. We'll leave as soon as we pick them both up.'

Dr Jeffrey's smile dropped. 'You have the authorisation from the army already?'

'We have military assigned to us,' I replied evenly.

'That's good, but you must have papers from the army to travel to Siguiri. Especially this close to the election.'

The short-lived optimism drained out of me. Even the two grey-haired old timers, Bob and the café owner, Sylvain, stopped swapping stories at that revelation.

I turned to my right. 'Manny?'

His sheepish grin confirmed the oversight. 'I'll call to the general now.'

★

We reached the Novotel two hours before Ryan and Luke returned complaining about their day and stinking of fuel. After Ryan reported on their success and failures, we reviewed our likelihood of reaching Siguiri within the next twenty-four hours. On the plus side, the CPDM authorisation should be in our hands at 9.00 a.m. the following morning. However, despite our best efforts during the afternoon, military authorisation hadn't yet been acquired. The chances didn't look good.

At least the expedition stores including spare fuel had been sourced and procured. The only outstanding items were the radios. A trader claimed that three decent VHF radios might be ready and waiting by the morning. Hedging his bets, Ryan had purchased a backup set of small AA battery powered Motorolas and a bag of alleged Duracell batteries.

The third vehicle hadn't shown up, although Condé assured us it would be at the hotel car park by 8.00 a.m. the next day. The medic had also been a no-show. Apparently unable to get an extra day off work on top of the time already requested for the trip up-country. According to Condé, the medic would arrive with the third SUV in the morning.

'In other words, giving us no time to turn down either,' said Ryan, wiping a smear of oil across his cheek.

'Don't touch anything, mate. You stink of diesel. Get off and have a shower. You've got time to grab a power nap as well. It'll be a late dinner. I'm still toppers from lunch.'

'I might just do that. But I'm starving, so don't make it too late. Food in that market was grim.'

After Ryan had left, there was another knock on my door.

'Who is it?'

'Bob. Alright to come in?'

'Yeah, of course.'

He closed the door behind him and refused the offer of a seat. 'Just a quick one. I can guess how much you enjoy a change of plan.'

I stopped tapping at the laptop on the small desk and shuffled my chair to point in his direction. 'What do you mean? We don't have spare time for anything major.'

'It's nothing new for you guys. Me though, I've just been on the phone to London and they need me in Monrovia at the start of next week. Means I need to be back in Conakry by the weekend.'

After a few seconds registering the implications, I looked at the plan displayed on the laptop. The now obsolete plan. 'Is that one hundred per cent confirmed?'

'Yeah, sorry.'

I massaged my temple. 'Not your fault. It means we'll need to split the team. And that means another vehicle. We can't drive you down that route from Siguiri with only one car.' I was speaking to myself as much as to Bob. 'Okay, leave it with me. I need to call Manny and arrange a fourth car and juggle the team. Thanks for letting me know.'

The big Aussie stopped after opening the door. 'Beers are on me tonight.'

'Damn right they are.'

That evening we went to a local restaurant recommended by Dr Jeffrey for its seafood dishes. I got caught in a satellite phone call with Cal, so Bob, Luke, and Ryan went on ahead with Manny. Seafood before a long drive might have been a high-risk play, but I asked Bob to order me something tasty sounding from the fish menu.

Cal confirmed Bob's Monrovia trip. A chance had surfaced for Pinnacle to meet with the president's people about a concession. With Bob in the region, it was too good an opportunity to pass up. We'd have to adjust our planning to cope.

'Keep me informed tomorrow,' said Cal. 'We can't afford to lose a day, but you need to be moving in daylight hours. No night moves, okay. Intel says bad people emerge at night on those roads.'

'There's no way we'll make Siguiri before dark. We'll either have to find a safe haven to overnight or push through.'

'No moves in the wee hours, John.'

We caught up with the others at the restaurant. Soon after we sat down, my mouth watered at the sight of Bob's meal as the waiter placed it down. Succulent white flesh on a weighty-looking fish. 'I hope you ordered one of those for me.'

Bob replied with a twinkle in his eye. 'We can't eat the same thing, mate. I ordered this one for you.' He pointed at an upside down, unreadable scribble on the menu. 'Sounds nice.'

None of the others were risking the seafood. The waiter approached and set down a bowl rather than a plate in front of me. I glanced enviously at Manny's steak before studying Bob's selection on my behalf. Chunks of fish bits floated in a black liquid. It looked like they'd scooped it from the harbour.

'Cheers, Bob. Great fucking birthday meal this is. I'll be shitting through the eye of a needle tomorrow.'

The whole table erupted with laughter.

Bob finally stopped howling and managed to slip out 'Happy birthday' through the tears.

CHAPTER 44

Standing in the Novotel car park at 08:15 the following morning, I felt bright and breezy all things considered. Contrary to expectations, I hadn't needed the Imodium Instants to counter the previous night's meal. After a couple of beers to celebrate my birthday in the hotel bar, I'd also done the sensible thing and gone to bed at a reasonable time. Now all we needed was for the cars and people to show up as promised.

By 08:30 our two regular Land Cruisers had turned up along with a pair of vehicles that had seen better days. The basic model Nissan Patrol appeared the more roadworthy of the two. The twin-cab Toyota Hilux had a bald tyre and smoked like a chimney. Ryan remonstrated with Condé and the driver of the Hilux, Alain's partner in crime Samuel, who'd helped with the escort to the diamond meeting in 2008.

'We're off to CPDM and then Camp Alpha,' I called over to Ryan.

He held his hand up to Condé and turned towards me. 'Hang on, John. There's another issue.' He beckoned me over.

'Salut,' I said to Samuel on reaching the group.

He grinned and returned the greeting.

A slender figure the other side of Condé had been hidden from my view. Shoulder-length black hair framed an attractive oval face. At a guess she was in her early twenties. Magnetic hazel eyes met mine, the speckled colours striking against the bright whites surrounding them and her immaculate, smooth brown skin. Her mouth crinkled into a shy smile.

'Who is she?'

'She's the medic.'

'You're joking.'

One young woman amongst a group of men, some of whom I didn't know. Alarm bells rang. That she was so pretty could only increase the risk of unwanted attention. At least the baggy field gear she wore disguised whatever feminine curves might lay underneath.

A petite hand extended and surprised me with its confident grip as we shook hands. 'My name is Isabelle. I am a nurse.' Her English precise with only a hint of an accent.

Momentary embarrassment engulfed me on realising I'd spoken about her and not to her. 'Sorry, I should have introduced myself. I'm John.'

'How do you do?' she replied with a beaming smile as Manny joined us.

'I'm well, thank you.'

I hesitated before choosing my words.

'I don't think this is a good idea. For you to come with us, I mean. You're very young and there are no other women here.'

Her face dropped. For all those occasions I'd told my daughters they could do anything they wanted, here was me dismissing a young nurse because she was a woman.

'No, John. It's okay. Isabelle is from Condé's family. She's his cousin. Real cousin.'

Condé nodded at me. 'Oui, c'est ma cousine. Je vais m'occuper d'elle.' *Yes, she is my cousin. I will look after her.*

'Are you sure this will be okay?' I asked Manny.

'Yes. He says he'll look after her. She's a good nurse. She has a pharmacy.' He pointed at a small, navy blue, messenger-style bag beside the tatty Hilux.

I turned to Ryan. 'What do you reckon?'

'She's here now. To be honest, I'm more worried about the state of those tyres. But you're the boss. She'll have to put up with me shortening her name to Izzy though.'

Looking into Isabelle's imploring face, how could I say no?

'Okay, it's great to have you aboard…Izzy. If anyone behaves badly to you, anything at all, then you must tell me straight away. Understood?'

She rewarded me with another beaming smile. 'Yes, I understand. But I know these men. It's not a problem.'

Ryan leaned towards me. 'Ya big softy.'

'Better than looking at your ugly mug. We'll need to keep an eye on her though. Just in case. I'll let you get back to having fun with the vehicles. Have you seen Bob this morning?'

Ryan straightened up and peered over my shoulder. 'He's just coming now.'

As the usually energetic Aussie ambled over from the hotel entrance, I could see he was blowing hard under his black, *Crocodile Dundee* style, Akubra hat – missing only the croc teeth in the hat band.

'Strewth, that bloody fish has gone right through me.'

Natural justice. I couldn't help laughing.

'You'll be pleased to hear I'm feeling great after that shark bait you fed me. What happened to that iron constitution you were telling me about last night?'

'No one likes a smart arse,' he replied and shuffled past to the car where Baldé and Demba waited.

★

By 13:00 we had all returned to the Novotel for lunch after a morning of small successes offset by one massive frustration. The CPDM authorisation had been issued and their geologist assigned; the expedition stores were complete apart from the better radios – we'd make do with Ryan's four small Motorolas; we had recruited the new medic, Izzy; and, after a struggle between Ryan and the drivers, all the vehicles had roadworthy tyres, spares, and running kits.

The reason we hadn't departed was the lack of an authorised movement order from the military. A fruitless morning chasing our tails had finally resulted in a 2.00 p.m. appointment to return to Camp

Alpha and meet with General Ndidi. He assured Manny we would have the paperwork that afternoon.

With the vehicles loaded and the assembled team busy munching through my logistics budget at the buffet lunch, we needed to depart soon, while everything and everyone was here and ready. A delay until the following day was not an option I wanted to consider.

Bob hadn't resurfaced since an emergency dash for the toilet when we reached the hotel. He'd tried to laugh off his stomach trouble all morning and the resulting scramble to reach a number of government washroom facilities in time. His descriptive disgust at the state of most of them left me and Manny in stitches. I took the piss of course, but his grey pallor concerned me. It left him looking all his sixty-odd years and then some.

Leaving Ryan to keep an eye on the team, I took one vehicle to Camp Alpha for the meeting with General Ndidi. Entering the gates of the military camp I couldn't help recalling the events of 2008. Me, Manny, Baldé, and Demba driving in a white Land Cruiser. The same suspicious glares from the guards.

'Any update about Mamba,' I asked.

'He's still in Guinea,' replied Manny. 'Not here though. Not in Camp Alpha.' He mouthed *I'll tell you later* and gestured at the two front seats.

A range of disbelieving faces greeted my presence inside the HQ building. Several officers stopped and watched as we passed. One interrogated Manny before allowing us to proceed upstairs. However, when General Ndidi closed his office door behind us, he greeted me warmly.

'How is my favourite Englishman?' he asked as he pumped my hand and offered me a seat in a sumptuous armchair.

'I'm very well, General. I didn't think I would ever come back to Guinea, but it's good to meet with old friends.'

'Yes, I was surprised when Emmanuel informed me. Many things have changed but some things remain the same. It has been a difficult time here. You must be very careful not to have a similar problem as before. The situation is more…more volatile. I think this is the right description.'

'I understand. Thank you for your help and for assigning Baldé and Demba. This time there should be no misunderstandings. Do you have the movement authorisation, and will it be enough on its own? In the rest of the country.'

'I am waiting to receive it from the Chief of Staff. He has to personally sign it.'

'That will be today?'

'He has assured me he will sign it this afternoon. As for your trip, I have another car ready for you. Three soldiers from the Beret Rouge led by a captain. They were due to travel to Siguiri tomorrow, but they will be here shortly to escort you.'

'And will they remain with us?'

'No, only for your drive. The prefecture should provide you with any additional papers and security if you need it. I doubt it will be necessary up there.'

We settled into a comfortable discussion about the merits of retiring to Paris over London, and the state of the UK housing market after the economic downturn.

Whenever I checked my watch, the time had surged ever closer to the end of the afternoon. At 4.00 p.m. a knock on the door signalled the arrival of the Beret Rouge contingent. The captain's brusque manner indicated annoyance at the extra duty imposed on him and his men. I couldn't blame him. A relaxing road trip across the country would be far preferable to escorting our merry band through the night and all that might entail.

An hour later, almost five o'clock, and the chief of staff's movement order was delivered. I thanked General Ndidi again before hurrying to the vehicles with Manny close behind.

Our journey to the Novotel, perched at the furthermost tip of the Conakry peninsula, was excruciating. Even the Beret Rouge car couldn't make much headway through the traffic despite the captain's best efforts with lights, horn, and good old-fashioned threats to the surrounding bemused and gridlocked drivers. My frustration made all the worse by the knowledge we had to return along these roads with the convoy on our way out of the city.

I considered attempting an RV with the rest of the team. An idea quickly scuppered by the difficulty in then getting hold of Ryan to discuss it.

On arrival at the Novotel, I gathered everyone together for a final briefing and to introduce the Beret Rouge captain and his men. The officer had chilled out after the hour spent with Baldé and Demba outside the Camp Alpha HQ waiting for us to emerge. Our guys reported approval of the new additions.

The tired and sweaty faces of the group caused me to flirt with the idea of a postponement until the following day. We had a drive of over 700 kilometres in front of us with the light already fading. Hands flailed at attacking insects as I pushed aside the thought of delay and instead confirmed the order of march.

'Five vehicles. Order of travel is in numerical order. One in front to five in rear. Vehicle One is Demba, Baldé, me, and Luke. Two is the captain and a wingman. Three is Samuel, Manny, Ryan and Bob. Good luck Ryan and Manny. You might need the windows open.'

Bob threw an expletive my way that was lost in the ensuing laughter.

'Four is Condé, the geologist – is it Yaya?'

'Oui,' came the answer from my left.

'Condé, Yaya, and Izzy.'

A figure darted in front of me from right to left and held up a hand. 'Sorry,' said Izzy. 'I thought I was with the other car.'

'Vehicle Five is Alain driving and the other Beret Rouge soldier riding shotgun.'

I ignored the puzzled looks at my use of slang and clapped my hands. 'Everyone happy? Let's get this show on the road.'

A chaotic radio check between each vehicle via the yellow Motorola leisure radios and we were off.

CHAPTER 45

Within 800 metres the convoy had ground to a halt. Six o'clock in downtown Conakry is not the greatest time to embark on an epic journey. And getting out of the city was a bloody epic. It took nearly ninety minutes through snarled traffic before we reached clearer roads.

Cal rang on the sat phone for a sitrep. When I reported that we had only recently set off and 'yes, it is dark already', he spluttered about risk management and insurance stipulations. I claimed a bad signal and hung up. He'd read the riot act soon enough if we didn't achieve our objectives because we ran out of time. Sometimes you've just got to say 'what the hell' and get shit done.

The presence of the Beret Rouge eased my sense of vulnerability from driving into the unknown of the pitch-black interior. That and the sprinkling of other armed personnel in each vehicle. Weapons of our own for myself and Ryan would have been even better, but that simply wasn't feasible or legal in this country.

The 'chat-net' that sprang up between the vehicles in response to the simplest messages caused me to stop the convoy once we'd cleared the city. Ryan recovered the radios and spare batteries from the Beret Rouge captain in Vehicle Two and Condé in Vehicle Four. I had Manny tell the captain it was necessary to keep them in reserve. We needn't have bothered. His glare indicated he thought I'd pissed on his chips whatever the justification.

With the radio net now confined to me in Vehicle One at the front, Ryan in Three, and Manny now swapped with Alain to drive Vehicle Five at the rear, it began to feel like a controlled convoy move.

Before we set off, I motioned Ryan and Manny to close in.

'Let's be careful with checkpoints.' I gestured to Ryan. 'Give yourself some room behind the captain. He's keeping right up our arse and I'll call it as soon as I'm sure there's no drama.'

'Roger that mate.'

When Ryan left to rejoin his car, I grabbed Manny's arm. 'What were you going to tell me earlier about Mamba?'

'He's not at Camp Alpha but he's still powerful. There are rumours he's running internal security or some sort of intelligence unit. Maybe from the Defence Ministry or the president's office. It shouldn't affect us. I checked with Alain and Samuel and they've heard nothing said about us at their units. Neither have Condé's other army and security contacts. No briefings, no warnings. There's no sign anyone is watching closely.'

'That's good to hear. I hope they're right. Come on, let's get up the road well away from him and whatever bunch of thugs he's running these days.'

As he walked away through the light rain, I called out, 'Get on the radio if you see anything suspicious. Anything at all. And if a gap starts to open, push Condé forward and tell me to slow in front until you catch up.'

He answered with a thumbs up.

The magnetic disc on the end of the wire aerial snaking out through my window kept the satellite phone signal connected. A blessing and a curse. During a combative second call from Cal in quick succession, we reached agreement before it dissolved into a shouting match. Every thirty minutes I would send a short text report and the lat/long readings from the phone's GPS. Now Cal could follow our progress, stay off my back, and let me get on with the job at hand.

With fifty kilometres on the clock, we reached the town of Coyah. On my last fateful drive into the interior, this is where we'd taken the southeast road to Forecariah. Today, we continued northeast.

I reviewed my maps by torchlight. We'd reached the edge of Conakry's urban sprawl. At every checkpoint we'd encountered so far, the soldiers had waved us through without a second glance. A five-car convoy with two soldiers in the lead SUV wouldn't be an obvious target to mess with.

A few kilometres past Coyah and darkness began to take over. In between roadside settlements, the jungle canopy encroached to the edge of the road and only our headlights illuminated the steady rain and occasional eyes reflected in the undergrowth.

When we crested a rise, the fuzzy glow in the valley beyond indicated some hardy souls lived out here in the sticks.

'Checkpoint,' said Baldé.

As we approached, a soldier swung a torch from side-to-side in the centre of the road. Demba dipped the headlights and braked sharply. Baldé reached for the authorisation paperwork for the first time.

'Ask him if this is a permanent checkpoint,' I said to Luke.

After checking with Baldé, he said, 'Yes, it's permanent. They stop every vehicle.'

The Beret Rouge vehicle, now christened 'The Ant Hill Mob' by Ryan, nestled behind us, slightly offset. Ryan kept a thirty-metre gap behind them.

I clicked the pressel switch on the Motorola. 'Permanent VCP. Will confirm when clear.'

'*Five, roger VCP.*' It hadn't taken Manny long to get the hang of convoy communications.

A stern, thickset officer marched from the direction of a single-storey brick building fifty metres to the right. Flanking him were two unsmiling soldiers holding AK-47s, butts in their shoulders.

The officer stopped next to the torch bearer to examine our registration plate. Then his eyes swept around our vehicle, before he peered above our roofline at the Ant Hill Mob and, presumably, the other three vehicles hanging further back.

'Pourquoi attendent-ils là-bas?' he shouted in a gruff voice.

'Why are they waiting back there?' murmured Luke.

'Thanks. Keep translating.'

'Nous sommes autorisés à voyager par le chef d'état-major de l'armée.' Baldé held up a sheaf of papers in his right hand.

'We are authorised to travel by the army chief of staff,' said Luke.

A shout came from behind. The Ant Hill Mob captain strode past to join the fray. An angry exchange sparked up between him and the checkpoint officer as they faced off in front of us.

When I put my hand across to stop him lowering his own, Luke craned his head closer to Baldé's open window.

'He's demanding we be allowed through, immediately. The lieutenant is saying his orders are to check papers for every vehicle. No exceptions.'

I lifted the radio. 'Hold position. Ant Hill Mob are kicking off.'

'Three, roger.'

'Five, roger.'

'Baldé.' I pointed through the seat gap at the papers in his hand and gestured at the squabbling pair. 'Show the checkpoint commander.'

'Le commandant?'

'Oui, montrer le commandant du poste de contrôle,' said Luke, repeating my message.

'Êtes-vous sûr?' asked Baldé.

I nodded and waved him out of the car. 'Yes, I'm sure. Go on.'

He stepped out of the car, leaving his AK-47 behind. After straightening his uniform, he turned with a final questioning look. I waved him forward again. 'Go on, show him.'

The two arguing officers focused on Baldé as he approached and interrupted them. He ignored the aggressive dismissal by each in turn and thrust the papers into the lieutenant's hand. The officer glanced at the documents and waved them at the captain. Then the shouting stopped.

'Now what?' I said to myself as much as to Luke.

His head remained cocked with an ear to the open window. 'I think the lieutenant just said we can go through.'

The captain stomped past us back to his vehicle. His face under the red beret set in a scowl. Baldé trailed him, papers in hand, and retook his seat next to Demba. 'Nous pouvons aller.' *We can go.*

The officer waved us forward.

I keyed the mic. 'Clear to go through. Prepare to move.'

When nothing happened, I tapped Demba on the shoulder. 'Aller.' *Go*

'Moving.'

'Five, roger moving.'

I lifted a hand in thanks to the checkpoint commander as we accelerated away.

'Stop, stop, stop.' An urgent command from Ryan.

Baldé lifted a hand to the steering wheel. 'Arrête.'

Demba brought us to a halt. The Ant Hill mob were on our tail, but I couldn't see around them to Ryan's car. Had the checkpoint commander pulled a sly trick to split the convoy?

I got back on the net. 'What's the problem?'

'It's Bob. He needs a dunny.'

Luke and I looked at each other and grinned.

'What, a toilet? Now?'

Ryan's answer came accompanied by a stream of obscenities in the background, largely directed my way. *'Yeah, it's either that or he's going to shit himself. Says he's still crook.'*

I couldn't help laughing. Christ knew what the checkpoint troops would make of the big Aussie defiling their ablutions.

Bob's voice boomed across the night demanding urgent directions to the nearest khazi. The sight of his shuffling run, with a toilet paper streamer trailing from one hand, had all our car cracking up. The Ant Hill Mob maintained their stony faces as Bob scuttled towards a small outbuilding, Ryan striding in his wake past the bemused soldiers.

'Twenty quid says he doesn't make it in time,' suggested Ryan's tinny voice.

'You're on,' I replied.

Ten minutes later we were underway again. Bob a few pounds lighter judging by the improvement in his gait, and Ryan twenty pounds lighter from the lost bet. The comic episode and my financial windfall were soon forgotten as we slid into the monotony of the long drive.

By midnight, I had fielded three increasingly acrimonious phone calls from Cal urging us to go firm for the night. The roads had been decent quality surfaces and almost empty of other traffic until that point. I'd hoped to reach 300 km before stopping, but the drowsiness that seeped into the car as we hit the witching hour couldn't be ignored. It had been a long day for all of us and the road quality had begun to deteriorate.

I picked up the radio. 'We'll halt at the next available spot.'

'*Five, roger. I need to stop driving.*'

'*Can't move for hotels,*' added Ryan.

'The map shows a town a few kilometres ahead. We'll find somewhere.'

'*Roger,*' the other two cars replied in sequence.

The 'town' turned out to be a small village clustered around a road junction near a river bridge. We pulled into a run-down fuel garage forecourt. It was difficult to tell if the pumps were still operational or the place had been abandoned. I stretched as the other four cars rolled to a halt and disgorged the rest of the shattered team.

No one complained at the news this was home for the night. Ryan drew up a sentry roster until 6.00 a.m. I took the first hour, which gave me a chance to update Cal and review the route for the morning. Everyone else tried to get their heads down despite aching backs and necks.

'Goodnight Jim-Bob,' called out Ryan with an American accent.

★

Sluicing water over my face at daybreak didn't do much for my gritty eyes. Hopefully the drivers had slept better, although it was doubtful. We'd need regular stops during the day's long drive to lessen the risk of fatigue-induced accidents.

After a quick breakfast taken from our provisions, we circled back onto the road and set off for Siguiri. By my calculations, we had approximately 400 km to drive. Three hundred to Guinea's second city, Kankan, with Siguiri another 100 km after that.

Manny had told me the roads would probably be slow and difficult until we reached Kankan. Boy, was he not kidding. The road top had disappeared in many places, and we were reduced to travelling under twenty kilometres per hour on suspension-testing surfaces. Ryan took to calling our journey 'the drive of doom'.

When we stopped for lunch at 2.00 p.m. in Kankan, only listless conversation passed between the haggard team members. The exception was a reinvigorated Bob, recovered from the stomach upset he still claimed had nothing to do with the fish he'd eaten.

Izzy was also a ray of sunshine compared to the bloodshot eyes and stubbly faces of the rest of us. Somehow, she still looked as fresh and vibrant as back in Conakry. Perhaps helped in part by her success in administering electrolytes to prevent Bob going down with dehydration. With her one patient recovered, her confidence and sense of belonging seemed to have taken an upward swing.

Luke went for a wander, causing a muttering Ryan to summon a Beret Rouge to join him to provide a sightseeing escort. The three of them returned twenty minutes later. Luke had bought a new hat from the market, which Ryan assured him looked great.

'Small victories, John. Small victories,' he said as he took Luke's spot in the back of our wagon.

I watched Luke showing off his ridiculous headgear to Bob, who told him he looked 'like a fucking idiot.'

'What do you think?' asked Luke, after returning to us with a face like a smacked arse.

Ryan stifled a laugh.

'You dick,' said Luke. He checked out his reflection in the window before looking over at me. 'It's not that bad is it?'

'It suits you,' I said with a straight face, made more difficult by Ryan crying tears of laughter next to me.

'Bastards.'

After two days subjected to our influence, Luke was already loosening up and fitting in well. The delightful lawyer wife he'd described during the journey might not be so impressed by his newly released darker side of crude jokes and bad language.

The road from Kankan to Siguiri was a vast improvement on our experience in the mid-section of the journey. When we crossed a bridge over the wide Niger river, the sun showcased a forested landscape of vibrant colours and human activity both on and beside the water. Everyone seemed re-energised by the scenery, the recent hot food, and the nearing of our destination. We finally rolled into the outskirts of Siguiri just before 4.00 p.m.

The map showed how close we were to Mali, and I noted how much quicker it might be to fly into its capital, Bamako and drive across the border. That would be for later though. I suspected our initial administrative and logistical requirements would anchor us to Conakry. In that case, internal flights would be the only way to avoid the epic drive across the country. Acquiring or chartering an aircraft jumped up my list of recommendations.

The 'hotel' at the disused Siguiri airport comprised a collection of wooden cabins radiating from an administration building with restaurant and bar. A vicious argument broke out over claims on one cabin between the Beret Rouge contingent and a boisterous group wearing t-shirts featuring the face of one of the presidential candidates. When an unseemly comment was directed at Izzy, Condé had to be restrained and it threatened to turn into a free-for-all.

'Leave them to it,' advised Manny when I suggested going over to sort it out.

'I don't know why they're fighting. If the Beret Rouge captain thinks I'm paying for him and his crew to eat and sleep here, then he's got another think coming.'

In fact, I did the captain a disservice. He was making sure we had our accommodation sorted before he and his guys left. Apparently, the argument had kicked off when he'd spotted two of the political group loitering in the doorway of one of our allocated cabins. When the excitement died down, I thanked the Beret Rouge team before they left us to it. Our team finally settled into five cabins in pairs and threes.

After dinner in the main building restaurant, I informed everyone it would be an early start the following morning: stood by the vehicles ready to go at 0600 hours. At that news, most of the grumbling team drifted away to their cabins. Five of us – me, Bob, Luke, Ryan, and Manny – stayed for a beer at the bar. Just the one.

CHAPTER 46

It took us ninety minutes, along roads that petered out into tracks, to reach the concession area. We received a warm welcome from the chief at the village of Fifa. He loved the idea of a nearby gold mine, provided it didn't encroach on his alluvial mining. I fudged the answer to that question and moved quickly on.

The priority was to review the logistics for the next few days. It soon became apparent there was no suitable accommodation available, and the villagers ate a diet that would test the constitution of some of us. I'd never seen water sold in plastic bags before either.

We couldn't afford to lose any days due to illness, so I decided we would remain at the Siguiri airport hotel and commute every day to the blocks. It meant three hours of driving, but at either end of the day there would be a shower and decent food. Not to mention the lure of a cold beer every evening.

From the first day we had an unwelcome surprise. The locations we needed to visit to replicate the previous survey were deep in the jungle and unreachable by vehicle. A pattern of daily yomping ensued. The team whittled down by three within the first 400 metres on day one. Demba, Alain, and Samuel elected to remain with the vehicles each day until the rest of us returned. They weren't stupid; they'd quickly realised how this job would pan out.

Each morning we loaded up with as much spare water as we could carry. Our rucksacks didn't get any lighter through the day though. Instead, we added bag after bag of rock samples shared between me, Ryan, Manny, and Condé.

'I don't remember any of this in the brochure,' said Ryan after hefting another sack of rocks into his bergen and then heaving it onto his back. 'I thought I'd left acting like a pack mule behind me years ago.'

My shoulders and back ached and I felt every one of my forty-two years, but an opportunity for inter-service banter was too good to miss.

'If you can't hack a bit of yomping, mate…'

'I can tab the arse off you, old man,' he replied, pulling out his map. 'Eight clicks to the PUP. Call it nine once we contour round that feature.' He pointed at a blob on the map.

I swayed to maintain balance after shouldering my own heavy bergen.

'Are you sure you can manage that?'

'Piece of piss. After watching you struggle, the lightness took me by surprise, that's all.'

'Dickhead. Bob was right, you are a smart arse.'

★

Three days of yomping later, we needed to wave goodbye to two of our vehicles so Ryan could escort Bob back to Conakry for his flight to Liberia. Alain and Samuel accompanied them for security.

Bob's larger-than-life character and good humour would be missed. He'd been at the centre of the trip's highlight so far. While we yomped around the jungle on day three, he and Ryan had been driven into town to recce the level of logistic support and supplies available to a future project. When Ryan met us at lunchtime near Fifa, there was no sign of Bob.

'He says he did enough humping in the jungle as a digger back in 'Nam. He's seen enough out here and wants to prep for the return journey.'

That surprised me. 'Digger? He was Aussie army?'

'Aye. And he's got some cracking stories from back in the day fighting the NVA and Viet Cong.'

Ryan shook his head. A broad smile indicated something amused him.

'What?'

'It's Bob, mate. This morning. I'll let him tell you in the bar later.'

When Bob entered the bar that night, Ryan lifted his beer glass in salute and said, 'Monsieur le president.'

Bob issued a royal wave and sat down. 'Maybe I should run for office.'

Everyone else around the table started laughing. It seemed I was the only person out of the loop. 'What's all this about?'

'You tell him, Jock,' Bob said to Ryan.

'Okay. This morning when we left, there were crowds of people lining the road all the way down the hill into town. As soon as we drove out of the gate, they all began to stand up and cheer.'

'An election rally or something?' I asked.

'That's right. Alain said there was a rumour the leading candidate would be flying into the airport in a private plane. They thought we were him.'

Bob's beer arrived courtesy of the barman and he lifted it into the air. 'Cheers lads. For a bunch of Poms, you're all right.'

A hearty 'cheers' rang out from everyone in the room, followed by a derogatory comment or two questioning the law-abiding nature of Bob's heritage.

After a slurp of beer, I asked, 'So what happened?'

Ryan wiped froth from his top lip, looked at Bob, and grinned. 'Alain said if they could see in the car they'd get a shock. "Le President est blanc". The president is white. So, what does the big man do? He winds down his window and leans out waving his Crocodile Dundee hat in greeting. The noise levels erupt all around us as we snake through the resulting melee. Sam got on the running board shouting at people to get back. It was chaos.'

'Bloody Crocodile Dundee. I've been wearing this classic hat since before you first peered through your mother's map of Tasi, you mongrel.'

I shook my head and tried to suppress my own laugh. 'Fucking hell, Bob. Impersonating the future president isn't exactly low profile.'

Ryan raised his beer glass. 'Tae the next president of Guinea. God help them.'

'To the next president' rang out from our table in reply, attracting confused looks from the other patrons.

The following morning, once half the team had punched out for Conakry, we were left with two SUVs and a tricky logistics issue. Each day we rolled out before any fuel stations opened and returned after they shut. As a result, we'd kept a vehicle behind each day to forage for fuel, fill jerry cans, and replenish supplies. With four vehicles it had worked okay. Now down to two, it meant some days would require a single vehicle move both to and around the blocks.

It became clear that achieving our objectives would need more time. The Pinnacle office in London rearranged our return flights for Friday 25th June, just two days before the election. Even with the extra time, it only gave us a total of six days in the concession areas.

After the others left, we spent two long, energy-sapping days completing the twelve priority samples from Block A and six rain-soaked samples from Block B. It left a day for a 'need to know' expedition to the Northern Blocks, C and D.

The CPDM geologist, Yaya, did not need to know. He was here to keep an eye on our activities on behalf of the government. On our final working morning, I assigned him to the admin vehicle that would run around Siguiri collecting fuel and supplies for the following day's drive to Conakry. He whined that he should be with Luke, but I said we had a meeting with the manager at the AngloGold mine – a meeting to which he was not invited. That part was true. However, I didn't mention we'd be heading north straight afterwards to collect illicit samples up near the border.

Baldé and Demba also remained in Siguiri. I argued they needed to look after Izzy and ensure our gear remained safe as the election date approached. In truth, I couldn't rely on General Ndidi's men not to blab about sneaking up to the northern blocks. Better they didn't know.

The team heading north therefore comprised the remaining trusted core: Condé in the driver's seat, Manny up front, me and Luke in the rear. Manny had a Makarov, and Baldé's folding-stock Kalashnikov sat in a car bag at my feet. He wasn't happy about us taking it, but I'd insisted. After that, he'd been relieved to stay behind; presumably in case I initiated another unsavoury 'incident'.

The South African manager at AngloGold Ashanti wasn't impressed by our presence in his fiefdom. Even less so when I refused to disclose what we were up to and then threw a reluctant offer of lunch back in his face. The visit to their camp proved worthwhile though. It gave me a sense of how Pinnacle's project logistics and life support might evolve, albeit ours would be on a much smaller scale. Army soldiers provided camp security. I planned to make sure Pinnacle received similar support, preferably from the Beret Rouge.

We drove north after the meeting, following a route on my improvised map. As the road became a track, which deteriorated into a boulder-strewn endurance test for passengers and vehicles, the chances of us reaching both blocks in one day diminished to zero. That optimistic goal was instead replaced with concern that the rough going might cripple the car and wreck all our plans.

A series of heavy crunches under the chassis had me fearing the worst and had Manny questioning Condé's driving abilities. We all sighed with relief after navigating a horrendous, bone-jarring 400 metres that resembled a rocky stream bed. We'd need another healthy dose of luck to survive the same obstacles on the return journey. I couldn't see an alternative option on the map but there had to be one. No one and no vehicle could regularly endure that route.

That led me to consider whether the 'obvious' route had been blocked intentionally and why? To keep outsiders away? Perhaps with an observation post to detect and deal with undesirables. Paranoia or a professional appraisal? Did it matter which?

For the first time since arriving back in Guinea, a familiar flutter danced in my chest. A sense of vulnerability wrapped me in a tight embrace. The idea of this one-vehicle road trip into the unknown crystallized as foolhardy.

'Let's keep our eyes open, guys. You see anything, then call it out. We don't know who runs this area and what they might think of us.'

'It's safe here?' asked Luke.

'The threat level is no higher than the other blocks. It always pays to be careful though.'

He looked about as convinced as I sounded. I reached into the rucksack at my feet and rummaged inside, clearing the way for rapid deployment of the Kalashnikov.

'Manny, keep an eye on the flanks. Let's assume we may have company.'

Our eyes met in the rear-view mirror. He nodded.

The improved going after the rocks meant we made good progress into the concession. It also reinforced my sense we'd now encroached into someone else's back yard. The speedometer climbed above twenty kilometres per hour.

'Men on the right in the trees,' said Manny.

The primary jungle had thinned to reveal stretches of open ground as we'd gained altitude. Here, the canopy on the right began thirty metres from the track.

The standing, stationary figures watched us drive past. They made no effort to hide from view.

'Roger, seen. No weapons by the look of it. Let's stop and talk to them.'

Condé hadn't understood my instruction. We drove a further fifty metres or so before he caught on to Manny's translated command and bounced us to a halt.

Climbing out of the car unarmed, I pointed at Luke. 'Wait there.'

Manny joined me on the track.

I studied the treeline. 'I can't see them, can you?'

'No.' He called out a greeting in French and then in English. No response.

Something bit my neck before I could slap it away. 'Right, if they're not playing then let's go. Keep your eyes peeled for drama.'

We rumbled on in near silence for twenty minutes. The forest thinned as we climbed higher, providing occasional glimpses of spectacular views across the undulating ground. When we broke out of the treeline almost twelve kilometres after the rocky road, the first signs of a settlement were evident: two roundel houses with smooth circular walls under pointed thatched roofs. Behind them and beyond a rise, similar dwellings lined either side of a muddy path of tyre tracks.

Past the first houses, figures began to appear along our route, cattle stood amongst them. Cows by the look of it, although scrawnier than the versions at home. Scrawnier and fiercer with it. Like the looks on the faces of the villagers.

Children ran alongside the car. Condé wound his window down and exchanged friendly-sounding banter with a boy racing to keep up. Not in French.

'What language is that? I asked Manny.

'Malinke. I don't speak it, but Condé has family in this region.'

'Are this lot friendly?'

Manny shrugged his shoulders. 'I don't know. They seem…nervous. I think we let Condé guide us.'

We'd entered the village proper – dozens of the thatch-roofed round houses spread over the top of an escarpment. Between the high ground it occupied and similar terrain a few miles west, the top of the forest canopy lay like a green carpet.

The men of the village stood immobile, staring at us, the interlopers. None of them obviously armed. The only women I could see were gathered near the doors of their homes, scrubbing pots, tending to babies, or otherwise productively engaged. Flashes of colourful movement came from running kids, streaming to join our growing posse. I spotted at least one Real Madrid and one Barcelona shirt. Here and there, more cattle seemingly trundled around as they pleased.

We pulled up next to a large group of older men. Like a shoal of fish, their weather beaten, lived-in faces and belligerent postures turned to face the car. They wore a mix of ankle-length white robes, colourful pyjama-like ensembles, draped furs, and copious bony and glittering accessories. Some impressive headwear topped off the local attire, along with more conventional skull caps.

Gold adorned the rig of the tallest man: embellishments on his robe, a nugget hanging from a black necklace, and sparkles shimmering on his outfit. Clobber that would rival the value of garments from the glitziest fashion shows.

A pair of hard faces belonged to two men wearing drab clothing. One carried a bolt-action rifle by his side. His stance was unthreatening, unlike his abrasive glare.

The houses had given way to a rough quadrangle of single-storey, angular buildings constructed from breeze blocks, corrugated iron, and odds and ends. A variety of foodstuffs and general supplies leaked out from most of the shop fronts.

Not that any customers were engaging. Like the rest of the village, the men here stood and stared. A handful of women stopped filling buckets at an old-fashioned water well and retreated from view.

'Get Condé to warm them up,' I said to Manny. 'Should we keep the weapons hidden or not.'

'We'll stay here while he introduces us,' replied Manny after a brief conflab. 'He says it will be okay. Leave the weapons for now.'

As Condé reached to shut the door behind him, his shirt flapped open and revealed the briefest glimpse of a pistol handle poking out from his waistbelt. A weapon I hadn't known about. Right now, good on him.

I took the spare, full magazine for the AK-47 out of the rucksack and slid it into my cargo pocket. The loaded weapon itself remained within easy reach.

Condé strode towards the well-dressed elders, raising his hand to his heart and conversing with the gathering crowd as he went. He disappeared behind the throng as they oozed towards the car with inquisitive looks and a rising clamour.

I checked my door was locked and motioned for Luke to do the same before poking my head between the seats to get a better view through the front windscreen. 'How do we know if he's okay?'

'They won't hurt him…us,' said Manny. 'There's no reason.'

It sounded like an attempt to convince himself.

'What are you doing?' I asked Luke. He'd lowered his window and begun handing boiled sweets to the multiplying number of small hands reaching his way.

He surprised me with his animated response. 'This is real Africa. People here are warm and friendly. Look at them. Just look at them.'

Fighting my instinct to think the worst, I took in the scene around the car. Condé's interactions had evoked laughter and a ripple of smiles. Now the solemn faces and rigid postures that first greeted us had dissolved into a riot of movement and excited chatter.

All very well, but I knew how quickly things could go downhill if the wrong person took a dislike to us.

'It looks okay for now.' I pointed at his half-open window. 'Let's just get that closed and wait to see what Condé has to say.'

CHAPTER 47

Five minutes later, the crowd parted and Condé swept through the gap, flanked by the two men in drab clothing. They didn't look ready to bust out party moves, but their eyes now scanned into the middle distance rather than locking onto us with menace. When Condé opened the driver's door, his escorts encouraged the obedient onlookers to retreat and give us space.

Manny listened to Condé's report over the rising din and passed on the highlights.

'This is Setka village. The chief wants us to visit his home. He thought we were bad men from the north. Now he knows we are from England, he welcomes us.'

I turned to Luke. 'I guess that makes you an honorary Englishman.'

Luke tapped his pocket. 'I'll be quick to show my Canadian passport if it turns out you lot caused any upset in his family tree.'

'What bad men from the north?' I asked Manny.

'I don't know.' Then he pointed to the bag at my feet. 'The chief wants you to bring the gun.'

'How the hell…?' I stopped and waved my own question away. Either Condé must have declared our weapons, or a villager had spotted mine through the window and reported it already.

We locked the car and set off on foot behind Condé and one of his new shadows. I trailed Manny and Luke, the rucksack containing the AK-47 on my shoulder. The escort with the hunting rifle brought up the rear.

A crescent Moon symbol on top of a flat-roofed building signified the village mosque. Shortly afterwards, we passed the dark entrance to a similar squat building, the wall next to the doorway adorned with a tatty 2010 World Cup poster advertising Budweiser beer.

Kids darted between us, one of them wearing an England football shirt. I pointed at my chest, gave an exaggerated thumbs-up and said 'England' with a wide grin. The ensuing chorus of jeers wasn't a surprise given the Three Lions poor results in their opening two games.

Our band of followers hung back as we reached the village elders. They were standing in two reception lines outside a large round hut with a colourful conical roof. Condé introduced me to the village chief at the head of the line and Manny translated. Remembering the mosque, I introduced another language into the mix. 'As salaam aleikum.'

The chief's eyes widened. 'Aleikum as salaam,' he replied, before launching optimistically into more Arabic. We shook hands, each pressing our spare hand on top in a show of desired friendship, before he ushered me into his home.

When I entered, the single room dwelling felt spacious. By the time the chief and the welcoming committee had piled in after us, it was rammed. When the huge horned head of an Ox poked through the open doorway on the other side, a skinny youth bounded across and steered it away before an emergency evacuation became necessary.

We sat cross-legged on dusty carpets. I gripped Manny's upper arm and pulled him close. 'Remember we're here to collect samples, and we don't have much time. Let's finish the pleasantries, then ask about the gold. And don't forget these "bad men from the north". We need to know who they are.'

I suspected the description originated from inter-village rivalry or ethnic tensions. Either of those issues would be relevant to any future community relations strategy.

Manny nodded as the chief sat next to me with Condé in tow.

I'd been in bizarre situations and meetings over the years and the following hour was one of the more memorable. Conversations in Malinke, French, and English crossed back and forth making it hard to keep tabs on the discussion. Manny negotiated a downgrade from a full-blown feast invitation to a few rounds of a spicy chai drink, served by the chief's wife and daughters. We had to promise to return for the feast though.

Then the chief had me demonstrate the AK-47 to him, before springing to his feet with the weapon in his hands and leading us along the main drag.

While I encouraged Manny to explain the basics of range safety to Condé, so he could explain it to the chief, the main man began blatting rounds at pottery targets set up by a group of young lads who now sat amongst them, cheering the hits. While I watched on helplessly, the chief emptied a magazine of single shots at the targets thirty metres away. People buzzed around us oblivious to the danger.

The old man loved it and had clearly used a rifle before. He finished with a ceramic-shattering flourish before I took the weapon back to clear it. Relieved we'd got away without needing to patch up any casualties, I pressed Manny to raise the subject of gold.

After a brief exchange, the chief set off again towards the outskirts of the village. Two hundred metres past the last house, a lunar landscape of bare earth dotted with holes appeared when we crested a shallow knoll. The chief motored on in his flip flops, speaking animatedly with Condé as we approached the edge of the bare ground.

'This is the closest of the gold mining areas,' said Manny. 'He says most of these holes are empty. They have more places further out.'

It was the first time I'd seen artisanal gold mining up close. The muddy holes were deep: a faint glisten of water in some, no visible bottom in others. Manny joined me and peered into one. 'It's tough and dangerous work.'

'Is this how the village makes it money?' I asked.

Manny threw the question over to Condé, who relayed it to the chief. A vigorous nod and beaming smile confirmed gold as their primary income source.

'Tell him we want to collect samples. Not here, not from his area. Ask him if he knows where we should look.'

The chief had walked over to me while I spoke. I waved a hand at the horizon and tried my best French. 'Où est l'or?' *Where is the gold?*

The chief's wide smile revealed a valuable collection of gold molars top and bottom. He turned to face the view across the top of the jungle and spread his arms wide. 'Voici, beaucoup d'or.' *Here is lots of gold.*

Apart from the chief and us four visitors, a distinguished gentleman in a natty outfit and skull cap sauntered along at the rear, and another pair of thickset individuals had joined our two shadows. Everyone else had peeled away when we marched out of the village perimeter.

When Manny mentioned collecting samples, an excited debate broke out in a mixture of the local lingo and French.

With the rest of the group engaged, Luke and I conferred. 'What do you think?' I asked.

'The signs are good, of course. There's clearly a lot of gold in this area. It's probably why the village is here in the first place. Although we'll have to strike very lucky to find a similar location in a single afternoon.'

Manny joined us after a couple of minutes.

'They suggested somewhere but it's difficult to reach.'

He pointed at one of the thickset chaps standing next to the chief. 'The chief's son can arrange three motos to take us. He'll ride one of them. It's forty-five minutes away. They are happy for us to collect samples there.'

His enthusiasm tailed off as he spoke.

'What is it, mate?'

He tapped his clenched fist against his lips. 'The chief asked me and Condé to promise that we' – he gestured to include me – 'wouldn't take their gold.'

Manny sighed, rubbing his jaw.

'I promised and Condé promised.' He paused, then jabbed an index finger in the air to reinforce his next point. 'We mustn't let Cal fuck these people.'

I held his gaze. 'I'll make sure of it. As far as I'm concerned, it's part of the community relations piece, and I'll control where operations are approved. That's if we find anything.'

I checked my watch. 'We need to get moving.'

'One more thing,' said Manny, his tone still subdued. 'The bad men from the north. The chief says across the hills are smugglers and bad Muslims. None of the villagers travel that way anymore.'

'Smugglers and bad Muslims. Does he mean in Mali? The border's less than fifteen kilometres away.'

'I think so. He says they've never come here. That's why he was so worried when our vehicle arrived.'

'Okay, that's something we must check out later.' I turned to Luke. 'You ready for some pillion riding. We're off for an afternoon of motocross.'

★

My numb arse and aching back hadn't recovered by the time we reached our base in Siguiri. An afternoon carrying an ever-heavier rucksack full of rocks on the back of a fume-spilling, bouncing motorbike had just about finished me off.

It wasn't as if Luke had produced a gold nugget from his digging and scraping. For all we knew, it had been a waste of time. He'd pointed out quartz and other mineral deposits that excited him, but my thoughts had been occupied with 'bad men from the north' and then concern about navigating the boulder-strewn road south.

When we left, with promises to return soon for the big feast, the chief provided a guide to show us an alternative route. I recorded and mapped waypoints as we followed the moto, squeezing along narrow forest tracks. It was rough going, but far preferable to chancing the rocks again.

After a shower, hot food, and a soft drink, I spoke to Ryan via the sat phone. He reported that Bob's trip to Liberia had been delayed and then cancelled. Instead, Bob was making friends in the hotel bars of Conakry.

'Just keep an eye on him, mate.'

Ryan laughed with the exuberance of someone who'd enjoyed a nip or two. 'I'll try. He's enjoying himself like he's back in downtown Saigon.'

Images of bar girls, drug pushers, and dank police cells flashed into focus, aided by a background of raised voices, clinking glasses, and shrieked female laughter coming through the phone speaker. 'I'm serious, mate. Don't let him get into trouble.'

'Dinnae worry boss, we're good. Enjoy your drive tomorrow.'

CHAPTER 48

CONAKRY

Still stiff from the jungle odyssey on the motorbike, the next day's fourteen-hour-long drive to Conakry reinforced the need to investigate air charter options. Even with a predawn start, darkness had settled over the capital by the time we battled through the evening traffic to reach the Novotel.

Ryan and Bob had taken the original authorisation papers for their trip, leaving us with photocopies. We'd had them stamped at the Siguiri Prefecture for added authenticity, and they afforded unhindered passage just like the originals.

Only a handful of checkpoints bothered to stop us, including Bob's favourite toilet stop on the approaches to the capital. The same sour-faced commander waved us through with barely a glance at the papers in Baldé's outstretched hand.

Upon arrival, we unfurled aching joints and ferried sealed boxes of rock samples from the cars to Luke's hotel room. Then I thanked the team as a group before approaching them individually.

From the old crew, Demba, Baldé, Alain, and Samuel had all again proved hard-working, trustworthy, and competent. My tiredness evaporated in the warmth of our parting exchanges.

The ministry man, Yaya, received no more than a lacklustre handshake. He had all the personality of a rock sample and I wouldn't miss his constant whining.

Izzy, on the other hand, had proved a real asset throughout. First with her taming of Bob's runaway stomach, and then with her effervescent and cheerful manner. All despite the spartan amenities and lack of empathetic female company.

Before leaving with Condé and Manny, she announced her fondness of the name 'Izzy' and asked me to thank Ryan for proposing it. Few of his renaming targets expressed gratitude. I promised her a job offer if the project got the green light.

After ringing Cal with a situation update and grabbing a bite to eat, I shifted my attention to tracking down Ryan and Bob.

Ryan answered my phone call within a couple of seconds. 'Yes, John.' His voice raised over blaring music.

'Where are you, mate? Is Bob with you?'

'Hello to you, too.'

'Please tell me he's there, mate. It'll be a long day tomorrow. We've got to get these samples bagged and submitted to SGS for testing.'

'Aye, he's here. Nothing heavy, don't worry. He wanted to see local live music. It's a decent place. I'll get the name and you can come over.'

Before I could suggest they move in the opposite direction back to the hotel, he was yelling a question at someone over a rising, thumping beat. When he returned, it was only to say, 'Sorry, mate. I cannae hear a thing. I'll get the name and call you back from outside,' before hanging up.

For wheels, I summoned Manny back to the hotel in Condé's car. He arrived at the same time as Ryan's text providing the name of the music venue.

Manny frowned when I passed on the information. 'Are you sure?'

'Yeah, Ryan and Bob are there already. Why?'

'You know that's the club we went to last time, right? The girl.'

'Oh, shit.' I considered the implications. 'Although that was two years ago, and I've had worse nights out.'

'Okay.' He rolled his shoulders, laced his fingers together, and stretched his arms and upper back. 'If you're sure.'

'It'll be fine. We won't be there long.'

He gave me a sideways glance before guiding the old Merc out of the hotel car park.

★

The foliage covering the front of the club looked less like a design statement this time and more like the jungle trying to reclaim territory. I couldn't help checking for signs of beasties as we passed a bushy outgrowth on our way inside.

For a Wednesday evening, four days before the presidential election, the turnout seemed good. Not as packed as the last time I'd visited, but almost as noisy and with enough patrons to generate a wait at the bar. When a space opened, I shouted my order for two Cokes.

'John,' said Manny from over my shoulder.

Before he could say anything else, a hand slapped onto my other shoulder.

'Ah my two favourite Poms.' Bob had a grip of Manny with his other hand. 'On the shorts already, I see.'

I held up my glass. 'Just a Coke tonight. We've got a lot on tomorrow and it's been a long day.'

'I'll get those,' Bob said to the barman.

Then he pushed in close and spoke into my ear. 'We're working. Me and Ryan are chatting to two Russkie flyboys who run cargo planes up north.'

'Russians?'

'Yep. We're sitting with them now. Can't hear fuck all though, with this music. Maybe we should arrange to meet them during the day.'

He bellowed his six-drink order at the barman, then pointed at my glass. 'You want a vodka in that?'

'Not today. Who are the other drinks for?'

Bob's face screwed up in concentration. 'A French fella, friend of the Russians, and a Lebanese bloke who hasn't said a word. Likes his Blue Label though.'

After Bob arranged for the drinks to be served at the table, we followed him amongst strobe-lit pockets of bodies to where Ryan and the others sat.

I clocked the Russians next to Ryan and my step faltered. The same two men from 2008. Their faces had sprung to mind when Bob mentioned Russkies, but I never imagined it would actually be them here tonight.

'Look who I found skulking at the bar ordering a cup of tea each,' announced Bob.

The closest Russian looked up from his conversation with the guy next to him – the Lebanese bloke at a guess – and his eyes widened.

I opted for a front foot approach. 'Sergei and...his little friend if I remember right. You own this place or are you gold card members?'

Sergei stood up and pointed at me, a wolfish smile spread across his grid. 'The English Kiwi who doesn't like women...' – he craned his head to see around me '...and his black shadow.'

Then he looked from Bob to Ryan and pointed again. 'You know these two?'

'Yeah, this is John who we told you about. Boss of the project,' said Ryan.

Sergei said something in Russian to his pal – Peter, now I remembered – and they both laughed.

'We'll be having one drink and then we'll be off,' I said, fixing my attention on Ryan.

'Okay,' he replied, frowning.

Then Bob piped up, 'He's not a fucking Kiwi. John here's a Pom through and through.'

Thanks Bob.

Sergei nodded slowly, still sporting the kind of wise-guy sneer that attracts punches. 'British, huh?'

I ignored the question and indicated the Arab and the swarthy, well-dressed guy next to Peter. 'Who are your other friends?'

The white guy stood and offered his hand. 'I'm Henri. You are John?'

'That's right. And this is Manny.'

Sergei shuffled round the table to invade my personal space as the barman arrived with a tray of drinks. While Bob distributed them and tipped the barman, Sergei leaned even closer. 'Bob says you are working up in the country. Ramzi here tells us it is Siguiri. What are you doing there?'

I checked out Ramzi – Arabic features, nondescript clothing, in this environment at least. He stared back. Then I jutted my jaw towards Sergei's face only inches from my own. 'None of your business.'

Bob pushed between us and thrust a drink into Sergei's hand. 'Now, now ladies. Let's all raise our glasses to new friends.'

As everyone repeated the toast and knocked back their drinks, I retreated to a seat next to Manny. 'Do you know either of those other two, Ramzi and Henri?'

'No. Never seen them before.'

Whoops and cheers broke out near the stage as the band finished their latest song. The noise levels weren't conducive to easy conversation, but the questioning looks emanating from Bob and Ryan suggested my arrival had soured the atmosphere.

Henri came over and began throwing out questions without offering much in return. I kept my answers as vague as his. He claimed to be a commodities trader, although he produced no business card.

I turned my attention back to Sergei and called across to him. 'What planes do you have?'

He studied me. 'You want to charter a plane?'

'It depends. What sort of cargos are you flying?'

He finished his drink and banged the glass down on the table. 'What cargos? The "none of *your* business" kind.'

Ryan jumped to his feet and blocked the view between us. 'Come on, drink up. Let's get out of here.'

CHAPTER 49

TWO WEEKS LATER

EPSOM, UK

Epsom Downs had returned to its tranquil, early morning norm. Running provided uninterrupted thinking time and today I needed it. Deployment options and logistic considerations for a follow-up visit to la Guinée competed for priority in my head.

England's World Cup campaign had ended early with a crushing defeat by the Germans. I, on the other hand, had returned to the UK with a successful mission under my belt, later enhanced with the news that the tested rock samples had corroborated the findings of the Barker study.

It meant the green light for the project.

Not only that, but the quick-fire samples we'd taken during our motorbike tour of the northern concession had shown positive results off the scale. We'd be returning to Setka village for the promised feast, that was for sure.

The previous afternoon's meeting at the club in London had proved a back-slapping affair. Although Pinnacle had not yet signed any contract, permission for a follow-up trip had been granted. Everyone around the table, the same gathering as the previous meeting, was buoyed by the success of the trip and the spectacular results obtained. The illicit probe into Block C in the north provided an added sense of self-congratulation amongst the group.

Foster had provided a sobering update on the results of the presidential election – a two-candidate run off as expected. The favourite had won the most votes by a distance, but he hadn't reached the fifty per cent threshold to win outright. Another old campaigner had secured second place by a small margin. Foster's prediction had proved accurate. The run-off between the last two men standing would take place within weeks.

'My team are not discounting the underdog. He's got some powerful backing, and his campaign may pick up steam if beaten candidates support him.'

'Where's the powerful backing coming from?' I asked.

'The scale of it isn't clear, but international investors and more than one government seem to be behind his reform manifesto.'

'He'd be the better president for us as well,' said Cal. 'He's looking to transform the mining sector and ferret out corruption. A squeaky-clean British outfit signing a deal and investing at the start of his term in office could be desirable.' He paused. 'That's according to contacts around him.'

All said with a straight face and not a hint of irony. Cal and squeaky clean couldn't be that well acquainted. Even so, for this project he might have a point.

'Our reversal in 2008 might even play in our favour, if we spin it right,' he added.

He met my stony reaction behind a placating palm in my direction. 'Not to downplay what happened back then.'

Sir Jeremy cleared his throat. 'The authorities in Guinea have given us permission to return, and John here is happy with the situation. Therefore, I propose we go ahead. Everyone agree?'

No one disagreed.

Plans for a two-week trip to Guinea were thrashed out, including objectives and provisional budgets. Bob and Luke would return, and I successfully argued that my supporting team should be enhanced to reflect the logistic realities we'd experienced on the ground. It was now down to me to make a convincing case if I wanted more than one additional body.

After exchanging a cheery 'good morning' with a dog walker and crossing the lush racetrack near The Derby start point, I considered the agreed objectives for the Siguiri project. A small list that packed a large punch.

1. Express interest/open negotiations with the CPDM for an exploration license for the Northern concessions. Priority is Block C. *Lead – Bob*
2. Comprehensive sample collection at all concessions. *Lead – Luke*
3. Assess options for mining operations in the Siguiri project area. *Lead – Bob*
4. Assess options for security and support operations throughout the project area and at primary and secondary potential logistic and transport hubs in Guinea (and surrounding countries as deemed appropriate). *Lead – John*

While Objective 4 was my chief responsibility, providing support to the other three objectives needed my focus and allocation of resources. The variables for splitting the team as we all went about our tasks were considerable.

Luke would be focused on the collection of samples in all the concessions, including the block in the northeast we hadn't even checked out yet. Operating in those northern blocks might still prove tricky unless we could secure authorisation from the ministry in Conakry. The problem with asking the question is that they might say no. Where would that leave us?

The uphill stretch at the back of the Downs took my attention until I re-emerged, breathing hard, into bright sunshine and settled into a comfortable pace on flatter ground.

Bob's maverick tendencies meant I needed to assign Ryan to him like a man-marking football defender. He'd need to roam the country independent of Luke's tasks and my own.

We needed at least two more warm bodies. Competent guys who I could trust to make the best decisions in any circumstances and make things work. I'd try to recruit Mike to join us this time, if he was available. Jamie too. My convincing case for that second extra body had become clearer. Now I wasn't sure if even that would be enough.

I increased the pace when I reached smoother tracks through a channel of open ground between woods either side. Crossing the racetrack again, nearer to where racing horses turn down the infamous Epsom slope, I glanced ahead to the car park. A latest style, gleaming black Range Rover caught my attention. Parked away from the handful of other vehicles, it was an unusual sight this early in the morning.

My speed quickened again once I reached the tarmacked road that swung downhill alongside the racetrack. A figure wearing a suit stood next to the Range Rover, thirty yards away.

Now suspicious, I kept to the far side of the narrow road and scrutinised the man as I prepared to pass within ten metres. He raised a hand in greeting and smiled. Tom Roper, former British Special Forces and, last time we met, an agent of the state at MI6 or one of its shadowy offshoots.

My run stuttered to a fast walk and I changed direction towards Roper. Sweat beaded on my forehead and under my t-shirt.

'Hello, Tom.' I made a show of glancing left then right. 'I assume you're here to see me.'

'I was in the neighbourhood.'

'And you happen to know that I run up here most mornings?'

'A lucky guess.'

'Really. So, to what do I owe the pleasure?'

He gestured towards the Range Rover behind him. 'I'm with someone who wants to speak to you.'

'Not my old friend Sandy Chapman by any chance?'

One of the black SUV's rear doors clicked open. A pair of shapely calves swung out and planted expensive-looking four-inch heels into the gravel. Unless Chapman had been through a significant mid-life transition, I was about to add a new name to my address book.

'Not this time,' said Roper. 'Although he sends his regards.'

Five years earlier, my adventures in Iraq with British intelligence had been directed by Sandy Chapman, an old-school, Oxbridge type. Unfortunate circumstances had resulted in my being one of very few people able to identify a high value target in Iraq. We'd clashed many times but by the end of the operation we'd rubbed along okay, for the most part. The last time we met, at the debrief after the 2005 mission in Iraq, he'd mentioned that MI6 might come calling again one day. All due to my operating in areas that could prove to be of interest.

Roper had been with me during the final part of the Iraq task and we'd got on well. I liked him. But that didn't mean I was going to like whatever they had to say. Chapman had used leverage to strong-arm me into helping them last time. They'd have a fight on their hands if they tried that trick again.

A thirty-something woman approached. Early rather than late thirties. Athletic poise, fresh-faced with light make-up that accentuated her blue eyes, auburn hair in a high ponytail. Girl-next-door pretty with a hint of mischief and a dollop of smart about her. About as different from Chapman as you could get.

Her inquisitive gaze locked on my face. A toned, tanned arm extended to offer a manicured hand.

'Ma'am this is John Pierce. John, meet Hope Crosby, my Section Head.'

'You can call me control,' the woman said as we shook hands, her grip light and feminine. No hand-crushing pissing contest to be 'one of the boys'.

I shot a look at Roper and considered how to respond. The woman laughed at my uncertainty. 'Only joking. I'm Hope. It's good to meet you after reading your file.'

Still off-balance, I glanced from one to the other before replying.

'Hi, you know who I am then. You're Tom's section head, an improvement on the last one I might add, but I don't really know what that means. Or why you might want to track me down and speak to me out here.'

'As Tom said, Mr Chapman sends his regards. He is in ultimate charge of this operation, but I control the day-to-day running.' She cocked her head slightly. 'Your involvement is his idea.'

Her sculpted eyebrows edged upwards. I detected an element of surprise that Chapman wanted me involved. Hopefully because I was a civilian and not because I looked incapable.

I took a deep draw of the cool hillside air and exhaled slowly. What chance did a guy have to look his best if he's interrupted during a morning run?

'I'm not operating in Iraq anymore. Things didn't work out. My current project is in Africa, and I'm due back there very soon.'

While I'd been shaking my head, Hope Crosby had been nodding hers.

'We know. It's Africa I need to speak to you about.' Her eyes glanced down to my legs. At a guess, assessing for dirt and sweat rather than taking in my splendid form. 'If you join me in the car, I'll explain why I'm here.'

When she led off, Roper didn't move. 'Not joining us?' I asked.

He shook his head. 'I'm going to take in the view. Nice place for a run.'

I studied his face. 'You already know what she's going to say.'

We were interrupted by his boss. 'You two will have plenty of time to catch up later.'

Once inside the Range Rover with the doors shut, Hope turned to face me across the back seat. 'We know you've been in Guinea recently, and we know you're returning shortly.'

She held up a hand when I opened my mouth to speak.

'If you'll let me explain our interest and outline our proposal, then you can ask questions.'

'Okay.'

'You have history with a person of interest to us, General Sylla.'

My mouth went dry.

'We have the report of your incarceration at his hands two years ago. You'll remember Gough from the embassy in Conakry.'

My reservations about where this might be heading intensified. 'Yes. He collected me from the cells and bundled me out of the country.'

'An appropriate course of action at the time, I think you'll agree.'

Not that she waited for my agreement.

'The good general has gone to ground during the recent upheavals as you might have discovered on your recent trip. However, he is suspected of coordinating the relationship between South American drug cartels, gold and diamond miners, and elements that warrant our attention. Namely al-Qaeda cells operating in West Africa, principally Mali.'

I processed the information with no idea where it was leading, other than a growing sense that my upcoming trip to Guinea was about to become a whole lot more complicated.

'I don't know how much you know about the relationship between the cartels and terrorist financing in Africa?'

This time she waited for an answer.

I took a deep breath. 'Consider me unenlightened.'

By the unblinking set of her face, it was clear that my irreverent answer did not meet with approval. The time for smiles and jokes was over. A waft of my own stale sweat competed for a moment with the light, crisp fragrance coming from the other side of the seat.

'Without going into detail, hard-line Salafist groups, broadly coalesced under the al-Qaeda banner, provide armed muscle to the cartels along the narcotics supply routes heading north across the Sahel from landing points in West Africa. You've been in the region, and from reading your file I'm sure you will be well aware of the failed state in Guinea Bissau and the increasing presence of the cartels as they spill over the border into Guinea Conakry.'

I nodded as she spoke. It was nothing I didn't know already but connecting the dots with regards to drug smuggling had never been my focus.

'Senior government and military officials in Bissau have been actively engaged in the drug trade for years. This has also been true in Conakry but to a much lesser extent.' Her tongue flicked across her undecorated lips as she straightened her posture. 'But what has this got to do with us, with HM Government, you might ask? Interdicting the narcotics trade routes is, of course, a goal, and we're certain that large quantities of the cocaine reaching West Africa is destined for UK streets.'

She leant forward again, eyes wide and intense, clearly relishing the subject.

'For us, the intelligence community, it is the link to terrorism that brings this topic into our domain. For the protection services they provide to the cartels, they are paid in diamonds, gold, and other easily transportable assets. These can then be used to finance operations against targets including Britain, the US, and our allies.

'As you would imagine, Guinea and other Francophone countries in the region are heavily monitored by their former colonial masters. Much of what we know is shared from the French. Now we have a man at the centre of a spider's web of money, drugs, and terrorists. A man with whom you have a more intimate knowledge than most.'

A predatory smile spread across her face. 'And then we have the reason you came to our recent attention.'

Her dynamic, confident poise compared to me: sweaty, knackered, stiffening. The hunter and the prey. These people weren't stupid. The sweat had mostly dried, although I wondered if there might be a wet patch on the cream leather upholstery.

The tinted privacy glass provided a cocoon where a world I thought I'd never experience again had come calling. A confessional perhaps?

My last dalliance with the intelligence world had been instigated by my own actions, however unwitting. I wracked my brain to think what else, other than my 2008 clash with General Sylla, could have initiated this current interest. Nothing sprang to mind.

'You've had a colourful recent past,' said Hope. 'My colleagues were dubious of your involvement in the operation in Iraq, and the file notes still leave questions as to your conduct leading up to that involvement.'

I interrupted. 'I'm sure Mr Chapman and Tom over there will have explained the background. I was assured that had all been put to bed.'

'Yes, that is not my focus here.' She swept a dismissive hand.

'In 2008, you popped up on our radar again, this time in Guinea. Another unfortunate set of circumstances that weren't your fault.' Her tone signalled her doubt on that point. 'And then we have your name splashed across a report currently on my desk.'

'I don't understand. What report?'

'A friendly agency providing details of you and others meeting in Conakry with men of interest to my counter terrorism operation.'

'What men?' I didn't make any effort to hide my scepticism.

'Russian pilots suspected of supporting the bad guys to run drugs, guns, and other contraband across West Africa.'

Silence descended on the car. I rubbed my stiff calves and rolled my shoulders as an image of two big, obnoxious Russians sprang to mind. Sergei and Peter.

'Now hang on, I don't know those guys. I mean, I know who you mean, but I've had nothing to do with them. We had nothing to do with them.'

'Just another unfortunate coincidence?'

I held her gaze. 'Yes, just a coincidence.'

'So, you simply happened to meet with two pilots flying for a rogue general who you spent time with in 2008? A rogue general at the centre of the sticky, vicious web I'm targeting. You can see why I'm a little cautious as to your involvement.'

Put like that, it didn't sound great. Change the presentation to include my torture at the hands of said general and my spiky interactions with the Russians and it would read very differently.

'That is why our friends across the water have been giving you the once over. Checking who you currently work for and making sure there are no new skeletons rattling in the closet.'

'The Americans?' I asked, my surprise evident.

'Not across that water. I'm referring to my colleagues at the Security Service. They haven't found any obvious red flags, and Mr Chapman and Tom both agree that you might be the right person in the right place to assist us. Plus, you're already bound by the Official Secrets Act and the very restrictive confidentiality contract you signed in 2005. Hence, here we are.'

It was all still clear as mud. I could see how they might have joined some dots but so what. A sudden wave of foreboding washed over me. Surely, they weren't going to ask me to go undercover to infiltrate General Sylla's network. That would be madness.

I swallowed and then coughed at the dryness in my throat.

'Water?' said Hope. She opened the central console and offered me a bottle. I gulped down half in one go.

When I began to shake my head, her eyebrows lifted. Did she have some leverage? Were they going to try and force my hand to help them again?

'Before you say something we both might regret, let me outline our proposition. I think you'll see we will all benefit, Pinnacle as well.'

Having taken a deep breath ready for an argument, I let it out and relaxed in my seat. 'Okay.'

She opened the window a fraction. 'Tom, can you join us?'

The door opened and Roper climbed into the driver's seat. When it clicked shut, Hope began to speak again.

'After reviewing the files, Mr Chapman and myself agreed that today's approach should be made. Tom is also fully aware of the plan. Discreet contact has been made with your current employers, Pinnacle Mining, and Tom met yesterday with Cal Simmons to sound them out.'

'You know Cal?'

That might explain a lot.

'No, none of us know him personally, but he is known to the organisation. He proved most helpful and agreed that Pinnacle would accommodate our requirements, provided you also agree and that it won't prevent completion of your tasks for them.'

I began to warm to the idea of getting involved. If Pinnacle didn't mind, then it couldn't involve anything too risky. Some ground truth reporting perhaps.

'You want to run an operation in Guinea? Where?'

'Tell me about your expedition to the north of Siguiri. We understand from Mr Simmons that you conducted work close to the border with Mali.'

'Not right on the border. A few kilometres away.'

'Close enough,' replied Hope. 'The border area is believed to host an al-Qaeda base. A facility suspected of being both a transit hub and a recuperation centre for injured and exhausted fighters. I assume you discovered nothing out of the ordinary on your travels?'

I thought back to Setka village and our frosty initial welcome.

'Nothing of particular note. Although a village chief did talk about "bad Muslims" and armed men to their north. We saw no sign of them.'

Hope's face brightened. 'I'm glad you mentioned that. It was, after all, noted in your post mission report. A report I read with interest yesterday.'

My eyes met Roper's in the rear-view mirror and he winked. I returned a caustic smile.

Hope continued. 'We believe these men might indicate the presence of the alleged al-Qaeda camp. If it is there, then I believe it will be to Pinnacle's and you own advantage to know about it.' That predatory smile returned. 'And to have that potential thorn in your side removed. Tom, do you want to outline the operational concept.'

Roper adjusted the mirror so we could see each other more comfortably. 'We understand you have a second trip to Pinnacle's mining area–'

I cut in. 'Potential mining area.'

'Okay, potential mining area,' he said with a hint of annoyance. 'Our plan is for me to accompany you on the trip, with added manpower as we decide is necessary, and for us to conduct reconnaissance in the border area. Our aim is to identify any sign of al-Qaeda elements or other suspicious activity.'

'That might not prove quite as easy as it sounds. You have a budget for the extra guys we'd need?'

'Within reason,' said Hope.

'And permission from the authorities in Guinea?'

There was a telling pause.

'That's a sensitive topic,' replied Hope. 'Especially with the elections.

The reason why we want to use the Pinnacle Mining visit as cover is because we need a discreet operation. One that remains undetected by the host country.'

There was always a bloody catch with these people.

I let out a heavy sigh. 'And what if things go wrong and we get compromised?'

Hope answered. 'You'll be mining contractors scouting for new prospects. The same reason you were there last time. Tom will be with you and reporting directly to me and the team here in London.'

'A fat lot of good that will do if Mamba gets hold of us. You've read my file. You know what happened to me back then.'

Hope lifted her chin. 'Mamba. General Sylla's nom-de-guerre. You're a big boy and must know the rules. Don't get caught.'

I shook my head. 'Is that it? "Don't get caught".'

Roper's eyes were on mine in the mirror. 'John, we're taking a careful probe into the area. This won't be a close target recce. We'll plan for all eventualities and use a convincing cover story for being there. Through Pinnace we already have the perfect cover and it's not a story.'

'Chapman is in charge again?' I asked Hope.

'He's the senior officer, but I'm running the operations side of Project Brimstone and we'll be monitoring you twenty-four-seven. And by the way, that project name is classified.'

Hope was right. If al-Qaeda had an R&R and transit hub up the road from a Pinnacle operating area, then I needed to know about it. The additional resources and support available for addressing it now, with Chapman's people, would never be matched by Cal and the Pinnacle board.

I took a moment to picture what we might need in terms of manpower, vehicles, and other support to make this work.

'We'll need more men. Perhaps four or more. And we should be armed in case we do bump into al-Qaeda. The cover story is more for the locals. We'll need to keep the weapons low pro, but they did see me with a rifle last time. It could work.'

A flicker of surprise crossed Hope's face. I hadn't mentioned being armed or the chief's target practice in my report.

'There's no need to go into the details here and now. You and Tom will have plenty of time over the next few days to work through that side. Can I take it you're in?'

I coughed a semi-laugh. 'I'm sure you've got something up your sleeve if I refuse.'

She fixed me with a triumphant look. 'A lady never tells.'

CHAPTER 50

That afternoon I met with Roper at an anonymous office in Kensington. He'd turned down the suggestion of meeting at my place. I guessed that was because MI5 had been crawling all over me, probably at his personal request, and he felt more comfortable meeting at a location he knew was secure. Another item for the list of things my wife need never know about.

Claire had accepted my new African project. Not without reservations but the money was welcome, and she'd even laughed at my stories from the first trip. Most of those involved Bob: his iron stomach and toilet troubles, his cameo as a presidential candidate, and his immediate and surprising friendship with the head of the CPDM, which rescued the trip from being canned at the outset. As far as she was concerned, as far as anyone was concerned, this follow-up visit would be more of the same.

The 'need to know' policy extended to me. Although Roper and I had an easy understanding and worked well together, he rebuffed any questions about Sandy Chapman, Hope Crosby, or anything unrelated to the immediate mission.

'The only thing you need to know is that we report to Hope who reports to Chapman. This is a sensitive operation,' he told me.

'Will we liaise with the embassy in Conakry?'

'No. This is being run directly from London.'

'But they know about the operation?'

He sat back in his chair. 'No. When I say this is sensitive, I mean sensitive. They're in the midst of a presidential election and Guinea is France's back yard. We work directly to the team here and no one else.'

I thought through the implications. None for me and Pinnacle that I could pinpoint. In fact, the fewer people aware of our involvement the better. Roper, however, could have problems if compromised.

'Okay, that doesn't affect us. What happens if you get into trouble? An undeclared spy in a foreign country.'

He laughed. 'I'm a security contractor working for Pinnacle Mining, just like you. Here.' He tossed me a passport.

The picture showed the Tom Roper I'd first met in 2005. No grey in the hair, fewer lines on the face. A different name though. 'Tom Robson. Could have been worse.'

We agreed a short backstory of how we would have met: contracting in Iraq. I didn't need to know much other than his military background. Only the bare bones, the same as everyone else on the team. Any mention of the SAS was out. Instead, he was now an ex-bootneck like me. 'Hoofing. Welcome to the Corps, Royal.'

We both laughed before he said, 'Gleaming. Get the wets on then. The galley is through that door.'

Over the next three hours we compiled a plan that dovetailed with the Pinnacle objectives. The longer we worked, the clearer it became that checking out reports of an encampment full of nasty bastards in the neighbourhood was of crucial importance to the company. We may never have known about them without the vague description from the village chief but having received the warning we couldn't afford to ignore it.

We discussed Setka village and whether to utilise or avoid it. Eventually deciding to engage with the villagers and harness their local knowledge of the terrain and nearby settlements.

Maps of the area arrived, courtesy of an efficient young woman. Three circles marked areas targeted for closer inspection.

'Can't you just watch it with a satellite?'

'If only it was that easy. The jungle canopy would be a problem even if we could task a satellite. This is our show and ours alone. It means no assistance from the Americans or anybody else. Even with Six, it's need to know only. Chapman wants to get a grip of the emerging West African threat before we're watching hotels, embassies, and Western interests burning on the evening news. With resources stretched, many here don't share his view that the region warrants attention.'

'I assume it's okayed by the chief, C or M, or whatever you call him, her?

Roper shrugged his shoulders. 'Above my pay grade to know the ins and outs of it. All we need to know is the mission is a go and Hope will have our backs. So will Chapman. He spoke highly of you when your name came up. Said he thought you were a good chap and meant well, if a little careless with the company you keep.'

'He's not wrong there.'

Over a coffee, I gave Roper chapter and verse about my experiences with General Sylla. It felt like I was talking about someone else as I described my time as his prisoner. The physical pain of the torture had long since passed, although the scars on my collarbone and elbow were permanent reminders.

When I finished speaking, Roper squeezed my good shoulder. 'If you're not up to this, then tell me now. I can see it's affected you.'

I shook my head. 'It's not Mamba. It reminded me of our dog, Taz. You saw her once, after Iraq when you dropped me at the house.'

'I remember. Black Labrador. A bit crazy.'

'Yeah, a Lab cross. She died when I got back from Guinea that time. Riddled with tumours. Taking her to the vet that last time was horrendous.'

'I know what you mean. I've been through the same.'

For a moment we were both lost in our own sad memories of past four-legged friends.

I downed the last of my coffee. 'Don't worry about me, I'm fine. In fact, I'm looking forward to the chance to help fuck up whatever evil shit General Sylla is involved in.'

Agreeing the personnel requirements proved straightforward. I briefed him about the various team members from the previous trip. I hoped and expected the local guys, and girl, would jump at the chance to sign up for Pinnacle's return trip. Roper laughed as I described Bob and his escapades and gave him the lowdown on Luke.

As for my security consultants, we agreed Chapman's mob would fund Ryan and three additional bodies. Ryan had already confirmed that morning he'd be along for the ride. There was a sharp intake of breath when I quoted £400 per man per day.

'I'm in the wrong game,' was all Roper said.

The recce team would comprise me, Roper, and two other trusted expats, one a medic. I needed to check availability, but Mike and Jamie were my preferred candidates.

It left me one more expat to find. Something I'd tackle over the weekend.

The subject of equipment provided a headache. Weapons should be doable via indirect routes, but we couldn't risk taking high-spec optics and communications kit through customs. The chances of attracting suspicion were simply too high. Manny and the locals could probably assist in part, but Roper didn't like the idea of involving them in that side. It was also doubtful that Manny would be able to supply the sort of kit we needed. Weapons yes, high-spec kit no.

'If not my guys, then who? You have any assets in-country? If you're not going to let the embassy into the loop, then it's going to be a problem.'

'I know, I know. I'll need to work on it. We have an asset in Freetown, Sierra Leone who could probably help.'

We examined the map and calculated distances to potential RV points. It would add a covert border crossing into the equation for whoever supplied us, and arrangement of a secure rendezvous. Neither of us liked the sound of these added complications.

'We might need to revisit keeping the Guinea station in the dark. The kit could be transported in diplomatic bags into Conakry.' He ran his hand through his hair. 'But the boss won't like that. Far too many additional people involved, here and out there.'

He studied the map. 'Maybe the RV will work. Our route runs near enough to the border and the town of Mamou. Davey Morgan is an old friend of mine, currently deployed with the IMATT training team in Freetown. Leave it with me and we'll see what he has to say.'

I took a closer look at the map as well. 'It's useful to know we have a possible safe haven in Sierra Leone. With this presidential run-off, there's still a risk of another coup or serious civil unrest, and Freetown is less than a day's drive from Conakry.'

As Friday afternoon drifted into Friday evening, we reviewed potential deployment dates. A check of the newswires revealed a fresh announcement that the presidential run-off, scheduled for 18th July, had been postponed until at least August. That prompted me to take another look at the calendar.

'I advised Pinnacle to wait until the dust settles after the election next weekend. With it cancelled, we could get in and out before the rescheduled date. How about we fly next weekend? Sunday the eighteenth. Election Day as was. It gets us in-country and ready to hit the ministry first thing Monday morning. Schedule the return for Saturday the thirty-first.'

'That gives us eight days preparation,' said Roper. 'More than enough for my side. And two weeks sounds about right considering all the hoops you say we have to jump through. I'll make the call.'

He took the maps and his notes off to the unseen parts of the spook lair.

When he returned five minutes later, he had his jacket on and waved me towards the door. 'Eighteenth it is. Two weeks on the ground. Come on, let's go grab a beer.'

★

The next morning, I woke with a thick head to Claire reminding me she had an early shift at the hospital, and one daughter needed to be ferried to ballet and another to drama school. Orange juice and strong coffee took the edge off the previous night's residue before I settled down in my office to start the real planning. Six forty-five a.m. – no wonder I didn't feel tip top.

By mid-morning I was alone in the house and making progress. Cal okayed the proposed dates and the two-week duration, provided Bob and Luke were available. He called me back as I made lunch for the girls with confirmation the Pinnacle mining team were good to go. Now I could rally my guys.

Once I'd fired off an encrypted email asking Manny to prepare the team for the 18th, I rang Ryan. He laughed when I told him he'd be babysitting Bob again. 'I'm ready, boss. Just tell me what day you need me to travel down.'

We threw a few names back and forth in case Mike was still sunning himself in the Caribbean and Jamie in the sandpit. It gave me a list of several seasoned operators we both thought would fit the Pinnacle task.

Ryan didn't know about the HM Gov angle, although I did tell him we needed to check out the area to the north as per my post mission report from the last trip. The fact we were all big boys used to playing in rough neighbourhoods didn't make me feel any better for not being straight with him. Unfortunately, that's a by-product of getting involved with spooks.

Before approaching anyone else, I wanted to establish if Mike and Jamie were free. I gave them forty-eight hours to respond – deadline Monday afternoon. To my surprise, by teatime both men were signed up. They'd each replied within two hours confirming their availability.

Speaking to them by phone, I made it clear this would be a security task with an element of threat.

Mike responded with, 'Bring it on. I need to keep my tan topped up.'

Jamie with a simple, 'And? You know me, brother. Always where the shit's at.'

Getting Mike and Jamie on the mission allowed me to relax. Together with me and Roper, the four of us comprised the reconnaissance team. With Ryan signed up to cover Bob, we only needed one more operator to look after Luke and his bags of rocks.

The rest of the weekend I focused on Claire and the girls. My high spirits rubbed off on Claire, even though she wasn't over the moon about me heading to Africa again. Our eldest, Natalie, announced she had a new boyfriend, which explained her buoyant mood. At seven and four, Becky and Daisy worshipped their big sister, and the five of us enjoyed a long day in London on the Sunday.

We watched the street performers in Covent Garden, Becky and Daisy aping one young woman's dramatic performance and receiving their own applause from the sweltering crowd. An expensive trip to the huge Hamley's toyshop on Regent Street was followed by an atmospheric meal at the Hard Rock Cafe along Piccadilly. The extensive queue outside the restaurant vindicated my decision to book in advance.

By the time the train pulled into the station near home, our two youngest were out for the count. I carried Becky to the car and Natalie carried Daisy. It prompted a pang of sadness. There wouldn't be too many more occasions I'd get the chance to carry seven-year-old Becky in my arms. Kids grew up so fast.

When Claire and I went to bed, we wrapped our arms around each other in a way we hadn't in months. Claire broke the contented silence. 'Thank you for today. I really enjoyed myself.'

'It was good fun, wasn't it? The girls were great.'

'I'm pleased we all went out together before you go away again.'

There was no hint of underlying tension in her voice, but I caught her eye to make sure. She flashed a goofy smile back.

'Love you,' I said. Something I didn't say often enough.

She leaned over and kissed me. 'Love you too.'

★

On Monday morning, planning for Africa resumed. The team would assemble at Pinnacle's offices early on Friday prior to being bussed to the Guinea Embassy for visa processing. With everyone else confirmed, I still needed to recruit someone for the role of Luke's guardian. The phone rang at eleven o'clock while I sipped my fourth coffee of the day.

'John, it's Hutch.'

That took me by surprise.

'Hello, mate. How are you doing?'

It flashed into my head to pitch him to join the team. A thought instantly dismissed. The last time we'd spoken, before the first African trip, it had been clear that was off-limits.

'I spoke to Ryan earlier.'

'Okay.'

'He says you've got another job in Africa and need one more guy.'

'That's right. Do you know someone?'

'It's just…' he paused and took a deep breath. 'It's just, I wasn't completely straight with you last time you called.'

'Right.'

'My job. I told you about it, but they laid me off. Before your call. It's one reason Liz was so unhappy. She doesn't want me to go back to Iraq again.'

'That's understandable, mate. Claire hates me going to Africa after the prison thing. It's just the money is so good. And what else do I know? Nothing that would pay anything close for a start.'

'Yeah, same here. Ryan said the trip last time was good. Hard work but no issues. No problems like you had before.'

'Sorry to mention that,' he added quickly.

'It's alright, mate. I'm over it now. Ryan's right, it was a good trip. Haven't laughed so much in ages or yomped so much either.'

'So, are you still looking for someone?'

'Yes. Right now, in fact. I've sent a couple of messages already. You're interested then?'

'A good daily rate?' He phrased it as a question, but Ryan would have given him a heads-up.

'Four hundred quid a day. I'd love to have you along but are you sure Liz wouldn't skin me alive?'

'Honestly? No. You and me both probably. But fuck it, we're running out of money and I could do with a laugh or two.'

The extra dimension to the mission, courtesy of Roper and co, spurred a note of caution.

'Although last time was plain sailing, I don't want to mislead you, mate. It's hard work chasing after the geologist and humping his rocks through the ulu.'

'I'm not a fat civvy yet.'

I laughed. 'Plus, four of us need to go and check out reports of not-rights somewhere between the concessions and the border. It won't affect you, but I want to lay all the cards on the table.'

'I appreciate it. Ryan says he's traveling to London on Thursday. Mike and Jamie are crashing at his sister's place in Kilburn, and I'm welcome to join the Taji reunion.'

'If you're sure, then it would great to have you on board.'

'Yep, count me in. As long as Liz doesn't kill me when I tell her.'

CHAPTER 51

18TH JULY

CONAKRY

A little over three weeks after the previous African adventure, eight of us emerged from the Air France plane into a sweaty night at Conakry's Gbessia airport. Last time two SUVs had met us. Tonight, five white Toyotas arrived near the bottom of the aircraft steps. Baldé hopped out smartish and opened the door to the familiar bulk of General Ndidi. My absolution from past sins appeared complete.

It was standing room only in the VIP waiting room. When our baggage appeared, it prompted a flash of concern. Grouped together it looked unexpectedly ominous; six large, military-style rucksacks, two black and four a muddy brown, arriving with a party of Westerners during a tense presidential election run-off.

No one else appeared bothered. Maybe I was unduly sensitive, but it was a relief when Bob's battered red suitcase and Luke's sky-blue hiker's rucksack arrived to add a splash of welcome colour and normality.

Luke joined in Paris for the second leg of the journey, and we'd only exchanged a brief handshake and hello until now. I encouraged him to move his bright baggage into the centre of the group. 'For those who haven't met him yet, this is Luke Moran, the Pinnacle geologist. He's Canadian, speaks French, and is learning to swear properly.'

After a chorus of hellos, handshakes, and gentle ribbing, Bob put his arm around Luke's shoulders. 'Your good lady let you come back to us then?'

Luke shook his head as he glanced from Ryan to me. 'No thanks to you bastards.'

That prompted a snigger from Ryan.

'Veronique said I came home swearing like an Englishman and she'll leave me if it continues.'

'Bloody Poms,' offered a grinning Bob.

'Actually, I told her it was Australian swearing, not British. She didn't seem to mind that so much.'

'What did she think of your hat?' asked Ryan in mock seriousness.

Like me, he'd seen the photos of Luke's wife and felt he was punching way above his weight.

'The hat had to go,' replied Luke with a deadpan expression.

General Ndidi joined me while Bob's efforts to explain why Aussie swearing trumped the English version was drowned by howls of derision. The general's beaming smile allayed my concern there might be suspicion of our motives for being there. He seemed to be enjoying the banter.

'Gentlemen, here are your passports. Welcome to Guinea. It's late and my drivers are ready to take you to your hotel.'

During the previous week, Bob's bromance with the head of CPDM, Dr Jeffrey, had paid real dividends. Roper and I had wrestled with planning options in the event Pinnacle didn't obtain permission to investigate Blocks C and D in the north. We needn't have worried. One phone call from Bob and a letter granting permission had arrived in London within two days.

One day for logistic preparations and gaining the necessary movement authorisations from CPDM and the military, and we should be on the move to Siguiri early on Tuesday morning.

Roper issued a satisfied nod in my direction as we shouldered our kit and Mike and Ryan lifted a large Peli Case of equipment towards the waiting vehicles. After a lot of angst from the bean counters in London, we'd risked declaring the expensive specialist kit, rather than attempting to route it via Sierra Leone for delivery at the Mamou RV.

The Peli Case contained medical kit, high-spec optics and cameras, night vision devices described as geological kit, and communications gear. The full manifest had been pre-approved by the Guinea authorities in London and Conakry, but having it cleared without any drama didn't necessarily follow. Maybe General Ndidi's presence prevented any obstructive officials trying anything on. Whatever the case, everything made it through.

Manny had confirmed our equipment from the previous trip remained in secure storage ready for use. It left only the small matter of weapons outstanding. Even if the planned RV in Mamou didn't work out, we'd find a way to source those locally.

The only important kit that hadn't made the trip was my lucky eyeball. Goofing around with Becky and Daisy the day before the flight, I'd managed to lose it under the floorboards. Not the most auspicious preparation, but the girls were more upset than me.

★

The following morning, the whole team assembled – locals and new arrivals. Fifteen men and one woman. Izzy had a confidence about her that caused me and Ryan to share a smile. She still looked relieved when I confirmed her place on the team.

'You've earned it. Anyone that can keep that old man healthy and put up with his jokes is invaluable.'

Bob lifted the peak of his treasured Akubra hat and caught me pointing at him. Clearly his hearing hadn't diminished. 'Hey, less of the old man. I could teach you youngsters a thing or two about humping gear through the jungle. Vietnam was no cakewalk you know.'

Rather than try to brief the team in the car park, I moved everyone into a vacant meeting room inside the hotel. In the private surroundings, I outlined the tasks for the day, our early start the following morning for Siguiri, and the team compositions.

On a manky whiteboard that defied my attempts to clean it up, I sketched out the team groups.

Support Group
Sierra One – Alain (Driver), John, Tom
Sierra Two – Manny (Driver), Jamie (Medic), Mike

Mining Group
Bravo One – Demba (Driver), Baldé, Ryan, Bob

Geo Group
Golf One – Samuel (Driver), Hutch, Luke
Golf Two – Condé (Driver), Izzy, Yaya (Geo)

All the vehicles contained both English and French speakers, and all would possess one or more weapons after the RV with Roper's contacts in Mamou.

Luke's two-vehicle Geo Group would collect further rock samples; Bob's single-vehicle Mining Group would roam the blocks collecting information and mapping the area; and my two-vehicle Support Group would provide mobile security and support.

'As most of you know, the chief of Setka village in Block C informed us that a suspicious group is operating to the north. This doesn't affect the other blocks near Fifa, but the Support Group will reconnoitre the block and the zone between the northern perimeter and the Mali border, just to make sure. Once we've cleared the area, then all of us will spend the last three days working on that block. Any questions?'

Apart from the murmuring of Manny and Izzy translating my words to the non-English speakers, no one spoke. Then Manny half-raised his hand and pointed at Condé. 'He asks if breakfast has finished.'

Before the laughter had subsided, Ryan flicked a hand up. 'What about the other one in the northeast, Block D. When are we fitting that in?'

'We don't have any time for D. This expedition will only cover Blocks A and B near Fifa, and Block C to the north. Maybe next time.'

★

Compared to our previous experience, the day proved successful on all counts. The support of Dr Jeffrey Diallo at CPDM and General Ndidi meant the all-important authorisation papers were signed, stamped, issued, and copied by mid-afternoon.

Conakry seemed little changed from before the election. Traffic filled the streets and people filled the markets. There was perhaps an underlying air of expectancy, although that might have had more to do with my altered perception of the situation rather than actual observation. Groups of men hanging around street corners were nothing new. Whichever candidate was elected, the circumstances for the general population would be unlikely to see much change, in the short term at least.

That night, Hutch thanked me for bringing him along. 'It's just what I needed, mate. I don't just mean the money. You and the guys. All of us back together and on the road. Thanks, John. I mean it.'

'You might not thank me after the drive to Siguiri tomorrow. It's grim. Watch out for that mosquito on your neck.'

He slapped a hand at the big beastie, which shrugged off his efforts and escaped towards the overhead light. 'I need more spray.'

Before meeting in the restaurant for dinner, I called the other security guys into my room and provided more detail on our recce plans for the Northern Block. I reiterated that it was in Pinnacle's interests to assess any threats to potential future operations and hinted at liaison with British government departments. Hutch and Ryan wouldn't be directly affected, but both joined in the discussion and offered to take part if needed.

'The main impact for you guys is the need to coordinate while we're up there. You've got locals with weapons and permits in each vehicle. The closer you can stay to each other, the easier it will be to provide mutual support. I'll speak to Bob about it. We can't have him doing his own thing and spreading everyone all over.'

'What about you guys?' Ryan said. 'What are you doing about weapons? You've only got Alain with a permit.'

'I was coming to that. We've arranged to collect four AKs at an RV in Mamou tomorrow, wrapped in a tent, of all things. We'll stop in the town and me and Tom will take our vehicle to the RV. It's at the back of a shop near the centre. Ten minutes and we'll be done. If anyone asks, we're picking up additional supplies.'

'Backup?' asked Mike.

'We'll be okay. I'm assured friendlies will see to it.'

Mike glanced at Roper and nodded. 'What about your drivers? Manny seems okay. How about the other guy, the policeman?'

'The drivers don't know we're going to be armed, but they saw me with a rifle last time we travelled north. Alain's a good guy as well and he'll be carrying an AK. I'll square it with Manny to talk to him nearer the time. The weapons will stay hidden until we deploy for the recces anyway. We're expecting four AKMS with folding stocks, so we should be able to keep them hidden in the bergens until after the drop off.

'The only guy to watch out for is the geologist, Yaya. He's CPDM's man, their spy if you like. We need to keep him well out of the loop.'

Of the four-man recce team, Roper and I had planned the tasks, Jamie was up for anything, and Mike already knew there was more to it.

Mike and Roper had recognised each other in London from their overlapping time at the Hereford gun club. Mike gave a knowing smile when I introduced Tom Robson to the team and afterwards told me he remembered Tom 'George' Roper. He'd also remembered Roper had migrated to the spooks. Mike hadn't pushed for details or let on to the others.

'He's a good man to have with us,' he said and left it at that.

Everyone looked fit and healthy as we assembled at 5.00 a.m. the next morning. We'd eaten at the hotel and all been careful with our meals. Bob's efforts to accept an invitation from Dr Jeffrey to revisit his favourite fish restaurant had been rebuffed, despite Bob's protestations that his previous stomach trouble had nothing to do with the food.

We flew out of the blocks, passing through the empty Conakry streets and reaching the open roads leading into the jungle hinterland before most of the city was awake. Our old friends at the large checkpoint outside the capital performed a perfunctory check and sloped back inside before we departed.

I asked Alain if the political uncertainty had caused nervousness in the security forces. Whether the choice of president would make much difference to them. He thought about it and decided it wouldn't, although he agreed that many in uniform were being careful not to align themselves too closely with either side. With Roper translating when Alain slipped into French, he described other officers and units who were fully committed to one side or the other.

'That shouldn't affect us, we're politically neutral,' I said.

Alain glanced over from behind the steering wheel. 'Nobody is neutral in Guinea. They're just careful when they show their colours.'

I thought back to Foster's briefings in London. In private, the Pinnacle hierarchy fancied one candidate over the other. Publicly, the company had no preference and would be ready to welcome whichever man took power. Not so different to how the locals were playing it.

After 250 kilometres of speedy progress, we hit the town of Mamou at 9.25 a.m. and everyone seemed happy to stretch their legs and grab a bite to eat. I announced we were off to collect supplies and shuffled into the driver's seat of my Land Cruiser with Roper alongside. The driver, Alain, stood next to the car looking non-plussed.

'We'll be back in ten,' I said and drove off without waiting for a reply.

Roper had a map with directions and instructions supplied by Dave Morgan. 'Slow down. Take the next left.'

We'd driven less than a kilometre across town and now found ourselves bumping down a dirt road between wrinkly tin shacks and tired commercial buildings, all bursting with boxes, crates, and goods. Piles of fruit, colourful textiles, and a mountain of shoes spilled into the road. The neighbourhood appeared to be a mixture of shops and small industrial units. Pedestrians wandered along each side of the road.

'Here, this blue one on the left,' said Roper.

I pulled up outside a brick building with peeling blue paint. We'd opted for a strategy of 'get in, pick up the gear, and get the hell out again'. No ham-fisted attempts at a recce or trying to play it cute. We were two white guys in an SUV in small town Guinea. We'd brazen it out like we were meant to be there.

I checked the rear-view mirror. 'A bike made the turn with us and stopped twenty metres back.'

Roper craned his head to peer into his wing mirror. 'That's okay. He's a friendly.'

'You sure?'

'They said a green shirt on a bike would follow us in.'

The large door opened, and a smiling middle-aged man came out and waved to us. His red polo shirt struggled to contain his stomach and how his filthy jeans stayed up I couldn't figure out. 'Ça va. J'ai ta tente prête à récupérer.' *I have your tent ready to collect*

'Ça va,' replied Roper. 'Je vais ouvrir le dos. Avez-vous besoin d'aide pour le transporter? *I'll open the back. Do you need help to carry it?*

'Non c'est bon.' *No, it's okay*

He whistled and two younger men carried out a large canvas valise. Roper's man in Sierra Leone had promised four AKMS folding stock rifles and twenty-four loaded, thirty-round magazines secreted inside an old 9x9 tent.

We elected not to hang around and check the contents. If anything was missing, there was nothing we could do about it. I stayed in the car with the engine running, ready for a quick exit if needed. Not that blocking the road would have taken much effort from anyone seeking to apprehend us.

Roper exchanged a few words with the big guy and slipped him something that prompted a deep laugh and a broad smile. Hard currency, no doubt.

Once we were loaded, Roper rejoined me in the front of the car. 'Down to the bottom. Take a left, then another left, and we'll be back on the main drag.'

I steered around a woman balancing an extraordinary amount of fruit on her head and we were back underway. Five minutes later we pulled up next to the team. Hutch stood by one of the Geo Group vehicles with its bonnet raised.

'Problem?' I asked.

'No, just filling the screen wash. How about you?'

'Yeah, we're good. Okay everyone, let's mount up and get back on the road.'

CHAPTER 52

TUESDAY 20TH JULY

SIGUIRI

Our convoy of five mud-spattered SUVs rolled through the floodlit Siguiri airport gate just after 6.30 p.m. Unlike our previous arrival, there was no competition for cabins other than from the mosquitos. The place was deserted.

The owners couldn't hide their glee that the beer-swilling Brits had rocked up again. Unfortunately for them, we had a hard-working schedule to follow and four of us would be spending several nights away in the north.

With no other residents, the main building hosting the restaurant and bar became our private clubhouse. Settled around a drink and a large map that evening, I outlined the plan for the coming eight days.

'Tomorrow we'll head into Fifa village, say our hellos, and get to work on Blocks A and B.'

My extendable pointer traced an oval in the space above the N30 'road' and Tinkisso river, between the Siguiri and Leifa gold mines.

'On Thursday, the Support Group will drive to the Northern Block and begin our recce of the concession area and the area towards the Mali border, where these bad guys are rumoured to operate.'

I tapped the cluster of markings fifty kilometres to the northeast, past a kink in the thick border line.

'You're taking it that seriously?' asked Bob.

'The board took it seriously enough to fund the extra security guys. Better we find out now if there's any bad neighbours, rather than have a guy in a balaclava tapping you on the shoulder with his AK in a few months' time.'

'Fair dinkum,' said Bob before lifting his pint glass to his lips.

'We're aiming to complete our checks in four days, by Sunday twenty-fifth. Bob and Luke, that gives you those four days, and maybe one more if you need it, to finish your work down here. Either Monday or Tuesday, we'll escort you north to Block C for your work up there. Bear in mind that we need to roll out of here back to Conakry next Thursday. Any samples will go into SGS on Friday, and we'll all be heading home on Saturday the thirty-first.'

'I'll be ready to go north on Monday,' said Bob.

Luke sucked in a breath. 'It will depend on the ground, the weather, and our work rate. But I expect to be ready by Monday.'

'Okay, well that's our provisional schedule then,' I said. 'Initial objectives completed by Sunday the twenty-fifth, a few beers back here that night, and up to work the Northern Block from next Monday to Wednesday. I'll drink to that.'

We all raised our glasses, beer for most, soft drinks for some.

'Oh, and Bob, no shirking off back to the bright lights of Conakry this time.'

★

We drove in convoy to Fifa early the following morning under bright, clear skies. The weather tended to be changeable in July. Sunny one minute, torrential rain the next, and back to sunshine. We could work around that ratio.

The villagers greeted us warmly and swarmed around the cars. The chief declared our return as a special day, whatever that meant. I presented Hutch as our main point of contact alongside Luke, aided by the latter's translation. When the other new guys, Roper, Jamie, and Mike were introduced, the chief's eyes widened as he took in the number of foreigners in his manor.

Manny explained that six of us, including those three, wouldn't have time to return because of our hectic schedule elsewhere. That prompted an invitation to a celebration meal. An invitation I quickly declined before the chief got carried away.

Despite the mood in the village for a fiesta, the focus returned to the job in hand when Bob and Ryan's Mining Group vehicle, piloted by Demba and Baldé, set off into the concession for Bob to begin his assessments.

Motorbike support from the villagers had helped us in Setka village in the north. At my suggestion, Hutch went bearing gifts to the Fifa chief: cash to encourage creative thinking. Before long, five motorbikes had assembled, and the chief had attached himself to Hutch's side. The remainder of the team posed for a group photograph around the bikes. Hutch's cheesy grin in the photo made me laugh.

'I know what you're thinking,' he said, 'and you're right. It was a good decision to come out here.'

'Don't thank me yet, mate. The next eight days carrying Luke's rock collection through the jungle might change your mind.'

Through the growing crowd, I picked out Luke offering chocolate to a group of small kids and beckoned him over.

'Luke, for today you've got your group and the Support Group. Let's make the most of it. Get your map out and let's conjure up a plan that makes best use of these bikes.'

In the clubhouse that evening, Bob and Ryan were on good form while the rest of us recovered from the day's exploits. The afternoon had passed in a blitz of yomping, load carrying, motorbike riding, sweating, and swearing. Mid-afternoon rains soaked most of us and, by the time we smashed our second extra sample location, the mozzie bites were stacking up.

Hutch leaned across the table. 'You weren't joking. I'm fucked. We're earning our money, that's for sure.'

'We cracked a lot more than expected today. Should mean the next few days won't be so hard for you. Remember, you'll only have Condé and Samuel to share the lifting. The Geo is about as much use as tits on a fish, Izzy's a good lass but carries the med kit, and Luke swans around looking important carrying a man bag.'

'What was that?' asked Luke from the next table.

'I said you swan around choosing the biggest rocks and carrying jack shit yourself.'

Before he could launch into a rebuttal, I held up my hand. 'I'm joking. You need to be getting down into holes doing your geologist stuff, I know.'

'I carry samples as well,' Luke said.

'In that satchel thing on your back. I thought it was just for your sandwiches.'

Luke's answer was lost in a tirade of piss-taking at his red cheeks and higher pitch. He gave up and rocked back in his chair. 'Wankers.'

'Now, now, what would Veronique say,' said Ryan.

I couldn't hear Luke's reply, but what I could lip read would not have pleased his good lady wife.

None of the team drank any alcohol that night. We all had an early start in the morning. The three Mining and Geo Group vehicles would travel west to Fifa and continue their assessments on Block A and the as yet little touched Block B. Once in the concession, they'd split up due to Luke and Bob's differing requirements for geology and mining engineering. Ryan and Hutch would use their satellite phones to maintain regular contact between the groups and ensure a proximity that would allow for rapid mutual support if necessary.

My two Support Group vehicles would drive up to the Northern Block, re-establish contact with the village chief at Setka, and begin a security reconnaissance of the entire concession and the terrain between its northern edge and the Mali border. Roper would probe the chief about the 'bad Muslims'.

After consideration, I'd swapped out Alain for Condé as our driver. Condé's family connections to the area and Malinke language skills were assets we couldn't do without. It might also be prudent not to have a security forces officer too involved with our armed patrols in the border area. If it all unravelled, Alain would be able to tell his superiors, hand on heart, that he knew nothing about our activities or the firearms we carried.

The three cars driving to Fifa left at 6.15 a.m. Once breakfast had been cleared, my group convened in the clubhouse. We put four tables together and spread large maps over them. With the room to ourselves, I outlined the plan for the next four days and Roper, Mike, and Jamie helped drill down into the detail. Condé dozed in the corner while Manny took an active interest.

The three locations we needed to target in our search for the rumoured jihadist camp were spread fifty kilometres apart on the Guinea-Mali border. The central location was the nearest to the Northern Block – only six kilometres from the northwest corner of the 11km x 6km rectangular concession. That would be our first target – code name Crystal One.

Assuming we found nothing suspicious, we'd then move to the eastern target, Crystal Two, eighteen kilometres northeast of the top right corner of the block.

Finally, we'd investigate the western target, Crystal Three. Located fourteen kilometres west of the southwest corner, where the Mali border dropped to the south along the centre of a minor river.

Setka village was located west of centre in the block, so the third target didn't fit so well with the chief's report of suspicious activity to the north. Either of our first two targets were a better match.

For each target we intended to mount an overnight reconnaissance mission, siting an Observation Post on high ground overlooking the area. From each OP, we'd log any movements, take comprehensive photographs using the high-spec cameras, and maintain communications with the rest of the team to our south. In addition to my Iridium satellite phone, Roper had one with an encryption dongle for secure comms with Chapman, Hope, and the Project Brimstone team.

We identified Drop Off Points (DOP), Pick Up Points (PUP), and Emergency RV locations and procedures if the plans blew off course. Then we studied the track network throughout the concession and agreed a rolling mobile reconnaissance effort added into the route planning for our movements.

Four days didn't provide much time to conduct three overnight patrols and check the entire seventy square kilometres of the concession.

Whilst the team patrolled on foot near the border, Manny and Condé would drive around the block, stopping at villages to establish new contacts and listen to gossip. With Alain and his government ID and AK-47 now embedded with Hutch and Luke in the Geo Group, those two would only have Condé's family links and Makarov pistol for protection. I warned Manny to be careful in case the rumours of bad guys had any substance.

'You get into trouble and there'll be no one to bail you out. Not unless you get lucky with the phone signal or the radios.'

'Don't worry,' he said, 'Condé's family will help us. I'm worried about you guys marching around with guns.'

'We'll be okay. We can call up the cavalry from London if we have to.'

Both vehicles were equipped with VHF radios and antennas. However, communication range would be limited to a few kilometres at best, even with our OPs on high ground. Another part of our recce included assessing locations for repeater stations to increase signal range in the future.

As for the GSM phone network, the signal availability was an unknown until we deployed and tested it.

An extra satellite phone of would have been ideal. Unfortunately, the other two were with Ryan and Hutch. Although I considered it, giving Manny my sat phone wasn't a serious option; our small team would need to split up at times and we couldn't rely on the VHF radio range in the jungle. Plus, satellite comms would be our lifeline if things went pear-shaped. Having mine and Roper's two phones with the recce team in case one became unworkable trumped other considerations.

I stood back from the largest map and flipped my waterproof notebook shut. 'There we have it, guys. Everyone happy?'

'Shit,' said Jamie. 'It's like being back with the Corps.'

'It's certainly going to be tight,' said Roper. 'Not much margin for delays.'

I looked at the map and pictured us toiling through the jungle. 'If we need extra time, we'll take it. Once we've cleared the first target area, Crystal One, the close one, it won't be so important to finish the others before the rest of the team join us.'

Mike nodded and stood up. 'As weekends go, I've had better. Best we get our kit together then, chaps. We don't want to be late for the ball.'

I led the way to the cabin me and Roper shared. We occupied the securest one available, a former storeroom. It had the sturdiest lock and crossed bars in front of the windows. Inside, I unlocked the alarmed motorbike security chain wrapped around the wardrobe and dragged out the canvas valise.

'Grab an AK and six full mags each. They've also thrown in some chest webbing if you want it. I'm going to stick with my safari vest.'

'Any chance to zero these?' asked Mike.

'They've been test-fired and zeroed by Davey Morgan in Freetown,' replied Roper.

Mike looked up from checking his rifle. 'Davey Morgan? I know Dave. Ran the sniper course. Good guy.'

'One and the same,' said Roper. 'Now at IMATT. He won't have given us duff gear.'

I folded the stock underneath my lightly oiled rifle to reduce its profile. 'I'll find us a remote spot to test fire on the way up.'

Jamie was trying on the olive-green chest rig, which consisted of four magazine pouches and two storage pouches. 'Just my size and colour.'

Mike and Roper both had sleeveless tactical safari vests like mine. They were designed with multiple internal and external pockets to accommodate the equipment a security contractor might need – rifle and pistol magazines, radios, spare batteries, field dressings, phones and tablets, concealed sidearms, hydration systems, the list and number of pockets went on.

We packed our rucksacks and personal rigs; each weapon stowed in the top of the bergens. Underneath those, our kit was individually waterproofed in sealed freezer bags and packed within heavy duty liners.

We carried enough gear to be self-sufficient for four days, although resupply of drinking water when RVing with the vehicles would be preferable to purifying river water. Apart from our tactical, communications, and medical kit, we carried jungle sleeping bags, hammocks, bashas, spare clothes, spare footwear, rations, water, insect repellent, bungee cords, water purification systems, solar chargers, and more.

Mike smiled as Roper shifted the heavy bergen on his shoulders to get comfortable. 'Been a while eh, George?'

'Seems like yesterday,' replied Roper.

Jamie looked around the room. 'Who the hell's George?'

'He means Tom,' I said, flashing Mike a look. 'Come on, let's get going.'

CHAPTER 53

THURSDAY 22ND JULY

BLOCK C – THE NORTHERN BLOCK

Using my route card to avoid the boulder-strewn track, our two vehicles made good time for the 110 km drive to Setka village. En route, Manny and Condé took us to a spot where making a few bangs wouldn't be noticed. Ten rounds each at improvised targets twenty-five metres away, and four happy campers were on our way again. We stowed our AKs 'made ready' – condition one – with safety catches applied.

We sighted the first roundels on the outskirts of the village at 12:45. Driving into the heart of Setka, residents noticing our arrival were cautious until Condé's yelled greetings elicited smiles and answering shouts. Word then seemed to spread faster than we drove.

In the central quadrangle, the chief took an immediate interest in the whip antennas on each vehicle. After a play with the VHF radios, he seemed satisfied. Our weapons stayed hidden; I wanted to avoid another range day on the edge of town.

My attempts to politely dispense with the extended pleasantries didn't work. I had one eye on the time as we sat in the chief's hut and sipped the proffered cans of Coke and Fanta.

Roper tried to pump the chief for information about the bad guys in the north. He grew frustrated with Condé's translation and then with the chief's refusal to engage in French and his seeming lack of interest in the subject.

He tried again after a three-way huddle with Manny and Condé. This time the conversation flowed better, and Roper came over to me after they shook hands and broke up. 'Took some effort, but we got there in the end.'

'What did he say? Anything useful?'

'He's adamant there is a dangerous tribe to the north. Other villages have reported women and girls taken at gunpoint and never seen again. Problem is, I can't pin him down on any details. Where they might be or how far away. He just says, "to the north". Worried about antagonising them, I think.'

The chief appeared at Roper's shoulder and spoke to me in the local lingo. Condé translated to French and Manny said, 'He asks if you've forgotten about the invitation. The feast.'

'Tell him I haven't and there are more of us coming in five days. We'd love to celebrate when they get here.'

When my reply went through the same chain of translation, the chief nodded and flashed his gold-toothed grin.

After relaying the chief's delight at my acceptance, Manny said, 'We have to do this. No backing out.'

Surrounded by intrigued, chattering spectators, we erected the 9x9 tent in a spot chosen by the chief near his hooch. Although it had only been a prop to facilitate the weapons move, since we had it, we'd use it. Rather than wasting time and fuel driving the 100 kilometres to and fro each day, the vehicles and drivers would be based at Setka.

'Home sweet home,' I said to Manny as he and Condé poked around inside. 'You two will be more comfortable than us four kipping out in the boonies.'

We pulled out of the village at 1400 hours. The route to the drop off took us north for ten kilometres before turning west and paralleling the border with Mali. A few kilometres away to our right, the demarcation line wound along the path of an unseen river. A similar distance to our south lay the northern edge of the rectangular concession. We encountered no people, no vehicles, no wildlife. The only evidence of life was the rutted track and occasional flyblown rubbish.

We reached the DOP on a track nestled between low hills at 14:50.

'Arêt ici,' I said to Condé. *Stop here*

Warm rain fell as the four of us moved off the track and into the treeline. The sound of vehicle engines receded and nature took over. Rain hitting the foliage dominated; the rustle of undergrowth and swish of branches a side note as we forged a way through.

Not that the jungle was thick. If you discounted the exotic flora and fauna, the terrain wasn't much different to a rainswept European hillside forest rather than a thick soup of rainforest vegetation.

One hundred metres from the road, I stopped under a thick outspread of leafy branches, gave them a cursory check for wildlife, and signalled for the others to close in.

'Just like we planned. Order of march, me, Jamie, Tom, and Mike bringing up the rear. Mike, we'll check the map and compass bearings now, and you make sure I stay on track. Jamie, pace count.'

He pulled the pace count beads out of his pocket and shook them at me.

'Good man. This yomp to the OP should be straightforward. I'm sure we could map-to-ground it. But let's get our drills squared away, ready for the tougher routes.'

We all set down our rucksacks to retrieve the weapons. Aiming to present an unarmed profile to any observers, I kept the stock folded and adjusted the sling so the barrel and most of the rifle was wedged inside the safari vest. The result – bloody uncomfortable. Rain dripped off my nose.

'Fuck that. I'm carrying it across my chest.'

Nods of agreement followed from the others. We all unfolded the stocks, slung the AKs across our chests, and heaved the packs onto our shoulders.

The route west was split into four legs. We'd contour the high ground, slip across a valley, pass through a saddle between two hills and traverse a second valley, then climb the feature selected for the OP. Total distance 4.8 km, give or take. The only known obstacles were the tracks running through each valley.

I intended to reach the OP before last light in order to eyeball the target area, identify any unexpected threats, and assess whether a night reconnaissance patrol would be appropriate.

'Remember the actions on compromise. Civilians, move through and once clear we'll throw in a dogleg and reassess. Bad guys, tactical retreat if we can get away with it, fighting withdrawal if we can't.'

'Don't discount assaulting through the position if we get bumped by an ambush,' said Mike.

'Fuck, man. Look on the bright side why don't you,' said Jamie before shaking his head and grinning.

I nodded at Mike. 'Yeah, follow the lead of the point man. If things go that bad, then we've seriously fucked up. Whatever option we take, let's use maximum aggression to get ourselves out of the shit. If we get split up, the emergency RV is the same as the scheduled RV: the northeast corner of the block, four klicks due south of the OP. Vehicles will be there from twelve hundred tomorrow.'

I wiped rainwater from my face and donned my jungle hat. 'Actions on compromise by the military, well, it shouldn't happen. The locals say there are no security forces in the area. If we do somehow stumble across them, then we'll try to cache the weapons and brazen it out.'

Roper's pensive expression told me he wasn't enjoying hearing all the ways his career prospects at MI6 might take a nosedive.

'Once we shake out, I'll give a radio check. Make sure these earpieces and mics are working. A reminder…' I prodded my chest. 'Sierra Alpha.' I pointed at Jamie, 'Bravo', at Roper, 'Charlie,' and at Mike, 'Delta.'

'The mobiles are Sierra One and Sierra Two. Just remember Condé in Sierra One won't have a clue what you're on about, unless it's in French.'

That raised a smile all round.

'Me and Tom have sat phones. The numbers for Ryan, Hutch, and Pinnacle in London are stored in the contacts. Pin code for the phones: sixteen sixty-four, birth of the Corps.'

The encrypted VHF radios supplied by Roper's people provided a crystal-clear radio check at close range, and the wireless covert earpieces and push-to-talk controllers worked a treat. The guys spaced out ten metres apart behind me as I set a brisk pace. There were four hours of daylight left.

Patrolling through the primary jungle in tactical bounds, it dawned on me how much I relished the operational environment. A forty-two-year-old civilian, it could be my last throw of the dice working for queen and country.

We took it in turns to cross the track in the first valley, each running in a crouch from cover on one side to cover on the other.

Whilst we were tactically sound, appropriately prepared and tooled-up, and actively searching for a suspected jihadist base, the whole scenario felt unreal. The idea that an al-Qaeda offshoot or other armed group might be over the next hill or through the next tree line seemed preposterous.

We pushed on up through the saddle, the sun now burning us dry. At the sound of a distant vehicle, we went firm. Trying to raise my head and observe through the binos with a large rucksack on my back proved impossible. I unclipped the bergen and rolled out of it. Roper crawled alongside to my left with his gear already detached.

'What have you got?' he asked.

'Vehicle moving north to south at two o'clock. Civvies by the look of it. No sign of weapons.'

We were perched amongst bushes in the middle of the saddle with a wide view of the terrain to our front. It provided glimpses of the track and occasional open ground through the treetops. I caught the glint of a passing windscreen, traveling ahead of the engine sound.

The idea of bad guys waiting around every corner seemed unlikely, but it didn't prevent the nerves from jangling. Whether on exercise or operations, slipping into tactical mode had always felt the same. I studied the ground through the binos before handing them to Roper. 'You could hide an army under that canopy. Finding these jihadis will be like looking for a needle in a haystack.'

'Maybe. Depends on the accuracy of the intelligence.'

We slithered back to the others. 'Let's take five, then push on to the next waypoint.' I moved next to Mike and pulled the laminated map and route card out of my cargo pocket. 'Bearing five one five zero mils, eleven hundred metres. Track crossing at seven hundred and fifty metres.'

'Bearing fifty-one fifty, roger.'

I rejoined my bergen and sank to the ground. Jamie was filling his face nearby, and I followed suit with a deep drag through the Camelbak mouthpiece and a handful of trail mix. I wiped my neck and face with the sweat rag on my wrist before rising and swinging the pack onto my aching shoulders. 'Moving out.'

We navigated the valley without any drama, detecting no further vehicle movements or other activity. Even so, we crossed the track with extreme caution.

At 17:15 we punched out north on the last, 750-metre leg to the final RV. It involved a climb of 600 feet, which we contoured while moving between the cover of scattered trees and bushes.

This close to the target, we were moving with increased vigilance. As we gained height, I could see a high ridge further north, at least ten kilometres away. The border was only a kilometre from our OP, so most of the ground between me and that ridge was Mali. Now the game got real.

It took us an hour to reach the top of the long spur. We closed together in a thicket fifty metres from the forward edge, according to the map and GPS coordinates. The irregular rock formation along the spine of the high ground meant we couldn't yet see over the target area. It bode well for concealment of the OP. We dropped our rucksacks and Roper and I snuck forward to select the best location.

CHAPTER 54

GRID 29PMP382472

OVERLOOKING THE MALI BORDER

Nature had produced a perfect hidey-hole for the OP. The rocks providing cover while gaps between them allowed observation of the unmarked border and the Crystal One target area. The view presented a familiar scene. The similarity to the 3D images we'd studied in London was uncanny.

'We couldn't have picked a better location,' said Roper.

'That's for sure.' I had the binoculars trained on high ground less than three kilometres to our front. An al-Qaeda base was suspected in the vicinity of the two-kilometre-wide feature. Not that I could see any sign of a camp or village. No giveaway pinpricks of illumination from lamps or fires as the evening drew in. My watch showed 18:25. We had less than an hour before last light.

I passed the binos over. 'Good light discipline if they're down there. I can't see anything.'

He scanned the same area for thirty seconds before lowering the rugged black field glasses. 'What do you reckon? Monitor overnight and reassess at dawn?'

'Yeah. First sign of light will be half five. Let's hold an O group at five. If nothing seen overnight, then let's consider a three-man probe towards the river crossings to check for activity. We'll need to be careful. Guinea military might monitor those, and Mali forces could be on the other side. I can't see any permanent border posts, but then it is three K from here.'

To our front, the river marking the border with Mali wriggled from one side to the other a kilometre away. Two kilometres at our nine o'clock there was a suspected river crossing point, with a second crossing a further kilometre past that. They were designated on the maps produced in London as Crossing Zulu and Crossing Yankee.

Closer to our ten o'clock and almost three kilometres further away, another point of interest to the Project Brimstone team was marked on the map. Although I couldn't make it out in the failing light. A piece of flattish land with suspicious sign had been assessed as a possible bush landing strip. London believed the Russians were flying cargo and personnel to and from the suspected base, so they had to be landing somewhere.

Behind the target area, a high ridge topped with plateaus stretched for ten kilometres across our centre view, dominating the surroundings. I nicknamed it 'Castle Feature' after a reference point on Woodbury Common, a training ground known intimately to all Royal Marines. According to the map, the slopes on either side of Castle Feature drifted into lower terrain containing roads leading north.

Roper collected Mike and Jamie and, once they had been orientated to the ground, we busied ourselves preparing the position. A basha strung over the rocks covered the OP position itself, which had room for one observer, two at a squeeze. Five metres behind, another low slung basha hovered above two sleeping mats where the off-duty guys would rest. Further back, another basha and rock combo created a rear-facing vantage point where one man would be on duty to guard against an approach from behind. On this rocky outcrop, the hammocks were redundant and stayed packed away.

Everyone delved into their bergens to retrieve the high spec optics and camera gear we'd shared out. With the kit assembled, Roper took first watch in the OP and Mike stagged-on for sentry duty.

Jamie and I changed into our dry kit and camp footwear before wolfing down self-heating American MREs. After giving our weapons a quick boojee, both of us slid into lightweight jungle sleeping bags with built-in mosquito nets at the business end. Fortunately, there wouldn't be too many mozzies at this elevation.

The routine would be two hours on, two hours off. During each two hours on duty, one hour would be observing from the OP and the other manning the rear sentry position. There were ten hours until the 05:00 O Group, so the first and last of those watches would be a single hour to even things up; everyone rostered for five hours on duty and five hours rest.

Jamie and I were the bleary-eyed duty pair from 04:00 to 05:00. At 04:40 I shook Roper and Mike awake and crawled forward on my knees to where Jamie observed with the aid of a Night Vision Device.

My natural night vision revealed the outlines of the rocks, shrubs, and sporadic trees in our immediate surroundings, but the target area remained a black hole.

No lights, no movement, no indications of a camp.

The only sign of life was the regular whine of a persistent squad of mosquitos, disproving my earlier confidence in their dislike for heights. I returned to the sentry position and considered the next options while munching on crackers and cheese washed down with coffee.

Come daylight, we'd examine every inch of ground through the optics and take high resolution photographs of the entire panorama for the spooks in London to pour over. Then at midday, we'd pack up our position and yomp the four kilometres south through the valley to the RV with Sierra One and Two.

If we wanted a closer look, here and now while on task in the vicinity, it needed to be at first light. We gathered behind Jamie at the observer position for the O Group.

'Let's recap the night,' I began. 'Personally, I saw jack shit. Tom, I know you saw three vehicles between nine and eleven. Anything else?'

'It was three vehicles at 21:24 and two vehicles at 21:47. All moving north from Guinea to Mali at Crossing Yankee. The lights were subdued, side lights only. They headed towards the west side of Castle Feature until I lost them in the dark.'

'Anyone else?'

'Some faint lights at our eleven o'clock at 01:30,' said Mike. 'Four or five K. Indistinct and impossible to gauge the origin. That was it for me.'

'I've got nothing, apart from bites,' added Jamie.

'Okay, options. We either remain in situ until twelve hundred and roll out to the RV and on to the next target. Nice and easy. The sensible, low risk choice.'

A mozzie buzzed my right ear, causing me to turn my head and flick out a hand.

'Or we mount a recce patrol down to the Zulu and Yankee crossings. Take a closer look at them and any border posts that might be present. We might just catch early risers as they set out for the day. Outbound would be covered by low light. The return leg could handrail the thicker forest next to the river. What do you think? Tom?'

'We're here already and we have the time. I say yes.'

'Mike?'

'I'm with you guys. Let's make sure the bad guys aren't here.'

'Jamie?'

'It's not like I can say no with you all keen to go patrolling.'

'I'll take that as a yes. Right, three-man team and one manning the OP for overwatch and comms link to the rear. Tom, you going to stay here?'

'To be honest, I want to go down and take a look.'

I considered that for a couple of seconds.

'Okay. Mike, you lead, Tom second, Jamie in rear. I'll provide overwatch. Move out in ten, 05:20.'

'Roger that,' said Tom, his visible teeth denoting a broad smile.

★

'Delta, this is Alpha, radio check, over.'

'Delta, lima charlie, over.'

'Alpha, roger. I have you loud and clear also, out.'

The patrol had been gone for thirty minutes and faint predawn light had begun to lift the blanket of darkness. No breakfast fires burned below my position. No torchlit journeys to an outside bathroom.

I thought of UBL in the caves of Tora Bora in Afghanistan and the Viet Cong living in tunnels underneath the battlefield in Vietnam. Might our targets have excavated into the hillside, hidden from all but the closest surveillance?

The wait until the next scheduled radio check at 06:20 dragged. Flying insects had made an unwelcome appearance to disrupt my concentration and the sudden urge for a shit wasn't helping. The reticules of the optic roamed first over the target hill and then followed the planned route of the recce patrol.

Running light without their bergens, Mike could push the pace. Each of the guys wore patrol rig: their vests or webbing augmented with a detached bergen side pouch containing essential kit and provisions. He'd hoped to cover the two kilometres to Crossing Zulu within the first and darkest hour. Depending on the situation there, they'd either push on to Crossing Yankee or go firm.

'Delta, this is Alpha, radio check, over.'

Nothing.

'Hello Delta, this is Alpha, radio check, over.'

'Delta…are…, over.'

'Alpha, you are broken, say again, over.'

Static mush made Mike's response unintelligible.

'You are broken, say again, over.'

'Delta, firm at Zulu, over.'

'Objective Zulu acknowledged. Your signal workable, over.'

'Roger. No issues, pushing on to Yankee, over.'

'Roger, out.'

My lofty position would be helping to maintain the working VHF signal.

I cocked my head left to listen with my free ear for any noise behind. Alone with the packed bergens to my rear, I was conscious of my vulnerability should any uninvited visitors approach from that direction while I concentrated to the front. The observer position was the only one we hadn't dismantled. The bashas, sleeping mats, and other gear were all packed in the rucksacks, ready for the move out to the RV at 12:00.

The team aimed to reach Crossing Yankee by sunrise – 06:45. One or two hours installed at that objective should catch a decent snapshot of the Friday morning pattern of life in the vicinity. If bad guys were camped up the road, then we might just catch sight of them.

At 06:44, a sudden burst of static and speech in my ear made me jump. *'Alpha…Delta, …at Yankee, over.'*

'Alpha, confirm you are complete at Yankee, over.'

'Delta, roger, complete at Yankee, over.'

'Alpha, roger, out.'

I scanned the area to the north of Crossing Yankee. No movement.

Two more river crossings were marked on the map, X-Ray and Whisky. They were evenly spaced a further two and a half and five kilometres beyond the team's current position.

I could see a speck of light approaching X-Ray. Of the four border crossings, it was likely to be the primary route: the shortest link between roads to the interior on each side. We didn't have enough time for a closer look.

With the appearance of the sun at last, I prepared the cameras ready to take an extensive portfolio of high-resolution photographs covering everything we could see from the OP. I needed to wait for better light before cracking on behind the lens.

A waft of my own body odour made me wince. None of us had washed with scented soap or shaved since leaving Conakry because man-made smells carried in the jungle and shaving cuts became easily infected. Three days growth itched on my chin and it took intense willpower not to start scratching.

To take my mind off that, I picked up the binoculars and studied the target area, keeping the view focused on different spots for twenty or thirty seconds at a time, expecting to see movement giving away our as-yet-unseen enemy.

Much as I wished otherwise, still nothing moved.

Mike moved the team back to Crossing Zulu after an hour and went firm there. At 08:45, the radio crackled in my ear. *'Alpha this is Delta, we are Achilles to objective green, over.'*

'Alpha, roger Achilles, out.'

Achilles was code for returning, and objective green was the OP. A precaution in case the team had been observed on the insertion and our comms were compromised. In that unlikely event, saying 'returning to your location' or 'returning to the OP' could instigate ambush preparations. Plus, it's not even a real mission if there isn't a Greek god somewhere in the orders.

At 09:35, while zooming in to points of interest and snapping off photos like David Bailey, I detected movement to my front right, close to the south side of the river.

'Delta this is Alpha, are you crossing my front and currently at my one o'clock, over.'

'Delta, that's a roger, over.'

'Alpha, roger, I'll get the kettle on, out.'

It took the guys forty more minutes to loop around into the valley on the eastern side of the OP and make the contoured climb to rejoin me.

'I know you've just got back, but can someone relieve me before things get unpleasant for all of us?' It was time for me to visit the 'shitting tree' in view of the sentry position, before having to Zip Lock my own shit and carry it around like a dung beetle.

'I'll take over,' said Roper.

'Thanks, Tom. See anything out there?'

Mike joined us and answered. 'Light traffic. Nothing suspicious. Range was restricted by the terrain at Yankee, that's why I moved back to Zulu. If you can't see fuck all, then better to be closer to the target. How about you, anything sus?'

'No.' I turned to Roper. 'All we can do now is get the best photos so your mates in London can try to spot something we can't.'

★

During the next forty-eight hours, the same scenario played out twice more. We yomped several kilometres into an OP position on high ground overlooking a target area on the Mali side of the border; a border demarcated in similar fashion by the same lazy river winding its way across our immediate front.

With no obvious camp infrastructure or movement patterns detected, we then mounted patrols before dawn to recce crossing points up close. If anything, the Crystal Two and Crystal Three target areas northeast and west of the concession had even less traffic than the first location.

We took it in turns to man the OP while the other three patrolled. Jamie watched over our Saturday morning effort in the northeast, and Roper sat out Sunday morning's breakfast stroll in the west.

Mike insisted on joining each morning patrol. I didn't blame him. After my eighteen hours static at the first OP, it had been a relief to get my legs and mind working again when we'd moved out to the RV with the vehicles.

Manny and Condé had criss-crossed the block looking for any sign of troublemakers and listening to the local gossip. Whispers suggested an armed band operated from across the border, but no one wanted to expand on the details. It was difficult to assess if there was any substance to the rumours.

Seventy-two hours after leaving Setka village for the first task, the four of us were wet, tired, bitten, and circumspect about our results. I'd envisaged detecting a busy al-Qaeda hub and being the toast of British intelligence after another great result. Sandy Chapman telling everyone that he knew I'd repeat my success of five years ago.

Instead, it was a damp squib for the spooks. Either the intelligence about an al-Qaeda base was wrong, or they'd had us looking in the wrong places. I'd directed Manny and Condé to snoop around near the border crossings and settlements, but it hadn't turned up any breakthrough information.

With light rain falling as we yomped from the third OP to the RV with the vehicles, I signalled a halt, consulted the map, and called Manny on the radio.

'Sierra Two this is Sierra Alpha, message, over.'

'*Sierra Two, send, over.*'

'Alpha, we will be at Hotel Three in figures four zero, over.'
'Roger that. See you there.'

On reaching the Hotel 3 rendezvous with the cars, we didn't hang around. Like me, I'm sure the others wanted to get back to Siguiri for a good dhobi, a shave, decent scran, and a beer. Billeted in the 9x9 tent, Manny and Condé hadn't been living in the lap of luxury either.

The following morning, Monday 25th, we'd be escorting the rest of the team from Siguiri so they could work their magic on this concession. I'd spoken with both Hutch and Ryan on the sat phone each day and both their groups were ready to move north as planned.

Likewise, Roper had been in touch with the Project Brimstone team in London about our progress, not that he could report what they wanted to hear.

★

Compared to us miserable gits who'd lived in the field and seemingly accomplished fuck all, the rest of the team were full of beans when we roused ourselves from a late afternoon 'gentleman's half hour' and walked into the noisy clubhouse.

Bob accosted us straight away. 'How was your holiday? Been sitting around while the rest of us work flat out, I'll bet.'

I didn't miss a beat. 'Still here, then? I thought you might have fucked off in the middle of the job like last time.'

A burning sensation hit the left side of my neck, and I recoiled to my right. 'Can't flash at a hot spoon,' said Hutch, before dissolving into laughter as he shielded a newly made coffee.

'Fucking blokes,' I said, rubbing my neck. 'You lot get any work done while the grafters were away?'

While a good-natured argument got underway between Bob and Jamie about who was having it tougher, a grinning Ryan brought over a beer. 'You look like you could do with that.'

'Thanks, mate. It's been a long few days.'

'Nothing at the last site either?'

'No. No sign of camps, airfields, armed gangs roaming the border area, nothing.'

'That's good though, isn't it?'

'Yeah.' I laughed. 'I don't know why I feel deflated. It's the best result for us and the project.'

Ryan lifted his half-full beer glass. 'Here's to the project.'

'Cheers.' I clinked my glass against his and took a welcome sip of cold beer.

A harried-looking Roper entered the clubhouse – a surprise because he'd been right behind me when I arrived a few minutes before. His head bobbed left and right until he zeroed in on me and strode across to join us at the bar.

'Can I have a word?' he said to me, before looking at Ryan.

'Don't mind me,' said Ryan, picking up his beer and wandering over to join the boisterous American-Australian discussion.

'It's London. I've been on the phone to Hope and the boss.'

'Chapman? They're keen on a Sunday evening.'

'Yeah. One of the analysts thinks there's something in the imagery. I don't know the details, but they're trying to arrange more detailed evaluation. By another agency at a guess. It's tricky because Brimstone is highly restricted. Hope and the boss must be pulling in favours and twisting arms. We'll know more tomorrow.'

'Which target? Number three, from today?'

'No. It's the first target area, Crystal One. The closest to your block.'

CHAPTER 55

MONDAY 26TH JULY

SETKA VILLAGE

The central quadrant of Setka village was a riot of colour. Strips of coloured cloth hung around the outskirts in a good approximation of bunting. Four folding tables had been erected close to the central well to form a square, and the team and village elders tucked into a spread of wild boar meat with rice, salad, and bread.

We'd all opted for dusty soda cans rather than the plastic freezer-type bags of water on offer. It didn't faze the locals, but swigging the dubious liquid would have undoubtedly condemned me and the guys to repeated visits to the khazi.

'First impressions?' I asked down the table towards Luke and Bob.

The team had spent four hours working on the concession until we'd regrouped at the village for the hastily arranged feast. The chief and his acolytes had even brought out an ancient crate of Heineken bottles to celebrate. I'd managed to spirit those away before anyone took advantage of their good nature and the rest of the day was lost to 'hearts and minds'.

'Strong indicators for gold,' said Luke from the other side of the table. 'As good as the sites I visited last time.'

Bob tipped back the brim of his hat and leaned out so we could see each other. 'If Luke's right, then this area might prove easier to mine than the ones to the south. Definitely easier than Block B. My boots are still damp from traipsing through that swamp.'

'We had some interest this morning,' added Hutch.

I looked up from sawing through the rare meat. 'Interest. What do you mean?'

'People watching us. One vehicle, a white twin-cab pickup, other side of the valley. Must have been over a K away. Two up that I could see. One might have had binos; his hands were lifted to his face. Fifteen minutes and they left, driving west. I called it in. Ryan and Mike acknowledged.'

'Show me on the map after.' I switched attention to Ryan, who was listening from further down the table. 'You see anything?'

'No, they didn't come our way.'

'How about you, Mike?' I called out.

'What was that?' Mike turned from a conversation with Izzy and Alain on an adjacent table.

'These blokes Hutch spotted. You see them?'

'I heard the message, but we were out of line of sight to the south, near Ryan and Bob. Didn't see anything.'

'Okay. We'll drive out for a spot of community relations work when we're done here. Call into the villages and say hello. Put their minds at rest. Mike, you keep Sierra Two close to Bob and Luke's groups.'

The convoy left Block C on time at 17:00 for the long drive southeast to Siguiri. Although we'd been invited to stay, the village didn't have the infrastructure and facilities to support a big influx of visitors. Plus, the team were unanimous that they preferred to start early and finish late, if it meant being able to eat and sleep in the sanitary conditions and comfort of the clubhouse and cabins at the old airport.

Bob and Luke both assured me that they could complete the necessary engineering tasks in the two remaining days before we returned to Conakry.

Me, Roper, and Condé had taken Sierra One to the spot where the mysterious watchers were seen: high ground eight kilometres south of where the same ridge dropped into the saddle we'd crossed on day one of our recce patrols. We found nothing there or any definitive answers in the nearest two small villages, although everyone we encountered took a keen interest in our arrival. My chief takeaway: if a project got the go-ahead, local curiosity would be a factor we'd need to manage.

Roper's satellite phone chirped from the back seat. He answered in a low voice. 'Hello. Yes. Yes. Will do.'

I turned in my seat to check he'd finished the call. 'London?'

'Yeah, we need to call them as soon as we get to the hotel. The boss wants to speak to both of us.'

An hour later, the convoy pulled up in front of the clubhouse lights. I grabbed Manny's arm. 'Normal routine. Take the other drivers to the store and pick up the jerry cans now, so we know it's done. Make sure they divvy up the water and fuel properly in the dark. Oh, and see if our laundry is back please, mate.'

Manny and Baldé corralled the other drivers back into their vehicles and led them around to where our hosts stored the fuel they collected on our behalf during the day. After our four days living in the field, they had also arranged for our minging kit to get an unscented cold rinse while we'd been out.

It proved impossible to lock on to a decent satellite signal in the cabin, so Roper and I borrowed the Sierra Two keys from Manny, drove to a secluded spot away from the cabins, and positioned the sat phone's magnetic aerial on the car roof.

'Dawson,' a tinny voice answered via the loudspeaker.

'Dawson, it's Curlew,' said Roper, causing me to suppress a smile.

'Wait one.'

'Tom, are you free to talk?' Sandy Chapman's voice was unmistakeable, despite the number of years since I'd heard his upper-class tones.

'Yes, sir.'

'And is Pierce with you?'

'Yes, he can hear you. You're on speakerphone.'

Roper lay the phone on the central console between us.

'Pierce, John, it's good to speak with you again.' Chapman had never called me John in the past.

368

'It's been a long time. I'm told you're running the show these days.'

A distorted cross between a laugh and a cough followed. 'Not quite, not quite. But this little task is one of mine. Hope is alongside me.'

'Evening, guys,' said a distant female voice.

Roper and I both returned her greeting.

'I'm going to cut straight to it,' said Chapman. 'More detailed analysis of the images from your first target, Crystal One, has revealed two antennas behind the primary target area. Four kilometres behind at the base of the large ridge to the north. I wanted to speak to you both because what we're thinking requires an escalation in the operational risk.'

'We only have two days,' I said.

'Exactly,' replied Chapman. 'We need to decide here and now if you can accomplish this expanded task and whether it would require an extension to your deployment.'

I spoke before Roper could answer. 'It will be difficult to extend everyone on the team for more time. The Pinnacle engineers have other places they need to be.'

Roper leant closer to the phone. 'What's the task?'

Chapman cleared his throat. 'We want you to return to Crystal One, except focus on the area with the antennas. It means crossing the border.'

'Into Mali?' I said, making no effort to disguise my surprise.

'Yes, over the border into Mali. Not far. You would be mounting an observation post on the same feature that you observed last time. As you are now well aware, there is nobody in that vicinity. Moving north of the border is more of a re-alignment. A necessity due to the geography and not an overt act of obvious escalation.'

Roper and I looked at each other without speaking. I closed my eyes and recalled the ground to the front of the Crystal One OP.

Hope's voice broke the silence.

'Four kilometres north of your previous position, there is a reverse slope that would provide you with a view of the area that was blocked by that same ridge last time. Our thinking is that you could insert tomorrow for overnight observation and a closer look at those antennas. Tell us what's underneath. If you withdraw on Wednesday, I believe you will stay on schedule and be able to fly out as planned on Saturday.'

'They've got it all worked out,' I said to Roper.

'I didn't catch that. Say again,' said Hope.

I mouthed 'an hour' at Roper.

'We'll need to speak to the other guys in the team,' said Roper. 'I'll call back in forty-five minutes.'

Roper flapped as the time for the call back approached and we still hadn't reached a consensus. Three-quarters of an hour wasn't long to round up the guys and explain the situation and the plan.

I'd insisted that Ryan and Hutch were included. If four of us were disappearing on an armed patrol over the border, I wanted our supporting oppos to know all the details.

Once the surprise at learning Roper worked for the spooks had worn off, we pulled out the maps and reviewed London's proposed plan. Then we'd taken a show of hands. As if by design, Manny had knocked with our cleanish dhobi just before the vote.

Roper and I drove back to our secluded spot and made the call five minutes later than the agreed time. Once Curlew had introduced himself, Hope came on the line.

'The boss has been called away, but he's asked me to advise him as soon as you relay your decision. I trust we're all on the same page with this.'

Roper answered. 'Yes, it's a go. The security team are all on board. We'll deploy tomorrow to the OP and repeat the mission profile at the new target area.'

'Excellent. I knew you wouldn't let us down. The new area is designated as Crystal One Alpha. We'll send you enhanced imagery and coordinates for the antennas. Is John there with you?'

'Yes, I'm here.'

'Thank you, John. And please thank your team for me. We'll be supporting you from here throughout. Now, I need to speak with Tom alone, if you don't mind.'

I left them to it and headed to the clubhouse.

CHAPTER 56

1635 HOURS – TUESDAY 27TH JULY

GUINEA/MALI BORDER

The river marking the border burbled five metres ahead. I signalled the team to go firm and wedged myself between a tree trunk and leafy bush. Out of sight behind us loomed the high ground that had hosted our first OP.

Concentrating to tune out nature's acoustics, I watched and listened for any sign of human presence other than my three oppos. While I observed ahead, Jamie, Roper, and Mike watched both flanks and the rear.

The night before, Ryan had tried to argue that he should replace Jamie on the patrol, ostensibly to make it an all-British affair since it was a British spook-mandated task. I suspected it had more to do with him not wanting to miss out on the action. Not that it mattered. Jamie had refused the kind offer to step down, and I didn't want to risk alerting the rest of the team that something out of the ordinary might be happening.

The only change I made was to swap Alain and Condé back to their original teams. I wanted Alain and his AK-47 and official ID back with our vehicles.

Two hours earlier, Sierra One and Sierra Two had passed the last hamlet in the northwest corner of Block C and driven along the track running north through the valley leading to the border. From our patrol across that valley the previous Thursday, we already knew the places where the trees and brush would quickly conceal us from view.

At a kink in the road, we'd rapidly de-bussed and dissolved into the undergrowth. Manny and Alain accelerated away to circle clockwise north, east, south, then west, until they would arrive back at their tent accommodation in Setka village.

We'd moved cautiously towards the border. Compared to our last outing here five days earlier, this felt more serious. Our intention to undertake an armed incursion across an international border raised the stakes. It shouldn't have made much difference – after all, we were already roaming with illegal weapons on the Guinea side of the border – but it did. And the cam cream adorning our faces was a constant visible reminder.

So why had we all agreed to Chapman's plan so readily? Was it the challenge? The craic? The buzz? Who knew? Probably all that and more. Maybe if Roper hadn't been among us, we'd have taken more time to consider it. But with the maps unfurled and a plan taking shape, everyone committed without question.

When he'd led that first dawn patrol the previous week, Mike had noted two fords where the river narrowed and could be crossed. At the time, I doubt he expected us to be the ones doing the crossing.

According to the map and the GPS, the selected option should be close. I locked eyes with Jamie ten feet behind me. A finger to my chest; an exaggerated two fingers walking; a turn to point ahead; a hand making a peak over my eyes while I rotated my head left then right. Jamie acknowledged with a thumbs up and turned to pass on the message – I would move forward alone to reconnoitre.

I slithered forward in a leopard crawl to the river's edge. Twenty metres to the left, rocks and sediment had created a partial mudflat around which the water flowed. A bend in the river and extensive foliage on the far bank restricted my view in that direction to fifty metres.

I studied the other side. From the left by the bend, past the ford, and away to my right. The only movement I'd seen in this area through the long hours at the OP had been our own returning patrol. Even so, I couldn't help feeling trepidation. A fear that I'd missed some detail – a human silhouette, a protruding rifle barrel, a tripwire near the crossing.

I shook my head. *Get a fucking grip. Stop flapping and stay switched on.*

Although it was only a few metres back to the team, a stab of alarm erupted when I pulled away from the riverbank and turned to see only greenery. The patter of light rain hitting leaves signified the onset of a late afternoon shower. Scanning the foliage behind me, the area I must have emerged from, it was only movement – Jamie's waving hand – that pinpointed the team's location.

Spaced six feet apart, we crept forward in single file. Mike and Roper took up covering fire positions, then Jamie and I splashed the ten yards across the shallow river to the far bank. Mali.

I tried to bound between the protruding rocks and stones to keep my feet dry. That failed. Water oozed across the top of my foot and around the toes inside my left boot. My right foot was okay. However, the bottom of that leg was instead covered in slimy goo where I'd planted it on the mudflat. As I signalled 'all clear' to Mike and Roper, my eyes fell on a size nine footprint in the mud. Bollocks.

When he ran across, Mike stopped to sweep away the sign with his foot. I thanked him with a thumbs up. He replied with a five-finger shuffle and mouthed 'wanker' as he scooted past.

In short, cautious bounds, I led the patrol away from the river and towards the next obstacle: a track running east–west two hundred metres to the north. From the OP we hadn't seen any traffic using this route. Despite that, we treated its crossing with care.

Anyone moving on foot would more likely choose the cleared path than take on the undergrowth like us. Not that the forest was particularly dense. Away from the abundance of vegetation near the river, it thinned out and enabled me to see fifty to seventy-five metres through and around the trees and bushes.

The drumming rain drowned out any other noise. Movement would be the element most likely to give someone away and, right now, we were the ones doing the moving.

Strapped to the inside of my forearm was a compass. I checked the bearing to the ground and identified a reference point two fingers right and two kilometres ahead: a prominent rocky outcrop on the mile-wide,

500-foot-high ridge rising out of the forest. Even so, I kept my eye on the compass bearing as I adjusted our route according to the available cover.

Jamie reported a number every time he counted one hundred metres travelled. At 'sixteen', the gradient had already increased as we approached the sharp incline. I went firm and checked the GPS.

'Waypoint four.' I held up four fingers to accompany my exaggerated whisper. Three thumbs up responses followed.

Two and a half kilometres to the south, our former OP overlooked us from the other side of the river. It was a shade taller than the feature we were about to climb. I shivered at the sensation of being under observation and hoped it was only our own ghosts of five days ago that occupied the old haunt.

The rain's drumbeat had ceased and been replaced with my heavy breathing by the time we crested the ridgetop. My response to a 200-metre climb over a kilometre of rough ground reminded me I wasn't quite the mountain goat of my service days.

The thick treeline provided us with cover from view, which was good, and blocked our first sight of the Crystal One Alpha target area, which was less helpful. Our final leg along the spine of the ridge as it curled north would take us to the new OP position, perched on the far end 750 metres away. With a bit of luck, we'd quickly locate a spot that gave us a good field of view over the target.

The clouds had thinned, and the sun had dropped below the horizon to our left by the time we reached the final RV. Jamie and I sacrificed stealth for speed as we checked the chosen OP area in tactical bounds. Where the ground fell away steeply to the front, a panoramic view opened before us.

'That'll do nicely,' I murmured.

The dogleg we'd followed pointed at the centre of the long, plateau-topped 'Castle Feature'. According to the map, the antenna marking Crystal One Alpha was at the bottom of the steep incline, three kilometres away at our ten o'clock.

Jamie shuffled next to me. 'Man, this is a different ball game. I see lights already at eleven o'clock.'

He was right. Faint lights perhaps two and a half kilometres away. When I scoped the binoculars down slightly, I could see two small, dark, single-storey buildings 800 metres closer and one larger and longer structure nestled behind them.

To their left, the ground was flat, and a pair of wide and narrow tracks ran parallel to each other 200 metres apart across our front, before the narrow one swung north to intersect with the end of the straighter, wider track.

A bush landing strip? It couldn't have been much more than 600 metres long, but a brave pilot in the right spec plane might fancy it.

'Bring the others in,' I said to Jamie.

Excitement bubbled in my chest. Whatever was down there, Malian village or al-Qaeda camp, we needed to take a look.

Already, I had three locations needing a Close Target Recce: the buildings and adjacent wide track; the area containing the faint lights; and the Crystal One Alpha antenna hidden by the encroaching dusk. It was going to be a busy night.

CHAPTER 57

0240 HOURS – WEDNESDAY 28TH JULY

CRYSTAL ONE ALPHA TARGET AREA

'Bravo, this is Alpha. Approaching Gold, over.'

'Bravo, roger. All clear, over.'

'Alpha, roger, out.'

After three hours of broken sleep sandwiched around one-hour watches, an all-British three-man patrol had set out at 0100 hours to conduct a round robin of CTRs. Jamie was our American eye in the sky, now three kilometres to the southeast. We were closing on the first and most important stop of the night: the Crystal One Alpha antenna, christened Gold for this patrol.

'Seven hundred,' a voice whispered in my earpiece. With Jamie loafing up on the hill, Roper had taken over pace counting duties.

We halted and closed up. Occasional moonlight, mixed terrain, and our natural night vision had so far meant no need for Night Vision Goggles. The previous night had seen a full Moon, and Roper's Met guy in London had provided the silver disc's expected illumination and trajectory through the night. We'd struck lucky – decent visibility ought to help us maintain a good pace to complete the 7.3 km patrol before dawn.

We'd been handrailing a track uphill for 700 metres since reaching a T-junction. The antenna should have been over the track and 160 metres to our right. Unfortunately, the Moon was AWOL behind thickening clouds, so all I could see was a dense blob of trees. I donned my NVGs; the whine of the power unit amplified in the still of the night. When I scrutinised the glowing green sight picture for anything suspicious, there was nothing to see apart from an armada of glinting flying insects.

'Count another hundred, over.'

'Roger,' answered Roper.

I led the way through the trees. Roper and Mike kept the distance between us down to a few metres.

'One hundred.'

I slowed the pace to a ghost walk – exaggerating each deliberate step and applying gentle pressure before allowing my full weight to shift to each foot in turn. *Where the fuck was the antenna?*

A twitch of light twenty metres to the right made me sink to the ground and signal the others to do likewise. Straight edges were visible amongst the trees.

'Buildings,' I whispered into the radio.

Two sets of double clicks acknowledged.

I held up three fingers and pointed right, centre, and left at the three single-storey outlines. A dim light shone from the window of the right-hand building. The tall trees limited my view, and I still didn't have sight of the antenna.

I headed left towards the nearest structure, using it as cover from whatever lay beyond. On reaching it, we knelt back-to-back in all round defence.

An elongated log cabin, twenty metres in length. The windows were too high off the ground to see through and there was no door. The back of the building.

I removed the NVGs and marked the location on my GPS.

'Cover at the far corner,' I whispered to Mike, chopping my hand to the right. 'We'll go left and take a peek.'

He pulled on his own NVGs and crept to the allotted position, which gave him a view of the building with the light. I watched through my fuzzy green display until he knelt with his weapon in the shoulder.

'Complete. More buildings ahead, no movement, over.'

'Roger, moving left.'

I led Roper to the left corner, both of us now using NVGs. We advanced along a ten-metre side without windows. Ten metres by twenty metres – thirty feet by sixty feet. Not your average mountain retreat chalet. And now I could see there were at least six buildings in total, all similar in appearance and size.

A peek along the front of the cabin revealed nothing of interest – just the expected dark windows either side of an entrance door. I swept my gaze in a wide arc from right to left. The six buildings were arranged around a two-hundred-foot-long, open rectangular space.

Then I spotted the large antenna protruding from the leftmost building, the furthest up the slope. The reason I'd spotted it – because a flash of light had burst from an opened door underneath and stabbed across the square. Two figures stepped through and ambled in our direction. Their rifles had been clearly visible when they were silhouetted in the doorway.

'Standby. Two tangos with longs approaching my location. Taking cover.'

This time three sets of double-clicks answered. That news would keep Jamie awake at the OP. I motioned down with my hand, just in case Roper hadn't got the message from watching me sink into a prone position against the building edge.

A flush of adrenaline surged when I pushed the safety catch off and it clacked like a fucking stone against a tin can. Bloody AKs. Roper's then did the same. Unbelievably, there was no sign of alarm from the two approaching night owls.

I took two deep breaths. 'Ten metres.'

A double-click responded. Roper didn't need to acknowledge; I could feel him laying against my left calf and he'd be watching these bozos bimbling towards us. They changed direction and stopped outside the building to our left. One of them entered, returning two minutes later.

Their voices were too low to make out the language used. Arabic would be the jackpot – a combat indicator for al-Qaeda's finest. French would leave the jury out; with the uncomfortable possibility this could be a Malian security forces base. I feared that fuckup more than anything else. Mind you, as the spooks' man on the ground, Roper had to be even more concerned.

Through the hazy green image, I couldn't tell if the two men wore uniforms. Five metres away, they passed the nearest corner of the adjacent hut and continued towards our position. Wedged low against the wooden wall, I held the AK into my shoulder, ready to bring it up on aim if the worst happened.

Before slipping the NVGs back on, it had been pitch black under the dense tree cover. I offered up a prayer to the big guy that the Moon stayed hidden and no one opened that fucking door and lit me up like a surprise party act.

As the nearest leg of the left-hand man approached, I steeled myself for a shout of alarm. At a guess, at least three of these huts were occupied. The one with the light nearest Mike, the building with the antenna, and next door where these blokes had dropped in.

Wearing NVGs and primed for contact, we could probably take them out before they got organised. Not part of the plan but not a disaster – unless they were Malian forces.

Ten feet. Six feet. Right over me, a foot next to my right shoulder. And on past.

I let the breath I'd been holding ease out. Sweat trickled into my eyebrow.

The footsteps stopped. 'Merde. Maintenant j'ai besoin d'une pisse.' *Shit. Now I need a piss.*

'Allez juste ici, contre le mur.' *Just go here, against the wall*

Fuck. Speaking French and stopping for a piss.

The sound of footfalls re-started. *Not this way. Not this fucking way.*

The French chatter drifted in the other direction. Thank Christ for that – no pissing up our wall. But now we had another problem. Mike was somewhere around the next corner.

'Tangos inbound to your location, going for a swamp. Take cover, over.' Whispered into the radio so quietly I didn't know if Mike would hear.

Two clicks in reply.

Roper and I pulled back to the rear corner of the building. Mike was nowhere to be seen at the other end of the back wall.

'They're speaking French. Could be Mali forces,' I whispered to Roper.

'Yeah.'

Ninety silent seconds went by.

'Tangos have passed my location. Stay firm. Wait on my message, over.'

I clicked twice on the pressel switch.

'We'll move on to Silver and Bronze next, see what's there,' said Roper.

'Roger that.'

Two minutes later, Mike popped up from a log pile and we re-grouped before resuming a slow patrol south through the forest, unsure whether we'd encounter more buildings or patrols.

Less than 100 metres from our close encounter, bright moonlight reached through the clearing skies and into the dwindling tree cover. It was a relief to stop and remove the NVGs. I wiped the sweat from my face and sucked greedily at the bladder bite valve.

After a pacey, uneventful yomp 900 metres to the east, we investigated objective Silver. Three buildings, each emitting faint light, and two SUVs parked outside. Roper noted the plate numbers and sketched the layout.

Then we dropped a kilometre south to objective Bronze. A collection of dark, lifeless buildings near to the wide and narrow tracks I'd observed from the OP.

My watch showed 04:10 – time was getting on. The night would start to lift at 05:30, reaching a workable twilight by 06:00. Sunrise would follow at 06:22. With the morning light would come movement and an increased threat of compromise. Home by 05:30 was the plan.

The largest building was rectangular with its longer sides facing north and south. The short, western side facing the flat ground was open to the elements. No doors. Inside appeared empty apart from scattered junk against the walls. It reminded me of a small hangar, and the windsock attached to a steel pole laid along one wall reinforced an aviation link.

'A small plane could fit in here,' I said to Roper as we conducted a rummage of the detritus while Mike kept a lookout from the doorway

He looked at the windsock. 'Have we got time to check the strip?'

'If we're quick. Need to leave this though.' I pointed my red-filtered torchlight at the junk.

'Doesn't seem to be anything here. Let's take a look outside.'

We moved west in extended line along the flat ground until we'd reached halfway. A ground inspection revealed wide tyre tracks that could have come from aircraft or could equally have been made by trucks. No signs or markings were obvious.

'Alpha this is Bravo, time check zero-four-thirty, over.'

'Alpha, roger. Achilles to green in figures five, over.'

'Bravo, roger, out.'

Mike appeared at my shoulder. 'Three hundred metres to here. I'd say six hundred total. Tight but doable for the right plane and pilot.'

The black menacing shape of the 1,000-foot-high Castle Feature loomed to the north, on our right. Moonlight reflected off parts of the wide sheer face below the plateau five kilometres away. If there was an al-Qaeda base close by, pound to a pinch of shit there'd be lookouts up there. I shivered as though someone walked across my soul.

In comparison, our OP was little more than a hillock two kilometres to the south. Not that I could make it out in the dark jumble of high ground beyond. Time to haul ass for home.

We trooped into the OP at 05:40. Exhausted, sweaty, bitten, and relieved to have completed our tasks without compromise. Jamie's eyes were sunken slits in the half light, but he insisted on holding the fort and keeping watch until 08:00. We again wrapped ourselves tight around the observer position so that one duty bod would suffice.

After ten minutes of personal admin and a welcome breakfast, I zonked out into a deep and all too brief slumber. Each of us had a length of paracord attached to one wrist. The other end led to Jamie. Pull in the event of alarm.

CHAPTER 58

After taking the 08:00 to 09:00 watch, I checked in via sat phone with Ryan. He reported that both Bob and Luke expected to complete all their planned tasks by the end of the day – our last before the long return drive to Conakry. Both groups intended to operate in the northwest of the block during the afternoon, the area nearest to us. I agreed to RV with them after we'd yomped south to our mid-afternoon pickup.

Roper wore a satisfied smile once he'd reported to London. We didn't know whether we'd found al-Qaeda, but someone was hiding out here and it won't have done his career prospects any harm to be the bearer of that news.

His sunny attitude matched the weather, although the trees provided cover from the sun's rays for us and the expansive insect life sharing the ridgetop. A third bite in as many minutes had me diving for the sanctity of my sleeping bag.

After an hour of unsatisfying drowsing, a yank on the paracord nearly twisted my arm out of its socket. 'Fuck's sake.'

I slipped out of my bag, extended the rifle stock, and switched on the radio. Mike was only feet away, but I'd cover the rear arc until I knew what had triggered the alarm. 'Delta, Alpha, sitrep, over.'

'I'm right here,' said Mike from behind me.

'Yanking my fucking chain.'

'Vehicle movement. Might be something,' he said, still watching from the observer position.

I crawled alongside him. A bleary-eyed Roper arrived on his other side.

'A packet of four white SUVs came around the west side of the feature at 10:15 and went into the trees at Crystal One Alpha.' Mike checked his watch. 'Three minutes ago. I've captured them on camera, although it's too far to make out how many or what type of pax.'

'Anything before that?' asked Roper.

'Only two cars heading from further west towards the border and one coming north in the other direction. None of them came into our target area.'

Another bite on my neck was an annoying reminder that I needed to reapply DEET and take my daily doxy tablet. 'I'll get the wets on. Tea?'

Mike nodded. 'NATO standard. Could do with the energy today.'

'Same here,' said Roper.

Apart from derisory comments about my wets-making prowess, nothing happened for the next twenty minutes.

At 10:41 Mike grabbed the scope and adjusted the focus. 'Standby, movement at Crystal One Alpha.'

Through my binoculars, I followed the track we'd handrailed a few hours previously. Three kilometres was too far to make out much detail, but a convoy of vehicles rocketed along it, south towards the T-junction.

'Come to papa,' said Mike.

We watched in silence. In the last week of OPs and patrols, we'd seen nothing like this level of energetic activity.

'Shit,' said Mike. 'Fuckers have turned right.'

At the T-junction, the vehicles had turned away from our position rather than towards us. We wouldn't be getting a closer look at them.

'Someone's in a hurry, wherever they're going,' I said.

'Third vehicle is a pickup,' said Mike. 'Five, maybe six guys in the back. Pretty sure at least two of them are carrying.'

Three minutes later, the four vehicles made a left turn at the next junction to head south in the direction of the border. Our view was curtailed by the surrounding trees and foliage.

'Lost them,' said Mike.

I looked at Roper. 'Let's see if we can pick them up again from round the side.'

Unlike the open panorama from the OP, it proved difficult to acquire an unrestricted view west. We thrashed through the undergrowth until finding an opening sixty metres behind and left of the OP. In the five minutes it had taken us, the vehicles could have travelled beyond our line of sight. I focused the binos along the river where the border lay.

'That might be them, near Crossing X-Ray. Must be six K though. I can't be sure.'

'I don't see them,' said Roper.

'I'll call Ryan anyway. Ask him to keep an eye out for them.' While there were more direct routes to the block, if those guys swung east anytime soon it would take them in his direction.

It took ten minutes and a move back to the OP before I reached Ryan on the sat phone. 'Mate, we've seen a convoy of four white SUVs – wrong, three SUVs and a pickup – roll towards the border to our west. Keep your eyes peeled. They visited one of our targets and are belting around the place. Two or more believed armed. Not your average locals.'

'Roger that. No sign of them here or anyone with a weapon. We're heading to a village a couple of K west of the block, Deebee or something like that. I'll get Baldé and Demba to make discreet enquiries. You guys must be about ready to pack up and call it a day.'

'Yeah. I'm planning to be at the RV for three. Are our cars with you?'

'They are, mate. Manny and Condé are here, and Bob says "Hi".'

'Good. I'll call you when we're at the RV and you can send them up. It'll be less than ten K if you're in the northwest corner. Oh, and good to hear that Bob hasn't tried to fuck off early again.'

An indignant Aussie voice cut in. 'Oi, I heard that you cheeky bastard.'

Ryan laughed. 'You're on speakerphone. Yeah, we've reached the northwest quadrant. I'll call Hutch and let him know about the suspicious cars. I don't suppose you have the plate numbers?'

'No mate, too far away. We'll get our shit squared away and join you later.'

I stowed the phone and looked over at Jamie's snoring figure. 'I'll wake sleeping beauty over there.'

We'd planned to leave the OP at 12:00. Now things had got interesting, Roper and I agreed to delay pulling out until 13:00. It might make us later than intended for the RV, but Manny and Condé wouldn't set off for the pick-up until I phoned Ryan.

We'd have time to link up with the rest of the team, drive to Setka village to say our goodbyes and recover the 9x9 tent, and still complete the 100+ km drive to Siguiri in time for dinner and a celebratory beer.

Come 13:10, we'd cleaned and sanitised the position and packed the last of the cameras and optics. There had been no further sighting of the four-vehicle convoy.

I delivered a brief set of orders over the unfolded map. It was way too early to be patting ourselves on the back for a job well done. We might not have found an enemy, but we were an illegal armed patrol the wrong side of an international border. Running into just about anybody else and being compromised would take the shine off the last twenty-four hour's work.

'We need to stay switched on. While we're not crossing the border at the same point, if anyone spotted us or our sign on the way in, there could be a welcoming party hoping to catch our return.'

My extendable pointer hovered over the alternative river crossing Mike had recommended.

'Try not to play grandma's footsteps in the mudflats this time, boss,' said Mike.

The four of us shared smiles as I folded the map and stowed the pointer. 'Last time, gents. Let's make sure we don't fuck it up.'

Jamie shook his head. 'Man, you Brits don't know how to do inspirational talk.'

The sun beat down between the trees as we patrolled along the ridge and down the steep incline. Skin had rubbed off my feet, shoulders, and near each armpit. I probably only noticed the painful spots now because we were so near the finish line.

Despite my own words during the briefing, I found my attention wandering. I had to purge thoughts of the drive back to Conakry, or the report I needed to write for Pinnacle, or getting home to Claire and the girls.

To counter the gritty-eyed tiredness and depleted energy reserves, I washed down an energy bar and a mouthful of chocolate and nuts with a large draw of lukewarm water from the hydration pack – some things never changed. And I had to admit, I loved this shit.

After an uneventful yomp, we crossed the river a kilometre east of our infiltration route. Once Roper and Mike splashed through the foot-deep water to join us on the southern, Guinean bank, I felt a wave of relief. A final leg of 1,700 metres and we'd be climbing into the vehicles for a stop-start journey that would last three days and take us home via Siguiri, Conakry, Paris, and London.

On completion of the last footsore strides of the patrol, we fanned out into all round defence in thick cover twenty metres from the PUP. I called Ryan and ordered our taxis.

When Ryan answered, there was a hint of fatigue in his voice. Everyone had been cracking long hours on this trip. 'I'll send them along now. They'll be ten minutes max.'

'Where do you want to RV?' I asked.

'One of Hutch's mob thinks they spotted watchers again. Bob's all done now, so we're going to check it out. We'll meet you at the little village by Ayers Rock once we've had a look.'

'Ayers Rock? Where the fuck's that?'

Ryan laughed. 'The flat-topped hill in the corner of the block. Bob's christened it. In fact, can't you see it from where you are.'

'In cover, mate, so no. But I know the place you mean. Fucking Ayers Rock. Is Hutch's group there already?'

'Just got off the phone to him and he says Luke is rechecking samples on the south side. When he's finished, they'll head to the village for Izzy's house calls after her packed clinic yesterday. A couple of bairns recovering from malaria.'

I checked my watch. 'It's fifteen thirty-five now. We'll be at the RV by sixteen hundred. Don't forget we need to call in at Setka before we leave. If you haven't reached the RV by sixteen fifteen, I'll push on there with Hutch's group.'

'We'll be at the RV before then. A quick spin over the ridge a couple of K to the south and we'll join you.'

After stowing the sat phone, I held up a fist and flashed a spread palm twice. 'Ten minutes.'

Knelt facing outwards to cover their arcs, the guys heard rather than saw me. They offered three identical left-handed thumbs up responses over their shoulders.

Seven minutes later, I heard a distant engine. 'Sierra Two, this is Sierra Alpha, radio check, over.'

Manny's voice blared in my ear. *'Sierra Two, hearing you loud and clear, over.'*

'Roger. Area is clear. Can hear your approach and moving to the track. Are you lead vehicle, over.'

'Yes, I'm in the lead. Slowing so I don't miss you.'

'Roger. See you in figures two, out.'

As the vehicles approached, I moved to the side of the track to signal our exact location. Behind the rising din of the cars, an unmistakeable popping noise broke out.

Gunfire.

The team arrived beside me. 'That's shots heard,' I said.

'Yeah,' said Mike. 'Definitely gunfire. Doesn't sound like a range day.'

The vehicles pulled up as the shooting continued unabated somewhere down the valley to the south. Mainly automatic bursts, which made it less likely my guys were directing some sort of unscripted, final afternoon fun shoot.

I listened for a contact report from Ryan or Hutch. The radio stayed silent. Roper and I were headed for Sierra One in rear, but I stopped at Manny's window and spun my pointed finger in a circle.

'We're going to turn around and hit the RV quick. That sound is shooting.'

I pointed at his vehicle set. 'Anything on the radio?'

Manny shook his head. 'Nothing.'

We loaded our bergens quickly and I climbed into the passenger seat next to Alain. 'Spin it round.'

His initial smile dropped. 'Yes, sir.'

I grabbed the vehicle radio mic. 'Bravo One, this is Sierra One, message, over.'

No reply.

'Bravo One, this is Sierra One, message, over.'

Much as I willed it, Ryan didn't answer.

'Sierra One, nothing heard, out to you. Hello Golf One, this is Sierra One, message, over.'

Nothing from Hutch either.

'Golf One, this is Sierra One, message, over.'

'Nothing heard, out to you. All stations, this is Sierra One, en-route to RV. ETA figures five, out.'

I grappled for the sat phone, extended the antenna, and attached the magnetic aerial to the SUV roof. Roper had already done the same from the rear seat with his sat phone.

'No answer from Hutch,' he said.

'I'll call Ryan.' Before I could press the green button, the phone chirped and showed Ryan calling.

I answered while lifting the handset to my ear. 'Yes, mate. You okay?'

Ryan spoke above shouting and gunshots. 'Hutch is in contact. I've lost comms with him. Multiple gunmen. Those four vehicles you reported, they're here. I've got one casualty–'

'He's dead,' a voice yelled, breaking Ryan's flow.

'You sure?' said Ryan, his voice distant as he replied to the English speaker. Bob?

'Yeah, he's dead. I've got his AK. There's some cover on the left.' It was definitely Bob's voice. There was shouting in French close by.

'Ryan, who's dead?' I asked.

'Fuck. Demba. He took a round through his window. Caught him in the head.'

Loud single shots blazed through the earpiece before he continued.

'We're close to the north-south track, south of Ayers Rock. Hutch's callsign is ahead of us, to our north. On the track. I can see one of their cars sixty metres to my front by the enemy vehicles. None of the team. We're on foot and trying to reach them.'

Breaking glass and clattering against metal interrupted him.

'Heavy incoming. Whichever way you come, watch your approach. There's a lot of them. We're outgunned.'

'Right. Get the fuck out of there if you can. Otherwise go firm and engage them from cover. You've got a principal with you, so he's your priority.'

I heard an Aussie cry of 'Got him. Take that you bastard.'

'We'll come in from the north. If you can't extract, then keep them occupied. We'll be there as soon as we can. Less than five minutes.'

'Baldé, donne-moi ton fusil,' said Ryan. *Baldé, give me your rifle*

Then the call dropped.

CHAPTER 59

'Sierra Two, this is One. Bravo and Golf callsigns are in contact, repeat in contact. We're going through the RV and driving into the contact point. Break.

'Be advised, enemy strength is heavy. Believed same vehicles we spotted earlier. Be prepared to debus and roll into a counterattack.'

After a two second delay, Mike answered. *'Sierra Two, roger. Stacks of smoke and straight up the middle.'*

'Shame we haven't got any smoke,' said Roper. 'Who's the casualty?'

'Demba.'

Roper clicked his tongue. 'Everyone else okay?'

'With Ryan, yes. So far. He's got no comms with Hutch.'

'Fuck. I'll get onto London now.'

'Yeah. I'll keep trying the radio.'

It wasn't until we'd passed through the village RV location and rounded Ayers Rock that I managed to re-establish comms. The hill must have been blocking the VHF signal. The shooting had been replaced with silence, save the rattling of the vehicle as we bounced down the slope towards the track.

'Bravo and Golf callsigns, this is Sierra One, we're two minutes out. Coming in from the north, over.'

My hope soared when a strong voice boomed out of the radio speaker.

'Bravo One, roger. We're firm south of Golf. No longer in contact, no further casualties. Enemy vehicles drove off to the south.'

'Sierra One, roger. Do you have a visual on Golf team, over?
'Negative. Can't see anyone.'
'Understood. Stay firm, we're coming in now.'
'There they are,' said Roper from over my left shoulder.

Two hundred metres ahead, a white Toyota Land Cruiser had come into view. Almost sideways across the track, its nose pointed left.

'One driving straight in. Prepare for hard stop if it gets hot.'
'Roger, right behind you.'

Alain must have lifted his foot from the gas because the vehicle began to slow.

Roper's forearm chopped between me and the driver. 'No, No. Keep the speed. Don't brake until you have to.'

My chest tightened as we raced towards the stricken car. All four doors were open, and something lay crumpled on the road by the driver's door.

A body.

Chances were the figure on the ground was one of ours.

At fifty metres, we hadn't received any incoming rounds. I ripped the safety catch on the AK down to single shot semi-automatic.

'Prepare to debus,' I yelled into the mic. 'We'll go right, you go left.'
'Roger.'

I slammed my hand on the dashboard. 'Stop, stop, stop.'

Alain braked hard, taking us from sixty km/h to a skidded halt just in front of the smoking, heavily pockmarked SUV and Samuel's lifeless stare from the road.

'Mon Dieu,' said Alain. *My God.*

I pointed at him. 'You stay here and cover us.'

I flung the right-hand door open and charged past the body to the rear of the Land Cruiser. On reaching the punctured offside wheel, I dropped into a kneeling position with the butt of the weapon in my shoulder.

'Sierra One, Bravo One, I've got you visual. We're sixty metres to your two o'clock.'

'Roger, hold there.'

Running footsteps preceded a body knocking against me from behind. 'Ready?' said Roper.

'Sierra Two, I have visual on a second vehicle near the stream. No friendlies or enemies in sight, over.'

'Hold there, Sierra Two, we're going to clear the vehicle. Can you cover us, over?'

'Two, affirmative, covering left arc.'

'Bravo One has overwatch of the track.'

I keyed the switch. 'Moving.'

'Let's do it,' I said to Roper. 'You cover. I'll check Samuel and inside.'

'Roger.'

As I reached Samuel's body, Alain watched me from a kneeling position by the front bumper of our vehicle ten feet away. He shook his head.

When I looked down at Samuel I could see why. His chest was a bloody mess. At least four or five entry wounds. His eyes were open, glassy, and unblinking. The side of his head had also seen massive trauma.

I rolled his shoulder and part of his cranium fell back like the cracked shell of an egg to reveal the obscene pink of brain matter. A hot flush of sweat engulfed me as I gagged.

'Samuel's dead,' I said into the radio, using professional detachment to force objective thinking.

I circled the vehicle. There were no other bodies, inside or out.

From the passenger side, I examined the interior. Blood coated the driver's seat and there were splashes across the passenger seat. No blood in the rear. Samuel drove Golf One – Hutch and Luke's car. Where the hell were they?

'Golf callsigns, this is Sierra One, over.'

As I spoke, a disembodied voice bounced the message at me from the vehicle radio set. My voice, although I wouldn't have recognised it. There was no reply.

The rear doors of another white SUV poked out of the brush fifty metres away, down a shallow incline that lead to a stream according to the map. Golf Two – Condé, Izzy, and the CPDM guy, Yaya. I batted away thoughts of how bad this might get. Maybe they'd reached safety like Ryan and his team.

Mike and Jamie were in light cover ten metres to my left, Roper knelt by the rear of the Golf One SUV I stood beside, Alain crouched by the bumper of our Sierra One Land Cruiser with his AK-47, and a weaponless Manny remained in the driver's seat of Sierra Two.

Now separated from the vehicles, I reverted to our patrol callsigns. 'Delta, this is Sierra Alpha, advance to Golf Two. We'll move right. Acknowledge callsign change, over.'

'Delta, change acknowledged. Moving left, out.'

'Bravo One, Sierra Alpha, everything clear from your position?'

'Bravo One, all clear.'

'Roger, yell if you see anything, out.'

The immediate vicinity consisted of scattered trees and bushes poking out of a sea of knee-high grass. Two hundred metres down the gentle slope, the trees merged into a dense, unbroken chain that meandered through the valley.

I aimed for a spot ten metres right of Golf Two. Roper moved into my eyeline and stayed level, five metres to my right.

We advanced with slow, careful steps, weapons in the shoulder, scoping left and right. My finger lay along the trigger guard, ready to slip inside if a threat unfolded. But the calm of the late afternoon induced a different and growing fear: that we'd soon discover more of the team dead or seriously injured.

'HUTCH. LUKE.' As a guilty afterthought I added, 'IZZY.'

I stopped to listen for a response and Roper did likewise. After five seconds of silence, he repeated my call, aiming his voice out to our right.

'Delta, figure in Golf Two passenger seat. It's Yaya, he doesn't look good, over.'

Mike and Jamie were screened from me by a thicket that also blocked most of my view of Golf Two. I assumed they were closer to the car.

'Alpha moving up on the right. You check the casualty, over.'

Roper and I moved level with the Land Cruiser and dropped into the cover of waist-high bushes while maintaining our spacing. Mike and Jamie's voices carried from around the car, where Jamie was performing his assessment.

Jamie broke the bad news. '*CPDM guy is KIA. Cause of death, gunshot wounds to the chest and head, over.*'

Christ, three dead so far and four members of the Geo Group missing. It was an uncomfortable, disrespectful thought, but better Yaya than any of the others.

'Roger. Any sign of the rest of the team, over?'

'*That's a negative.*'

'Okay. Let's line up and sweep this area towards the treeline.'

Mike's torso appeared by the vehicle and he raised a fist with a thumbs up.

I shouted over to him. 'Forget the radios. Make plenty of noise and listen out for replies.'

His thumb went into the air again. 'Roger that.'

When we began our slow walk forward in extended line, I shouted out the names of the missing again, adding Condé to the list.

No reply and no sign of anyone. I hoped that meant they'd managed to escape as a group.

'John, one o'clock,' said Roper.

I followed his instruction and heard the crashing through the undergrowth before the branches began to shake.

'Movement to our one o'clock,' I whispered into the radio.

A pair of acknowledging clicks were followed by an answer from Ryan. '*Bravo One, roger. All quiet here.*'

Roper and I had both dropped into kneeling firing positions. I was checking for other movement to my front when a figure flew out of the bushes five metres from Roper. I swung the barrel and locked the iron sights onto the centre mass.

'Izzy,' shouted Roper.

A strangled sob escaped the girl as she ran to Roper and wrapped her arms around him.

'Go firm, Mike. We've found Izzy,' I yelled.

'How is she?'

'She's alive and mobile. Send Jamie over here.'

'Will do.'

Jamie ran towards me and I directed him on past to where Roper was attempting to calm Izzy and ask her about injuries. Her sobs only quietened when he asked, 'Where are the others?'

'They killed him,' she wailed.

'Yaya?' said Roper.

'Yes, they shot him while we drove. They shot the car in front of us. So many bullets.'

Jamie eased her from a sitting to a prone position. 'Hey, lie down Izzy. You're safe now. Let me take a look at you. There's a lot of blood. Are you shot or hurt anywhere?'

'No, I don't think so.'

I listened while scanning the terrain to my front. The thicker treeline was about a hundred metres ahead. Hopefully, the rest of the team had regrouped there.

Roper asked, 'What about Condé, Hutch, and Luke?'

Izzy snivelled before answering. 'My cousin ran the other way, over there. He told me to go this way. You must find him.'

'And the men from the other car, Hutch and Luke?'

'I couldn't see. The firing started and the car in front turned and stopped. Other cars were on the track in front. Condé tried to drive away through the trees, but he said the tyres had been shot. I didn't see what happened to the others.'

'Tom, which way did she say Condé went?' I called out.

'Mike's direction.'

'I'll scout the area with Mike. Jamie, if she's walking wounded, then get her up to the cars on the road.'

I joined Mike ten metres to the left. 'Izzy says Condé went this way. You seen any traces?'

'None. What about Hutch and Luke?'

'She didn't see what happened to them. It sounds like a deliberate ambush. If they didn't get off the X and they're not in the car, then kidnapped maybe?'

Mike blew out a long breath. 'Let's hope they got away somehow.'

We spread a few metres apart and headed left.

'Shit,' said Mike. 'Blood trail.'

Sporadic drops of bright red liquid decorated the grass. I expected to encounter Condé's body at any moment. My boot landed on something hard. A handgun.

'Mike, I've found a Makarov. Maybe Condé's.'

He squatted and searched in the grass 'There's spent casings scattered here. Nine mil and seven-six-two short. I think Condé took them on. Hang on.'

'What is it?'

'Blood smears. As though someone crawled or was dragged. Maybe they grabbed Condé as well.'

'Let's keep searching. He might be laid up in cover.'

Jamie escorted Izzy to the cars while Roper joined our search for Condé and the others.

By 17:30 we had regrouped on the track after finding nothing more in the forest. Much as I wanted to stay longer to find our teammates, we couldn't rule out the hostiles returning in strength.

Ryan moved his vehicle onto the track and his team kept watch as we examined the ambush site. Mike and Roper searched the track and a patch of light cover where empty brass casings had been spotted, while I conducted a fingertip inspection of Golf One.

At the cars, Jamie monitored Izzy and organised Manny and Alain to help him collect the three dead bodies and lay them in the rear compartment of Sierra One.

It didn't take me long to find Hutch's radio, switched off and stuffed under the passenger seat along with his satellite phone. The logical explanation was that he'd realised he couldn't get away and hid the radio to prevent our comms being compromised. *Good effort, mate.*

If he and the others had been kidnapped, we might have a chance to recover them. After all, we were pretty sure where their attackers had sprung from.

I parked that thought when I noticed Samuel's jacket was pushed between the driver's seat and the central console. When I pulled it clear, it revealed his AKMS wedged into the space underneath, stock folded. Low profile. Its presence was another sign that Hutch hadn't escaped.

'We're certain the ambush positions were in that copse and those bushes,' said Mike, pointing to the areas they'd searched. 'Well over two hundred rounds fired. A lot of hits and even more misses.'

Roper took over. 'Based on the physical evidence, talking to Ryan, and what Izzy said, it looks like the ambush hit the first car hard. It killed the driver, crippled the engine, wrecked the tyres, and wounded the front seat passenger, Hutch.'

He took a deep breath. 'Hutch got off a contact report, but he and Luke were probably grabbed by the enemy shortly afterwards.'

Roper moved clear of the SUV and pointed down the slope to Golf Two. 'The second vehicle goes off-road into the forest, taking a number of hits into the engine block and front tyres. The front seat passenger, Yaya, was probably killed in that barrage.'

He looked over to Ryan's car, where Izzy was wrapped up and being fed sweet, warm tea.

'When Golf Two crashed to a halt, Condé takes on the enemy with his Makarov and is either hit then or had already been hit during the initial contact. Meanwhile, he tells Izzy to run in the opposite direction. She gets away and hides until we turn up. Condé is either still here somewhere and we just haven't found him, or he's been taken with Hutch and Luke.'

Mike indicated the high ground on the other side of the track. 'While this was happening, Ryan approaches from up there to provide support. That's when Demba gets hit through the window. He manages to stop the vehicle in cover and the team debusses to return fire, hitting at least one of the enemy.'

He focused on the track where it led south.

'They remained in contact and pinned down. Couldn't see much. We're guessing the enemy grabbed Hutch and Luke, and maybe Condé, before they bugged out down that way. We rocked up a few minutes later.'

'A few minutes too late,' I added.

Mike shrugged. 'Nothing we could do about that, boss. Those fuckers had it planned. And we know where they are.'

He looked from me to Roper and then back to me. 'We're going to get them back, yeah?'

CHAPTER 60

Mike had said what I already knew in my soul: we were going to get our friends back. As I met his gaze, a sense of purpose welled up to nullify the exhaustion that had begun to settle.

'Yeah, we'll find them and bring them out and eliminate anyone who gets our way.' I turned to Roper. 'What resources can you call on, Tom? We need to act fast before those motherfuckers whisk them off to Timbuktu and do Christ knows what to them.'

Roper held us his palms. 'It's not that easy. I can't just call in a squadron to do a hostage rescue. We don't even know where they've been taken.'

'We know a fucking place to start looking,' said Mike, his normal laid-back manner replaced with a fierce intensity.

'You need to slow down. I need to report this in and talk to the boss.'

I fixed Roper with a hard stare of my own. 'We're going back into Mali for the guys no matter what the people in London think.'

Roper looked at both of us and shook his head. 'It's not my decision. I'll call London and see what they say.'

'Do that now then because I'm going to pull everyone together in five and thrash out a plan.'

Roper sighed, pulled out his sat phone, and stepped away to make the call.

Mike gripped my shoulder. 'Thanks, John, I knew you'd do the right thing. We can't leave the guys here.'

'I know, mate. I know that better than anyone.'

The team was quiet after I explained the suspected sequence of events at the ambush site. Shell-shocked might have been a better description. I'd gathered them next to Ryan's vehicle so that Izzy, wrapped up inside on the back seat, could hear what was said.

I paused for questions. When none were forthcoming, I continued.

'That's what we believe happened. Now, let's focus on what we're going to do next. First of all, we have three serviceable vehicles left. Sierra One and Two crews will remain unchanged. Bravo One will now be manned by Baldé as driver, Ryan, Izzy, and Bob. Izzy and Bob, we're going to take you to Setka village and ask the chief if you can stay there tonight.'

'What are you going to do?' asked Bob, pointing at me.

'Depending on those arrangements, we're going to return to an area to the north where we suspect the attackers originated. I'll need to jig the teams a bit to bring Ryan along and have Manny and Baldé stay with you at the village.'

Ryan's head bobbed in approval.

Bob flicked up the brim of his black hat. 'You expect me to stay there while you take on these bastards and recover Luke and the others?'

'Look Bob, we need to find them first. Tom is speaking with people in London to see if we can get some official help.'

Bob stepped forward, sucked in his stomach, and pulled his shoulders back. 'Well I'm coming with you. It may have escaped your notice, but I'm the only one who's dropped any of these mongrels so far.'

'You're an engineer. Pinnacle would go mad. You did great earlier, but this will be a whole different ball game.'

'I saw more combat in 'Nam than the rest of you put together. I'm staying right here, and Pinnacle can go fuck themselves.'

'And me too,' said a small female voice from the car. 'I don't know how to shoot a gun, but I'm a medic and I can help. I'm staying as well.'

Roper approached our loose semi-circular gathering. I looked from Izzy's defiant face to Bob's scowl under the re-lowered brim of his hat. Mike cocked an eyebrow when our eyes met.

400

'What does London think?' I asked Roper when he stopped next to Mike.

'We should speak in private,' replied Roper.

We moved out of earshot, passing a distraught-looking Baldé facing south where the hostiles had gone.

As we passed, I gripped his shoulder and Roper murmured something in French.

'So, what did Chapman say?'

'I didn't speak with him; I spoke with Hope. She authorised me to make the decision on the ground.'

'Okay, good.'

'But I'm only authorised to confirm they've been taken hostage and find where they're being held.' He fixed his eyes on mine. 'We're not authorised to go shooting up the place in Mali on some hare-brained hostage rescue.'

I held his stare. 'And if we find them, what then? Will there be a Hereford or Poole team on standby? And how far away?'

He relaxed his shoulders and looked away. 'I don't know, John. If we find them, then we'll deal with that. If. And it's a big if.'

'Mate, you and I both know that if we find them, then we'll have the best chance to take a shot there and then. Save their lives before they get moved out of reach.'

'Or get them killed,' he replied. 'This is Hope's instant reaction at the news. It's good. We have permission to go back over the border and try and find the guys. They'll be working their sources and, if we pinpoint them, they might have assets in place, British or French, that can get the job done. Let's focus on finding them.'

He was right, we needed to concentrate on that first. I wasn't confident Chapman would have a special forces team poised to strike, but there was no point arguing about it until we located the prisoners.

I glanced at my watch: 17:40. 'Okay. We'll drive to Setka, square ourselves away, put together a cunning plan, and deploy up north tonight.'

The diminished team clambered into the three remaining vehicles. Thoughts of our missing friends and the three inanimate teammates laid in the rear of my vehicle prompted a wave of guilt. Three of my people were dead and another three were fate unknown.

'*Bravo One, ready to move.*'

'*Sierra Two, ready.*'

There'd be time enough later to castigate myself for what I could have done differently to avoid this disaster. For now, I needed to focus on the three people we could still save.

'Sierra One, moving. Actions on encountering enemy, follow my lead and let's hit them hard, over.'

'*Bravo One, roger.*'

'*Sierra Two, roger, out.*'

We followed the track south where the four attacking vehicles had gone. They were unlikely to have hung around, but it paid to be prepared. As we bumped along the track, I scanned ahead and to the flanks. In the wing mirror, Ryan's Land Cruiser, Bravo One, followed on our bumper. Mike and his guys brought up the rear.

The ten kilometres to Setka would take twenty minutes. I considered the resources available and began to formulate a plan.

Our arrival at the village had been expected, unlike the news we carried of the afternoon's events. Without Condé, we'd lost our primary Malinke speaker. However, Izzy emerged as a strong replacement.

Her youth and obvious distress granted her a level of immunity from the deeply patriarchal conventions. A couple of the village old timers tutted and shook their heads at the candid way she addressed the chief. The traces of blood on her shirt and her recount of the earlier violence soon shut them up.

Roper and I also engaged in French and English to communicate the situation and a request for assistance. We didn't need much – just to leave the three dead bodies at the village while we tried to locate our missing teammates.

The chief agreed without question. He also wanted to raise a posse to go after the devils who had attacked us. It took repeated efforts from both me and Roper to persuade him that wasn't necessary. I did note and appreciate the offer though. Depending on what transpired that night, we might need their help.

While Manny organised the transfer of the bodies from my car to the temporary morgue, five of us gathered in the 9x9 tent around an unfolded map of the Crystal One Alpha target area. We didn't have a table, so I unhooked the tilly lamp and placed it on the ground to better illuminate the map sheet. I knelt on one side, looking at it upside down, and Ryan, Mike, Jamie, and Roper knelt on the other.

'Okay, gents. I'll give you an outline of my thinking, then let's hear some feedback. We're light on resources, options, and time. There's going to be plenty not to like. If you think you have a better idea, then for fuck's sake mention it now.'

The guys all acknowledged they understood.

I pulled out my pointer and extended it.

'Still got your birthday present, I see,' said Ryan.

'Only just. Right, based on Bob and Izzy's demand for involvement, I propose three teams. Manny, Baldé, and Alain will be the drivers and comprise the mobile team. Tom, Bob, and Izzy will be the OP support team.'

I ignored the questioning look on Roper's face.

'Us four,' I circled a finger to include Mike, Ryan, and Jamie, 'will be the patrol team.'

Before Roper could complain, I said, 'Tom, you're the link with the cavalry in London, and you need an overview of the situation and the ground before calling in whatever support they can provide. I need you with satellite and VHF comms on that hill. Let me outline my plan and then you can say your piece.'

He toned down his scowl. 'Okay.'

'Our objective is to locate the three hostages and coordinate their rescue.'

I looked at each of the men, pausing to meet Roper's eyes.

'I say again, our objective is to locate the three hostages and coordinate their rescue.'

Roper glowered but didn't interrupt.

'I propose a five-phase plan. Phase one is the insertion. The team will drive across the border at the river fording point to the waypoint at the bottom of OP hill. The vehicles will be camouflaged and remain at that position with the three drivers until called forward or until we extract.

'Phase two will see the remaining seven of us move up the feature and along the ridge one and a half K to the OP position. From there, we'll observe the ground for any sign of the enemy. Tom's team will go firm and overwatch.'

I focused my attention to Roper. 'You should have VHF comms to both the mobile and the patrol teams from that hill. Both will also have satellite phones.'

I moved the pointer to a location we all knew well.

'Phase three sees the patrol team move to Crystal One Alpha and conduct a CTR. We saw those four enemy vehicles visit that location this morning before they set out, so we now assume anyone in that vicinity is also enemy forces.'

I trailed the pointer towards the map edge nearest to my foot.

'If we don't locate the hostages at Crystal One Alpha, then we move up on to Castle Feature, two K up a sharp incline, to check what's behind that ridge. Those vehicles came from that other side and might have taken them into that area further back.

'Phase four is the rescue. Of course, if we don't find the guys then there won't be a phase four. Even if we do find them, the rescue part is fuzzy.'

My eyes shot back to Roper. 'We don't know yet if Tom's bosses will have anything arranged or we'll be left swinging in the wind. We may need to take some tough decisions if we get eyes on our people. It might mean staying in situ for an extended time.

'Or?' Mike prompted.

'Or it might mean getting the job done ourselves.'

I lifted my hand up in Roper's direction. 'I know what you're going to say, Tom, but it's an option on the table.'

'Not a realistic option,' said Roper. 'A four-man team is highly unlikely to succeed in doing anything other than alerting them and kissing goodbye to any hostages, forever.'

'You're right,' I said. 'That's a fair assessment. It's why I want you to get Chapman, Hope, and their paymasters in London to get a fucking squadron down here and get the job done properly.'

Roper shook his head and his eyes flashed with anger. Probably because I'd mentioned the names of his bosses in front of the others. Tough shit. I spoke over him as he complained about it 'not being that easy'.

'Phase five is the exfil. If phase four is woolly, phase five after a rescue would be a whole ream of unknown unknowns. The place would be stirred up to shit and we'd need to be well out the way before SF rolled in and out.'

I regarded Roper's flexing jaw. 'And Tom's right, we don't want to be launching any boy's own adventure bullshit unless we have to and unless we get a clear shot.'

I paused to find the right words.

'I'm just worried that if we don't recover the guys now, we won't see them alive again.'

Mike spoke up again. 'Sounds to me like we'll need to improvise, adapt, and overcome. Same as always. It's what we're good at.'

'That's about the size of it. We'll have the mobile team ready to be called forward if we recover the boys. Either that or we might get lucky and steal a car or two. Otherwise, I expect we'll be walking out again. Maybe with a lot of hostiles on our ass.'

'I'm okay with that plan,' said Jamie. He looked at his watch. 'But ask me again in twelve hours' time and I can't guarantee the same answer.'

'Works for me,' said Mike. 'I suggest you consider dropping two at Crystal One Alpha and pushing two on to the top of the ridge for that recce. We'll be close enough to reinforce if either team gets eyes on.'

'Good idea,' I replied. 'Timings are going to be tight. We've been on the go for most of the last twenty-four hours, so we need to rest up before this patrol. It will only be three or four hours max. Better than nothing.'

Ryan looked up from his waterproof notebook and tapped his pencil on the page where he'd made notes. 'Are you sure you want to take the cars over the border? It keeps them close but increases the risk of compromise.'

'It's a trade-off. I'd like to punch out of here by nineteen hundred while we have the last of the twilight. I'm thinking three of us can drive to the waypoint. We'll use NVGs if we lose the light.'

'We could hold them back here or at the other village,' said Ryan.

'Yep, we could. But to be honest, I want to keep Baldé close to us. He's already told Tom we should be notifying the authorities. I'm worried he'd Foxtrot Oscar in one of the cars and do his own thing if we left him and the other drivers behind.'

Ryan looked at Roper and nodded. 'Fair enough. We'll need to camouflage them as best we can then.'

'What else you got?' I asked.

Ryan scanned his notes. 'No problem with the plan. A couple of questions about kit and equipment.'

'Go on.'

'Radio and NVG batteries, sat phones and battery strengths, weapon and ammo allocation, water, rations – the usual. Oh, and are you sure we want Bob and Izzy out there with us. Bob did well this afternoon and can handle an AK, but Izzy? Couldn't we leave her here?'

'I'll try. You heard her though. She's determined and she's a medic. I hope we don't need her or Jamie to work their magic, but you never know. As for the VHF batteries, we've got spares and they're high capacity, twelve hours or more. Each team will only have one radio operational to maximise capacity. We'll run with me, Mike, Tom, and Manny. Sierra Alpha, Delta, Charlie, and we'll keep Manny as Sierra Two.'

I indicated to Ryan. 'You'll be Sierra Echo if you get on the net.'

He nodded in return.

'We'll give Manny the ones with no juice so he can replenish them in the vehicle chargers. We're good for NVG batteries, and my sat phone is okay. Hopefully, that goes for the rest as well. Everyone needs to check. We should have enough water to top up and we'll need to divvy up the remaining rations.' I rubbed my stomach. 'Might all lose a few pounds in the next day or so.'

After waiting his turn, Roper spoke in an even tone that surprised me. Perhaps the shadows cast by the lamp had engendered an impression of ire that wasn't warranted.

'I have no issue with the plan concept. It probably does make sense for me to coordinate from the OP. But I'm concerned about this idea of launching a hostage rescue on the fly. I want this to work as much as any of you, but we all need to understand the risks if any sort of opportunity like that arises.'

Before I could answer, Mike said. 'You know me from way back, Tom. If it stacks up, then I'll say, "take the shot". But only if stacks up.' He gestured around the room. 'Us four have worked together through tough situations. We're too long in the tooth for any John Wayne shit unless we have to.'

'Yeah, I'm concentrating on finding the guys,' I added, 'and hoping you and the London people can work a solution if we do.'

'As long as that's clear, then we're good. All on the same page,' said Roper.

The fleeting looks I exchanged with Mike and Ryan suggested otherwise.

A 'him and us' divergence had opened up, that was clear. Understandable too. His motivations for involvement in this gig were different to ours but ultimately we all wanted the same outcome – find our friends and bring them home.

Fifteen minutes later, the entire team assembled by the tent. I'd used the military aide memoire prompts at the front of my waterproof notebook to fashion a briefing. It had been a long time since I'd given a set of military orders and these wouldn't have wowed the DS at Lympstone. They did the trick though and nobody took the piss, although that was probably influenced by the gravity of our situation.

CHAPTER 61

Bang on 1900 hours, we rolled out of Setka past lines of sombre villagers, leaving our three dead comrades in their care. I drove Sierra One in the lead, Ryan took the wheel of Bravo One behind us, and Mike piloted Sierra Two at the rear. We each had NVGs ready in case the light dropped en route.

With Demba and Samuel's redistributed Kalashnikovs, there were eight rifles – enough for all but two of the team. Manny volunteered to make do with Condé's Makarov pistol. Izzy refused to countenance carrying a weapon, even though Alain offered her his Makarov.

Ryan and Bob had got through the best part of two thirty-round magazines during their earlier skirmish. Once we divided up the ammunition, the patrol team each carried five full mags, Roper four, and Bob, Alain, and Baldé two each.

Thirty minutes later I steered off the track near the afternoon's PUP. We'd passed the two forlorn Land Cruisers keeping a silent vigil at the ambush site. A sobering image. Not that anyone needed reminding of the risks we faced, and the stakes involved.

The sun had set on the clear evening at 19:05 and the daylight evaporated fast. To reduce our profile, we were driving without lights and with the interior bulbs removed.

I keyed the mic. 'Stop, stop, stop. Switching to NVGs.'

Two pairs of clicks answered over the radio.

Driving with NVGs wasn't easy – they reduced spatial awareness. The windscreen clashed with branches from several trees as we bounced towards the river.

Our patrol route took us along much of the same ground as the previous night. Ground we knew but which might have attracted hostile interest if our last incursion had been detected. We'd just have to hope we tip-toed in and tip-toed out leaving everyone else none the wiser.

And now we needed to do it all again, except bigger and bolder. What choice did we have? They were our friends and no one else would save them.

Roper, Alain, and Baldé jumped out when we approached the river. They moved ahead to secure the ford. We used the second option from earlier that day. I'd already tangled with the mudflat at the first crossing and didn't want to risk any of the vehicles either getting stuck or leaving obvious sign.

Once across the river, I made good time to the waypoint at the base of the dog-leg hill. The Moon wasn't due to rise for another hour and the night had almost closed in.

We spent fifteen minutes positioning the three vehicles in cover as best we could and gathered armfuls of foliage to augment the camouflage. Although in the dark it was impossible to tell whether the three white SUVs might stick out like a bulldog's bollocks come the morning. I conferred with Manny about checking and adjusting the position once daylight returned.

Before leaving, I reminded him of the comms plan. 'Just listen out for Sierra Two as usual. Happy?'

'Sierra Two. Got it.'

'Don't respond to the regular transmissions between the rest of us. But you need to listen to that radio in case we call you in. Nobody falls asleep on watch.'

Alain and Baldé stood listening. I pointed at Baldé. 'Make sure he understands how important it is to remain awake.'

Manny spoke in French and Baldé answered with an indignant 'Oui, oui.'

I placed a hand on Baldé's shoulder. 'Pour Demba et Condé.' *For Demba and Condé.*

His head twitched in acknowledgement.

Leaving the mobile team at the waypoint, we shook out and filed up the slope in the pitch dark. Order of march: me, Ryan, Roper, Izzy, Bob, Jamie, and Mike, where I always relied upon him, securing the rear.

The tranquil surroundings didn't suppress my anxiety about advancing along this same ridge for the second night running and reoccupying the OP position. Setting patterns was a big no-no and went against every instinct. However, no one had come up with a better idea.

I'm sure the others felt just as relieved when we settled into the OP without any drama. It bothered me that we sat atop a prominent piece of high ground – a location I would have regularly swept if I had a base on Castle Feature. With no evidence of compromise so far, we'd have to hope the enemy didn't feel the same way and roll down here anytime soon.

The Moon crept over the horizon within ten minutes of our arrival. The four of us in the patrol team snuggled into our bags and left Roper, Bob, and Izzy to cover the watches. Even a kaleidoscope of harrowing images from the aftermath of the ambush couldn't stop me from crashing into a deep sleep soon after closing my eyes.

A hand shook my shoulder three and a half hours later.

'Mister John, it's twelve-thirty. Time to wake up,' said Izzy. Her soft voice wildly at odds with the violent and bloody dream she'd interrupted.

My eyes had pinged open the moment she gripped me through the jungle bag.

'Thank you, I'm awake.'

We'd left most of our rucksacks and supplies with the vehicles. The three bergens we did hump to the OP contained optics and essentials. I'd kept it to three so that Roper, Bob, and Izzy could haul them out if necessary. No one knew how this might end.

My patrol team wore vests and daysacks packed with gear and ammunition. Jamie crammed his personal kit into chest webbing and carried the larger medical pack. We stuffed our sleeping bags back into the designated bergen, bolted down boil in the bag MREs, and prepared to move out at 01:00.

If the previous night had felt tense, moving forward on this patrol felt like stepping into a pressure cooker. My skin prickled and my stomach churned. Fear of failure engulfed me. Failure that would cost the lives of three of my friends and possibly more.

The lengthy, forbidding ridge of Castle Feature dominated the skyline and watched our every move.

I concentrated on what I could control – the task at hand – and my initial anxiety eased. We were four against superior numbers but the further we patrolled without compromise, the more likely we retained the advantage of surprise.

Three hundred metres west of Crystal One Alpha, Mike and Jamie peeled away to recce the same buildings as the previous night.

Ryan and I had a steep climb to navigate to the left edge of the Castle Feature ridge. Mike had first seen the four enemy vehicles appear from the road that wound around that edge to whatever lay behind. The imagery suggested a forested 'hidden valley'. A long, narrow re-entrant that might provide an attractive hiding place.

Looking up at the ridge and imagining an exfiltration under fire, I hoped Mike would find our guys down here.

'Sierra Charlie, this is Sierra Alpha complete at RV One. Delta is moving to Crystal One Alpha, I am moving to Crystal One Bravo, over.'

Roper answered immediately. *'Sierra Charlie, RV One acknowledged, over.'*

'Sierra Alpha, roger, out.'

I looked up to our lofty destination. 'Hope you've got your yomping boots on.'

'Anytime, once you've finished having a rest,' fired back Ryan. 'We can tab if you want to get there quicker.'

'Twat.'

Halfway up the slope, my thighs burned with lactic acid, my shirt was drenched, and I was blowing like a steam train. The sweat rag around my wrist was soaked. Sweeping it across my face provided negligible relief to my stinging eyes.

Ryan hadn't complained about the fierce pace, but his laboured breathing matched mine. We sought to maintain tactical awareness while pushing hard to reach the objective on time. Both of us spurred on to match the other. Our only communication – my occasional hand signals to go firm or restart the advance.

'Sierra Charlie, Sierra Alpha, this is Delta. Indications are Crystal One Alpha is dry, over.'

'Sierra Charlie, roger.'

Shit. Mike and Jamie had drawn a blank.

'Alpha, Delta's sitrep acknowledged. On schedule to reach Crystal One Bravo at zero four hundred, over.'

'Delta, roger. We're continuing our CTRs, over.'

'Sierra Charlie, Objective Bravo at zero four hundred and ongoing CTRs acknowledged.'

'Sierra Alpha, roger, out.'

It was encouraging that we had good comms with both Mike and the OP four kilometres away. Roper was either the world's lightest sleeper or he was pulling an all-nighter.

Surrounded by forest, I couldn't see our objective, but I'd judged the pace so we could afford to slow for the final, cautious approach. If al-Qaeda had a holiday park over that ridge, it was a fair bet we'd encounter sentries positioned at the top. Wandering patrols might also provide a problem.

By now, my general anxiety had disappeared and professional determination to complete the mission had taken over. I battled to ignore the inner voice whispering that our friends were long gone.

I dropped to one knee and signalled Roper to do likewise. The final 300 metres to the objective rose in a sharper, forested incline. I locked onto the bite valve and sucked in two long drags of tepid water. My watch showed 03:15. I held up a hand with the fingers splayed and whispered, 'Five minutes.'

Ryan acknowledged with a thumbs up.

'Sierra Alpha is three hundred from objective. No issues. Moving out in figures five, over.'

A comforting pair of clicks answered.

My final energy bar didn't last long despite my efforts to chew in slow time. Once we pushed out from here, all bets were off. We might find a big load of nothing, or we might stumble into al-Qaeda's back yard. I expected the former but couldn't rule out the latter.

Our priority was avoiding detection. For that, the covered route to the top of the ridge worked in our favour. However, it also limited our field of view and meant we might not spot hostile forces until at close range. I stopped every fifty metres to listen and observe. The night gave nothing away.

The trees thinned until we reached the edge of steep, rocky ground. Moonlight illuminated the last 100 metres to the top. After pausing for a careful check with the NVGs, we crept forward between the rock formations and outcrops.

I advanced in bounds of ten strides, then knelt to scrutinize the way ahead. Sound travels further at night, so I planted each step with extra care to avoid unnecessary noise and strained to detect any hint of nearby human presence.

Twenty metres from a rocky overhang jutting out from the forested ridgetop, I heard something. My hand shot up to signal a halt. Remaining motionless, I strained to listen over the sound of my ragged breathing.

There it was again. Voices. Not loud, not urgent. Voices in conversation. Almost imperceptible, but definitely there. I signalled 'enemy' to Ryan and pointed at the overhang. He responded with an exaggerated nod.

We needed to get 'eyes on' and find out what we were dealing with. Popping up this close was asking for trouble, so I improvised a hand signal for 'box around' that Ryan acknowledged.

Hunched into a crouch, I picked my way through the stark landscape of rocks and shadows as we navigated a circular approach to the top of the ridge.

We had no way of knowing if the voices belonged to bad guys or innocent locals. Quite what innocent locals might be doing here at this time of night was debatable. Stargazing perhaps? We also didn't know how many people might be in the vicinity or how widely spread they might be.

I ran my thumb over the metal safety on my AK. It remained in the safe position for now, while we navigated the rough, steep terrain. I didn't want to risk the disaster of a negligent discharge while traversing the rugged hillside.

At 04:10 we crested the ridge on our stomachs in a leopard crawl. The final hundred metres had taken us fifty minutes. Because of the trees and foliage, I couldn't see the outcrop near where I'd heard the voices. We cleared our immediate area and I sent a sitrep.

'Sierra Charlie, this is Alpha. I am complete at Crystal One Bravo. Voices heard in the vicinity. Limited visibility due to jungle terrain, over.'

'..Charlie...broken...again, over.'

I repeated the message but comms with the OP remained unworkable.

'Alpha, this is Delta. I have you loud and clear. Will relay your message to Sierra Charlie, over.'

'Alpha, roger, will advise when recce complete. Anything new at your location, over?'

'Negative. Same profile as last visit. Let me know if you need support and we'll join you.'

'Roger, wait out on that. Will relay all future messages through you.'

Much as I would have liked Mike and Jamie alongside us, I judged it better for them to stay put. For now, at least. I didn't want to lose our eyes on Crystal One Alpha, the most suspicious location surveyed so far. Not unless Ryan and I hit paydirt when we scouted our objective.

We stalked through the flimsy trees coating the ridge top. The Moon's ghoulish silver glow moulded bushes and branches into elongated torso outlines and rifle stocks. They melted away as the angles of the shadows changed with our slow progress. My thumb lay on the safety lever of the AK, ready to force it down in an instant.

The outcrop came into view and the murmur of voices floated in the air.

I sank to the ground and directed Ryan into a prone position alongside me.

'I'll go forward. Wait there.'

I snaked across the hard, uneven ground, exerting the least pressure possible with each placement of elbow and knee, and trying to glide the rest of my body with minimal contact to the floor.

Within ten feet I could see the source of the noises through wispy vegetation: three men illuminated by moonlight near the edge of the ridge. Behind them, a poetic vista of epic landscape: smooth hills and a jagged patchwork of jungle, scree, and grassland. The terrain I knew so well distorted and unfamiliar from this elevation.

I placed the rifle gently by my side and used the NVGs to verify that I hadn't missed anyone mooching in the shadows. With that confirmed, I slithered backwards to Ryan in slow motion.

'Three men armed with rifles. Two sitting, one standing. Chatting without a care in the world. There's no obvious shelter, so they may be a wandering patrol. I'll log the position and call it in later. Let's bypass them and move into the objective to see what they're protecting. The night will start to lift in an hour. We need to be either firm in a hide or making like swastikas back down the hill by zero six hundred. Zero six-thirty at the latest.'

'Roger that.'

I didn't want to risk radioing an update from here in case the armed men heard me like I'd heard them. We needed to distance ourselves first.

Once we'd retraced our steps fifty metres to where we'd ascended, I tried Mike on VHF. Back on the lip of the ridge, the signal remained strong. I advised him of the location of the suspicious armed men and the likelihood my next sitrep would arrive via sat phone. Either SMS or voice.

After we dropped into the valley, I expected to lose VHF comms. According to the imagery, the fold behind the ridge stretched 1.5 kilometres in length. It looked like a 600-metre-wide ice cream scoop had gauged a 200-foot-deep, v-shaped hollow in the otherwise flat-topped plateau. Without line of sight, we'd be limited to reporting by satellite phone.

The time was 04:35 and we had two hours before sunrise. Two hours to scout the sizeable, forested target area and assess whether we were looking in the right place.

I pulled out the map and orientated it to the ground under the faint glow of my red torchlight. With our view restricted to a wall of black foliage, we needed to march on a bearing.

'Four hundred metres once we hit the slope, on a bearing of six thousand mils,' I whispered, setting the dial on my compass.

'Then what?' asked Ryan

'We should be at the bottom. If nothing seen, we'll turn right and head east-northeast until the end. If we still haven't seen anything by then, we're probably barking up the wrong tree.'

'Fair enough.'

'If we get separated with no comms, then meet back here at zero six hundred. If the other is a no-show by six-fifteen, then move down the hill to link up with Mike.' I thought about the ramifications of that scenario. 'Let's not get separated.'

'I'm with you there.'

Ryan switched on his radio and we each blew twice into our microphones for an informal radio check. Then we advanced across the ninety-metre-wide ridge and dropped down the thick forest slope on the other side.

Three hundred and fifty metres later, the dark, hulking shape of a single storey building materialized. Up close, the wooden structure was identical to the cabins at Crystal One Alpha.

We edged round to the front, which faced towards the bottom of the re-entrant, until we had a view that had me reaching for the NVGs. Blood thumped in my chest and pulsed in my temple as I swept the optic from left to right and back again. Glowing green images of buildings, tracks, and parking areas with groups of vehicles, all stretching into the distance.

I was gobsmacked. The two of us had just stumbled into the rumoured base. Whether it was al-Qaeda, smugglers, or even ill-disciplined Malian security forces that lived here, it had to be the Project Brimstone target. I couldn't see Ryan's features, only his head wafting from side to side like mine.

'Now what?' he whispered.

'Sitrep first. Then sweep the area for any sign of Hutch and the guys.'

Bob's deep Aussie voice crackled over the sat phone. 'Hello.'

'Bob, it's John. We're at the objective, in the bottom of the valley, and we've found a camp. The camp. I'll give you the grid and a description. Have you got a pen?'

'Sure thing, mate. Err hang on.'

CHAPTER 62

After providing the situation report to the OP, Ryan and I set about reconnoitring and mapping the area. On each side of the central track stretching into the hollow, identical buildings stood like lorries that had been reversed under the canopy. The layout provided excellent cover for us to slink through the camp and observe from the deepest shadows.

We advanced in short, measured bounds – me first, then Ryan drawing level. Each adopting a kneeling firing position before signalling the other to move.

Twelve of the large cabins straddled the track. In addition to their dimensions, one thing they all had in common was black windows. They defied our attempts to peek inside, even aided by weak red torchlight. At a guess, they were fitted with blackout blinds. An understandable measure if the occupants wanted to avoid detection by aerial surveillance due to poor light discipline.

We counted twelve SUVs, four pickups, and three trucks. All of them parked under camouflaged sunshades or tucked into the forest adjacent to the buildings. The one thing conspicuously absent: people. That was until we discovered a scattered complex of different sized structures inside a fenced compound at the far end. The gate to the sixty-metre-wide compound was closed. Two men armed with Kalashnikovs paced behind it.

We circled the compound checking for signs of further guards. It didn't take long to spot them. Another two pairs of armed men patrolled the fence perimeter. One pair hugged the 120-metre-long northern fence line, and we spotted the other pair near the southern fence. We also counted another three SUVs nestled among the tightly packed structures.

Rudimentary camouflage netting hung like a giant spider web across the entire compound, supported by a network of tall poles and the tallest building rooftops. It reminded me of a giant version of the set up at the camp in Taji. The ingenuity impressed me. A reminder these people should not be underestimated.

After completing our circuit, we settled into thick bushes on the slope, twenty metres from the nearest fence corner. The position provided an unimpeded view of the gate and a restricted view under the netting and over the tops of the nearest buildings into the heart of the cobweb covered lair. Good enough. An ideal location from which to monitor the comings and goings, record patrol activity, and scrutinise movement along the main drag.

Shortly before 05:30, we froze when a three-man patrol appeared ten metres from our hide. We hadn't encountered anyone else outside the compound apart from the three at the top of the ridge. This might have been them returning, or an indication there were more forces around than we figured.

The gate was opened to allow the three armed men to enter. I followed their progress to a square building towards the centre rear of the compound. There they merged with at least five more figures. A marginal improvement in the light conditions registered for the first time. Improvement being the wrong word for us. It signalled that we needed to be making decisions right now as to the next course of action.

The improving light revealed a large, disguised antenna next to the square building. Larger than the one at Crystal One Alpha, it soared through the cam net and had an array of dishes close to the top below a simulated tree canopy. Indicative of a well-disguised comms centre or headquarters building.

Did this compound house our captive friends? It was the only guarded part of the camp we'd found, although we hadn't investigated west of our entry point into the valley or seen inside any of the buildings along the track.

Should we bed ourselves in here by the compound or sneak to the open end of the valley that led to the local roads? If we didn't commit one way or the other soon, we'd be caught in daylight like a pair of vampires fleeing to a crypt after a night overdoing the bloodsucking.

I'd already decided we needed to remain in the valley. Using the sat phone, I would report to Roper and urge him to finish Brimstone in a blaze of explosive, hostage rescuing glory — just as soon as we could confirm our men were held prisoner here.

And if Chapman, Hope, Roper, and their ilk elected to do nothing? If we found the prisoners, mapped the target, and studied the patrol patterns, then all options remained on the table.

Mike and Jamie could join us that evening to launch a four-man rescue mission. And the mobile team could advance to a staging position much closer to the valley entrance. Instead of fleeing on foot with bad guys in hot pursuit for hours on end, we could be over the border via Crossing X-Ray or Yankee in ten minutes.

A myriad of positive images cascaded on top of each other as hope bubbled deep inside. But nothing could be done until we verified this was the right target and our boys were here.

'Stay here or snurgle down the other end? I asked Ryan.

'Stay here. There's too much movement to risk it. Look, there's more coming out now.'

He was right. Six bulky figures carrying long weapons exited through the gate. Three veered onto the slope and passed twenty feet in front of us. The curved magazines in the rifles, indicative of Kalashnikovs, were expected. The fuzzy silhouettes of their heads and shoulders less so.

Scarves and headdresses. The different profiles indicated either Arabic Keffiyehs or perhaps tagelmust, a head and face-covering garment worn by the Tuareg Berbers who inhabited vast swathes of the Sahara that stretched into northern Mali.

On reaching the forest edge on our left, they slotted into single file and hugged the treeline as they moved away parallel with the central track.

'Those weren't regular soldiers,' I whispered to Ryan. 'We're in the right place. I just hope we're not too late.'

The other three men bimbled down the track that passed between the twelve cabins. From their boisterous manner, it wouldn't have surprised me if they'd been the same guys from the top of the ridge.

'Shift change,' said Ryan.

'Maybe.'

I tapped out a message on the sat phone, but it wouldn't send. The display showed no satellite reception. Great. Just when I needed it, no fucking comms.

I was about to voice my frustration to Ryan and tell him I needed to sneak up the hill to obtain a signal, when a faint hum caught my attention.

Then a much closer cough of a combustion engine spluttering to life, followed by another, then a third. From silence to engines sparking up all over the manor in twenty seconds.

The wall of man-made sound grew louder as multiple vehicles approached. In the feeble dawn light, I made out the boxy shapes of three SUVs and two pickup trucks. All driving without lights.

The two pickups spun around on reaching the gate to face back down the track. Several human outlines perched on each flatbed. The three SUVs, Toyota Land Cruisers by the shape of them, entered the compound.

Male voices barked orders above the commotion, while another sound enveloped the valley from above. The hum had intensified.

I turned to Ryan. 'That's a fucking plane.'

We both raised an ear to the sky.

I focused back on the bustle of vehicles and people moving in and around the compound. 'Shit. If the hostages are here, then maybe they're about to be moved. Flown off somewhere.'

The angry buzzing of a turbo prop plane began to wane into a muffled drone. I pictured it landing on the other side of the hill.

'Can you reach the OP for a sitrep?' asked Ryan.

I checked the sat phone. 'No signal, mate.'

Attempts using both our radios failed to raise either Mike or the OP.

I queued another SMS update on the sat phone and shifted position for a better view through the gate into the compound.

Sunrise was only twenty minutes away and the retreating night had morphed into a twilight that unveiled the locale. I pulled out my binos and zoomed through a gap into the group standing next to the SUVs, which were now parked in front of a large dark building.

From the right, two men without headdress carried a stretcher between them. A partially obscured figure with an arm in a sling stumbled while propelled by an armed man gripping each shoulder.

'Fuck. Watch it.' Hutch's agitated reprimand was unmistakeable.

An explosion of relief and adrenaline was followed quickly by alarm at the unfolding situation. Behind Hutch and his heavy-handed new friends, Luke was similarly bundled forward. The party moved out of sight behind the close-knit SUVs and the obstruction of a closer rooftop.

Ryan leaned in close. 'There's too many of them. We can't do anything here.'

'I know. As soon as we're sure they're in those vehicles, we need to be on our toes up the hill. I hope you bought your running boots.'

'You too, old timer.'

When the first Land Cruiser moved out of the way and rolled towards the gate, it revealed our friends being loaded into the vehicle behind. The immobile person on the stretcher, who I assumed to be Condé, was lifted off the ground and folded into the car.

Including the twelve I'd counted on board the pickups, there were at least twenty armed men in the vicinity and a lot of ground we couldn't see. Any attempt at a half-arsed two-man rescue here would be a suicide mission that would kill us and the prisoners.

'Prepare to move,' I said to Ryan. 'We need to traverse the hill at an angle towards the RV. Above us the top is open ground as flat as a bloody pancake.'

I adjusted the dial on the compass strapped to my forearm and indicated up the hill behind us to our left. 'Eleven hundred and eighty metres. Three seven sixty mils. Let's call it ten minutes.'

'Piece of piss. As long as we don't run into the three amigos we saw a few minutes ago.'

'If we do. Take no prisoners, mate. We put them down as quiet as we can and push through.' I tapped the knife on my belt.

The three SUVs exited the compound, formed a convoy with the pickups front and rear, and snaked off along the main track. When the rear pickup pulled away, we tore off up the hill.

Tactical movement was out the window and any encounter with hostiles would necessitate improvisation on the hoof. We had to inform the others what was happening asap and try to join with them to prevent losing our friends for good.

There wouldn't be time to summon special forces with their resources and expertise; not unless they were already sipping tea with Roper. And that meant we'd have to pray for a realistic shot at success with the assets we had.

Within 500 metres, my face was scratched and bleeding and the chocolate and nuts I'd wolfed down for breakfast had almost come back up. I pushed through another stubborn barrier of spiky branches and found myself on a narrow, cleared path leading directly up the steep incline. It made sense for the camp guards to have an easy access route to the ridge. The 'three amigos' Ryan had referred to might be on the path somewhere, above or below us.

I caught my breath and peered up and down the improvised path. Visibility was thirty metres in either direction. 'Fuck it. Let's use this and review our options at the top.'

'Risky,' said Ryan.

'If we spot anyone going up ahead of us, we should have time to take cover. If we run into someone coming the other way, they won't even tell we're not from the camp until we're in their faces.'

'Makes sense.'

The twilight was lifting fast, but it still offered some protection:

vital seconds that we could use to our advantage to nullify any threats. Gunfire would alert the whole grid square and blow any chance of a rescue. We'd need to get up close and personal and use overwhelming aggression to avoid that happening.

We set off up the path at an urgent pace. Buzzing critters swarmed and swooped, eager for their first feed of the day. I gave up trying to swat them away and preserved my focus on the trail ahead.

When we breached the treeline and arrived at the desolate ridgetop, I collapsed into a prone position and offered a silent thank you that the next legs would be flat then downhill.

Ryan dropped beside me, his face a mask of sweat-smudged cam cream. His breathless 'Fucking hell' summed it up without needing a reply.

The ridge looked clear. No sign of enemy patrols. The sun hadn't escaped the horizon but visibility with the mark one eyeball was already considerable. Although we hadn't seen anyone, risking a charge across the 150-metre-wide ridgetop would be pushing our luck.

'It's six hundred and fifty along the treeline to the RV,' I panted, the sweat now running in rivers because I'd stopped moving.

'Either that or we chance it across the top.' I pointed ahead over our flat, rocky frontage.

Ryan looked right towards the forested, RV end of the ridge and then at me. 'We haven't got time to fuck about. Let's do it.'

Pushing our luck it was then.

After sucking in greedy breaths and greedier slurps of water, I said, 'On three. One, two, three.'

My leg muscles howled as I clambered to my feet and accelerated to a gallop across the open ground. I held the AK across my chest and hunched my shoulders to reduce my profile. Ryan pulled ahead of me, forcing me to increase the pace.

I inched in front again and heard him call out, 'Run Forrest'.

I couldn't help laughing despite the perilous situation.

Forty seconds later we both slid to the ground in a scattering of thorny bushes, one of which ripped another gash in my cheek.

Checking around us revealed no sign of compromise. We'd made it.

'You fucking idiot,' I said, while Ryan chuckled in a heap alongside me.

'Sierra callsigns, this is Alpha, message, over.'

'Charlie, send.'

'Delta, send, over.'

'Crystal One Bravo is hot. Repeat hot. We've had eyes on the prisoners, figures three, roger so far, over.'

'Charlie, roger so far.'

'Delta, roger so far, over.'

'The pax have been moved in a five-vehicle convoy. Three SUVs and two pickups, over.'

'This is Charlie. Be advised Delta has eyes on a similar configuration at Crystal One Alpha. We also have an aircraft landed between Delta and my location, over.'

'Alpha, understood. We're on the south side of Castle Feature, preparing to move. Will reach the airstrip in two zero mikes, over.'

'Charlie, roger two zero mikes. Delta reports heavy armed presence with the convoy. Do not engage with any hostiles at this time. Please acknowledge, over.'

Fucking Roper – worried about his pension more than the lads. Probably unfair, but this was my team and I'd decide if and when we engaged with these pricks. This wasn't the time for that argument though.

'Alpha acknowledging your last. Advise you call in the cavalry, over.'

'It's in hand, out.'

Next, I called up Mike and told him we could RV 100 metres west of a track junction sprouting from the airstrip. The offshoot running north led to the second of the three targets from our first recce patrol here. He confirmed the grid reference and suggested he and Jamie made their way to the RV asap.

It was a gamble. I hated the thought of losing eyes on the convoy transporting the hostages, but I doubted they'd remain stationary long enough for us to form up and launch a four-man rescue.

Assembling by the airstrip had a better chance of working. Why fly a plane into this particular location and move a bunch of freshly captured Westerners unless you intended to spirit them away?

At the airstrip we'd have oversight from Roper watching from the OP, less than two K to the southeast. It would also reduce the time and distance required by the mobile team to come screaming in to sweep us back over the border.

'Agreed Delta. Make your way to the RV. We'll see you in two zero mikes, over.'

'Delta, roger. Moving, out.'

CHAPTER 63

As Ryan and I hauled ourselves back to our feet, the joke was starting to wear thin. I was hanging out and hotspots on my heels and toes indicated blisters on the way.

The sun sprayed across the hillside forest beneath us as we began our descent, which soon evolved into a frantic scramble to avoid serious injury. All semblance of control had been lost as we pitched down the steep slope, running, falling, recovering – total chaos. Somehow, we remained together as we battered our way down the hill.

My knee exploded in pain as I planted a foot and the momentum twisted my body. Fortunately, I lifted off again and the next stride suggested a tweak rather than anything worse.

Two bulky figures swung into my path as I brushed yet another tree trunk with graceless good fortune. Both had their heads covered, their part-revealed faces peering our way as we bouldered through the undergrowth. Matey on the left began to raise his AK-47 while I steered myself at him like a human cannonball. This was going to fucking hurt.

I lowered my head and braced before smashing into him and spinning arse-over-tit into a knot of bushes. The stock of my AK caught my jaw, but I tumbled to a halt on my knees with no pain receptors flashing. Well, none flashing any more than all the other alarms my body was trying to ignore.

I'd scored a bullseye. My target lay crumpled on the floor and moaned. His arms lifted into the air and his hands shook as though asking the big guy the 'why me' question, before he tried to prise himself up off his back.

I pulled out my knife and charged the ten feet to pounce and plunge it into his chest. His wide eyes registered shock and incomprehension as he stared into mine. His features were Arabic or North African rather than sub-Saharan.

I used all my weight to push the knife in to the hilt and stirred it to cause maximum damage. Him or me – and it was him.

Blood soaked my hand as his eyes rolled and shut. A rattle escaped his throat.

Five metres to my left I saw Ryan's arm bring a blade down multiple times like a scene out of *Pyscho*. This was fucking mad.

A prickle on my neck caused me to look along a fallen tree to my right. Another wild-eyed face, this time belonging to a man whose posture confused me. It took a moment to compute what I was seeing – a man with his arse pointed over a natural seat, desperately trying to pull up his trousers.

I ran at him with the blood smeared knife gripped in my right hand, AK-47 banging across my chest on the sling. He lifted his hands away from his trousers and held them up to ward me off. I spotted a rifle laid on the ground as I reached him and thrust downwards at his neck with everything I had.

The blade planted into the soft skin and sank deep towards the vital organs. My momentum knocked him off his perch and we fell together over the tree. I lost my grip on the knife and rolled to one side, bringing my head up quickly to get a visual of my quarry. He lay with his hands clutching the knife sticking out of his neck, an obscene two-tone gurgle accompanying each dying breath.

Ryan stood next to me, panting, and reviewed my two victims.

'Good drills, Royal. Two for the price of one. Not sure that stabbing a gadgie going for a shit is a fair fight, mind you.'

I crawled on my knees to the dying man and ripped the knife across his throat and out the other side. I didn't ponder on the resulting carnage other than to satisfy myself he was dead.

'That'll do it,' said Ryan, wincing at my grisly handiwork.

I looked at my hands, slick with bright red blood, and at the dark splatters coating Ryan's hands and shirt.

'Needs must, mate. Let's grab their weapons and ammo and get to the RV.'

I caught glimpses through the trees of the static white aircraft as we jogged down the shallower base of the hill.

The time was 07:01 when we reached the RV after a cautious final approach. Mike and Jamie regarded us with concern.

'Whoa, are you injured?' asked Jamie.

I shook my head.

'You okay?' asked Mike.

'Yeah. Ran into three hostiles. They're down, weapons are ditched, and we've picked up five full mags.'

'How about you?' Mike asked Ryan.

'Aye, we neutralised them without compromising everything. What more is there to say?'

He handed Mike and Jamie a full, thirty-round AK mag each from our new stash.

Mike's eyes lingered on Ryan's blood-stained hands and he nodded slowly. I guessed what he was thinking, but now wasn't the time to worry about any psychological impact from our brutal encounter.

'We're good,' I said, wiping my hands on my cargo trousers before pulling out the map. 'Let's get a cunning plan together.'

It took three minutes to agree our next move: advance through the jungle parallel to the airstrip for 200 metres to a final RV; slip forward to the edge of the treeline with eyes on the plane; if and when the prisoners entered the stage, hope that Roper conjured up a military display that showcased UK Special Forces in all their swashbuckling glory; alternatively, cuff an improvised rescue if the odds of success were better than fifty-fifty.

A chunk of Jamie's chocolate and an electrolyte drink lifted my sagging energy levels. It would have taken something a lot stronger to assuage the throbbing pains radiating from all parts of my bruised and stiffening body.

I looked at my ripped and filthy shirt and trousers and wiggled the toes inside my muddy boots. Could be worse. I'd got away without serious injury. The primary cost had been my jungle hat, lost in the flailing bedlam on the hill. The blood from the cuts on my hands and face had dried and I scraped a congealing blob from my cheek. Just my luck if I survived all this unscathed and caught some howling blood-borne lurgy instead.

The only obstacle between our current position and the final RV was the track leading north. We crossed it one at a time with the rest of the team providing cover. Safely across, we pushed on until the GPS indicated we'd reached the selected grid reference. I drew the others in until we knelt back-to-back in all round defence.

'Charlie, this is Alpha, complete at FRV, preparing to move forward. Any news on the Blades or Shakies? over.'

'Sierra Charlie, waiting on an update. Situation on target is three tangos and two aircrew in the vicinity of the Cash, three vehicles with unknown pax, and one Hilux offloading cargo to the hangar. Roger so far, over.'

'Roger so far, over.'

'Another group of twelve tangos is inside the hangar. Believe one or more high value targets amongst them, over.'

High Value Targets. What the fuck did that mean? I didn't know the spooks had any specific targets identified yet. Not unless…fucking hell. General Sylla – Mamba? A flush of adrenaline sluiced away my fatigue.

'Roger. Will advise when in position, out.'

I hadn't understood every reference and whispered a single word question over Mike's shoulder, 'Cash?'

'It's an Antonov An-28. One of the few planes a bush pilot could land in that space.'

Jamie leant back and twisted his head. 'Blades or Shakies? Are you Brits even speaking English?'

I snorted. 'SF. Hereford and Poole. I don't care which, but we're going to be seriously outnumbered if that convoy rolls down here.'

The radio crackled to life in my ear as if prompted.

'*Alpha this is Charlie, be advised there are vehicles moving south from Crystal One Alpha, over.*'

'Alpha, roger. Keep me updated. Moving, out.'

I shuffled around. 'Right gents, the convoy is moving. We need to get eyes on. Single file crawl behind me. Should be twenty metres. Then we'll fan out into extended line.'

I advanced in a catwalk, crawling on my hands and knees with the slung AK in my right hand. Red ants swarmed over my other hand when I disturbed an unseen gathering under a desiccated branch. Pinpricks of fire erupted as far as my elbow. I shook and swept them off before continuing. Moving into a leopard crawl was going to be fun.

When I finally slithered to the edge of the treeline, the view and position were perfect. The 'hangar' we'd investigated was sixty metres away to my ten o'clock. Thirty metres in front, at twelve o'clock, squatted the white Antonov perched on three black wheels.

The plane was fifty feet long with five windows trailing behind the cockpit and under wings that protruded from the top of the fuselage. An engine with a motionless, five-bladed propeller hung from each wing. The tail sloped up to chunky fins on either side.

It faced right, pointing along the short airstrip towards the west. That meant the passenger door was out of sight on the other side. The cargo doors hung open from the tail, although two men were in the process of pushing them shut.

I signalled for Ryan to go firm on my right and Mike and Jamie on my left, with the former SAS Senior NCO nearest. I valued his judgement and wanted him close. Mike's calm, rational input would be a useful counterweight to mine and Ryan's risk-taking tendencies. And we couldn't afford to get this wrong.

'Charlie, this is Alpha, in position waiting on your call, over.'

'*Roger. Five-vehicle convoy approaching, over.*'

'Alpha, roger, out.'

The growl of approaching vehicles rose above the rowdy banter between the two men struggling to slam the aircraft tail doors shut. The convoy motored past within touching distance. Lying prone, we were at the wrong angle to see the passengers inside. Not that it mattered. The reappearance of the three Land Cruisers bracketed by the two pickups carrying their squads of rifle-wielding goons indicated the prisoners were being delivered for relocation. Mike looked my way and I nodded.

The convoy wheeled right and slowed as it approached the hangar, stopping in front of the cavernous entrance and blocking the view. The front passenger doors of two of the SUVs opened. The third SUV remained sealed and the goons riding the pickups stayed mounted.

'Alpha, this is Charlie. Have you got a visual on the tangos at the hangar entrance, over?'

'Negative. My line of sight is blocked.'

'Understood. See if you can ID any of the party leaving the hangar. We're too far away for close ups.'

'Will do. What's the status on that support?'

While I waited for Roper's answer, a figure wearing khakis and an untucked short-sleeve shirt ducked under the tail of the plane and wandered under the closest wing, stopping to inspect the engine and propeller.

My old mate Sergei. I would have recognised his ugly mug at this distance even without the binos. He yelled something guttural in Russian and a second, similarly dressed, muscular guy barked a garbled answer as he rounded the nose and scrutinised the landing gear under the cockpit. Peter. Hope had been right — those two motherfuckers were in this shit up to their necks.

The convoy pulled away from the hangar and made a tight right turn to loop into a position behind the plane. The lead pickup halted facing us, level with the right-hand tail fin. Nobody dismounted. By contrast, when the SUVs lined up and stopped, doors flew open and shouted orders filled the air.

While concentrating on the convoy, I'd tuned out a message from Roper.

'Say again, over.'

'*Charlie, support is not presently available. I say again, support is not available. My people are tracing the plane's tail number. We won't lose them, over.*'

'Alpha, wait out.'

I swivelled the binos left at a group of a dozen men approaching the plane from the hangar. The tall, broad uniformed figure in the centre was unmistakeable. Mamba. General Sylla was here. He was actually here and fucking with my life again.

I also recognised the face of the man next to him with South American features. A drinking buddy of the Russian pilots if I remembered right. I lowered the binos and wiped the sodden sweat rag across my face.

'Hutch and Luke,' whispered Mike.

I leaned left to try and obtain a better view around the sloping rear of the Antonov but couldn't see our men. I'd missed them while distracted by Mamba.

'You sure?'

Mike nodded. 'Definitely. Jamie concurs. He's got the best view.'

A figure was then dragged out of an SUV and hoisted into a standing position. Condé's contorted features prompted mixed emotions. Relief he was alive tempered with concern for his health. He let out an anguished cry as two men struggled to walk him to the aircraft.

'It's now or never,' I said to Mike. 'There's a lot of them, but how about you and Jamie go left, and me and Ryan go right. We'll be on them before they know what's happening. You take out that first pickup while we neutralise the pilots and grab the hostages. Then we smash the rest in a fighting withdrawal and get the fuck out. What do you think? If we've gotta go, then let's go hard.'

Mike shook his head and turned his cam cream-streaked face to me. 'Not this time, John.'

The three SUVs that had been parked by the hangar now roved into view. They pulled up less than ten metres from Jamie's position and another handful of Kalashnikov-wielding troops emerged.

'Shit.'

In my heart of hearts, I'd known this wouldn't be feasible ever since we observed the convoy configuration. It didn't stop a wave of frustration crashing through me.

Foliage rustled to my right. 'What do you reckon? They're mob-handed,' said Ryan.

'Too many,' I replied, attempting to sound upbeat. 'Tom's people will track the plane and we'll find them again. It will give the grown-ups time to sort out some fucking support.'

The Antonov's engines burst into life one at a time. We watched with impotent fury as it taxied away from the vehicles and then accelerated down the makeshift runway. After a bumpy 400 metres the aircraft rose, skimming the ground for a few seconds before climbing steadily heading southwest.

'I bet they're going to Conakry,' I said to no one in particular. 'The Russians, Mamba, the South American, all from Conakry.'

It took twenty minutes for the remaining worker ants to scamper around the hangar collecting and loading boxes before they disappeared with their surreptitious haul. Once Roper gave the all clear, we patrolled to an RV at the mobile team's unchanged position.

Each blistered step and chafed head-turn kindled irritation at the gnawing sense of failure. No matter how prudent the decision might have been, a burning knot of betrayal twisted and gouged inside.

The haunted faces of the other three reflected the same. Had we just condemned our friends to suffering and death? Or avoided a tragic, unwinnable shootout that would have caused dozens of unnecessary and pointless deaths, including theirs and ours? Perhaps both. Only time would tell.

The mobile team were relieved at our arrival. Manny's initial smile couldn't hide his unease. 'What are we going to do now?' he asked.

'Go back to Conakry as planned. We'll leave Baldé at Setka with the bodies. You need to persuade him to give us twenty-four hours before he raises the alarm with the authorities. By that time, we'll have ripped the city apart looking for those bastards. If we don't find them before Saturday, us four are staying here. The others can fly home.'

After the plane left, we'd deliberated in our hide. The bitter frustration at sitting and doing nothing as our kidnapped friends were paraded before us had unleashed a storm of sworn vengeance.

We'd start with those Russian pricks. They had no idea what was coming.

It didn't matter what Roper or anyone in London thought about our plan. These were our people, and we'd do whatever it took to get them back.

Five minutes after we'd reached the RV, Roper led his team down the slope. Bob at the rear, and a rucksack with legs in the middle. Izzy was swamped by the wide, heavy pack, but she marched with an unruffled, determined face.

Baldé protested when we left him at Setka. Protestations that weren't altogether convincing. I think he was relieved to be doing the right thing. Despite Manny's reassurance, I wasn't convinced the army man would give us the twenty-four hours I'd demanded.

When the village chief agreed to arrange transport for the following morning, he also expressed satisfaction that we were hunting those who had brought evil to their peaceful district. With the chief onside, Baldé then appeared to defer to our request for the twenty-four-hour delay. His natural respect of authority and his shock at learning of General Sylla's presence tipped the balance.

Roper kept his counsel. When we first linked up at the RV, I'd given a terse report and declared the intention to return to Conakry as planned and leave Baldé to deal with the repercussions from the ambush.

He lifted his jaw and clicked his tongue at my vow to find and interrogate the Russians but didn't attempted to dissuade me. He'd read the mood amongst the four-man patrol and the rest of the team. Our pointed efficiency and lack of small talk spoke volumes. Together, we formed a seething band of motivated, well-armed fighters and healers.

'When we reach Siguiri, we'll speak with London. Get a steer from them,' he said.

'They should be able to confirm the destination for the plane by then. It must have a flight plan filed.'

'The tail number was false.'

'What? So, they've lost them?'

He raised conciliatory hands. 'No, it'll just take a little longer.'

'Find the Russians and you find the plane.'

'John, I know you're angry, but you need to look at the positives.'

'What fucking positives? For you maybe, but not for Hutch, Luke, and Condé.'

'I mean, we now know a lot. We have enough information to formulate a reaction, to apply the right pressure.' He met my glare. 'Just don't get your hopes up about a "Who Dares Wins" rescue. Remember where we are and the politics of the situation.'

'Fuck the politics.'

Roper let out an exasperated sigh and glanced at Mike and Ryan who now stood listening, fierce faces set in concentration. Any hope of support from those two was misplaced. 'We'll see what London says.'

CHAPTER 64

1130 HOURS – THURSDAY 29TH JULY

SIGUIRI

Roper woke me with a gentle shake. Through bleary eyes, the old airport gate bounced past as we entered the hotel grounds. He and I had agreed to alternate rest on the way down from Setka. I'd been too wired when we set off, so Roper had the first slot. Once we reached decent roads, Alain made good time, spurred on by me. Forty-five minutes later, and a long way from the scene of the recent drama, I'd swapped seats with Roper and fallen into instant oblivion tucked amongst the kit.

Mike and Ryan organised a working party to refuel and load the three cars and consolidate our deceased comrades' belongings in the room Roper and I shared.

The hotel owners expressed disappointment we hadn't thrown a leaving party but welcomed the extended booking for one cabin. I masked my bubbling emotions with the lame pretence of a ham actor. Fortunately, I was aided with the perfect prop to pull it off without suspicion – hard currency.

When I joined Roper, parked in our favourite spot under the trees, he was already engaged with the Brimstone people in London.

'Pierce,' barked a familiar voice, 'Sandy Chapman.'

'Good Morning.'

'I've got Hope patched in. Unfortunate about your people but full marks on finding them and our friends with the black flags.'

'Hello, John. Yes, well done with the task.' Hope's tone was smooth rather than excited.

'Hi, thank you. Although it doesn't feel like a job well done. We're on our way to Conakry as planned. We'll be leaving straight after this call.'

'Yes, Tom has told me of your plan to find the two Russians. I'm not sure whether that's a good idea.'

'You've found the plane then?' I asked.

'No.' The word lingered on Chapman's tongue. 'However, it does match the description of the plane operated from Conakry Airport by our Russian comrades.'

'We need to find them and find where Hutch and the others have been taken. General Sylla is a nasty bastard as I know from personal experience. At least two of the guys are already wounded. They won't survive long if he's got them. They won't survive long if he gives them to jihadis either.'

'Understood,' replied Chapman. 'Unfortunately, we're operating in a grey area in a sensitive theatre. Tom has given us the bullet points, but Hope, I think it's a good idea to hear from John exactly what happened.'

'Yes. John, can you run through the details of events since the kidnapping?'

I described from memory everything that had occurred since 16:30 the previous day. Roper referred to a raft of notes to correct any omissions or inaccuracies.

I glossed over the brutality of mine and Ryan's tangle with the three-man patrol on the hillside, but I admitted it hadn't ended well for them. Both in the car and over the satellite link, there was silence as everyone digested my revelation. Roper hadn't been aware of that titbit before.

'That complicates things somewhat,' said Chapman. 'We already have to assume compromise to some degree to explain the kidnapping of your chaps, or suspicion about your presence at least. Three corpses are going to raise a red flag. Make it difficult for us to revisit the area.'

'They probably won't have been found yet,' I said. 'That gives us a window of opportunity to act. The authorities won't know about the ambush for twenty-four hours and no one will expect us to strike back in Conakry.'

Chapman snorted. 'You're not striking anywhere. Guinea's in the middle of a presidential election. If your men are in the hands of an intelligence unit, even an unsavoury one supporting the cartels and jihadists, there is no way I can allow you to start a war on the streets.'

Roper whisked the phone from its position laid between us and held it clamped to the side of his face as he stared at me, eyes wide and pleading. He'd seen the red mist descending across my face as Chapman spoke.

'Boss, John's idea to locate the Russians has merit. I recommend we run with it. If you're already assuming compromise at Crystal One Bravo, then taking action to recover the hostages doesn't impede any ongoing op over the border. Not if we act fast in hot pursuit. If we find them, we can revisit the options.'

There was a fifteen second delay before Roper laid the phone back down and returned it to speakerphone mode. I assumed Chapman had given his opinion on the idea.

'Hope, what are your thoughts?' asked Chapman's tinny voice.

'Tom's on the ground and seen the team perform. If he's happy to run with it, then I say go ahead. Realistically there's nothing we could do apart from enlist the assistance of Gough at the embassy. It would mean widening the distribution.'

I jumped back in. 'We've got good local support, ex-special forces, ex-para reg, ex-MARSOC, I'm an ex-bootneck, and Tom's ticked a couple of those boxes and now works with you guys. We can do this.'

Roper made a frantic 'cool it' gesture with both hands.

Chapman answered my appeal by ignoring it. 'Very well, Tom. As Hope's willing to let you run with this, let's see what you and Pierce's team can achieve in the next twenty-four hours. But do bear in mind that if you find the hostages, the options for recovery will be limited.'

Roper threw an open palm in my direction like a wizard casting a spell. It worked because a caustic response died on my lips.

'Thank you,' he said. 'I'll report again before we reach Conakry.'

'You haven't finished your report, John,' said Hope. 'We reached as far as the tangle with the men on the hill.'

Tactfully put.

I described our move into position close to the plane and the appearance of the Russian pilots and then General Sylla and his entourage.

'Did you get any photographs?' asked Chapman.

'No. We didn't have any cameras. Tom would have taken plenty from the OP.'

I wanted to add more into the static. Make sure everyone understood we hadn't fucked up down in the valley. Happy snaps hadn't been in our itinerary.

'You should have received some already. I'll get the rest to you as soon as I can,' said Roper.

'Did you recognise any of the others with the general?' asked Hope.

Roper pointed at me to answer.

'I've seen one of the South Americans before. In Conakry, with the Russians. I didn't recognise any of the soldiers. Nor the Arabs or North Africans, whoever they are.'

'Okay, we'll get our people working on the images and see if they can be improved for facial recognition. From what you've described, it does sound like this could be a link on the drug smuggling routes north across the Sahel. Protection and security provided by rogue elements of the Guinea military who pass it off to al-Qaeda or a spin off. Good work.'

'I just want to get our friends back,' I said. 'If we find them, can you promise me that all options will be explored to get them back?'

'Find them first, Pierce, then we'll talk options,' answered Chapman. 'That's all, and I wish you good luck with your search.'

With the call ended on an agreement that Hope would manage communications with Cal at Pinnacle, I rested my head back against the seat. 'Thanks, Tom.'

'I'm not the enemy here,' he said. 'I want the lads back as much as you do.'

From a team of sixteen in five cars, we had now morphed into a bedraggled nine squashed into the remaining three Land Cruisers along with all our kit and equipment and Luke's endless bags of samples.

Everyone grabbed the opportunity to take quick, cold showers and change into fresh clothes. Removing my cam cream revealed angry cuts and abrasions sprinkled across the frazzled image in the mirror. I scrubbed at my hands, neck, and face anyway. The grime and dead men's blood soon replaced with a fresh red flow in numerous stinging spots.

Refreshed and splashed with mild antiseptic, I focused on the next objective rather than the recent calamity – driving more than 600 kilometres to Conakry over shitty roads and through numerous checkpoints. All the time knowing that Mamba had returned and might be orchestrating dark elements of the state machine against us.

He knew I was here; I was sure of it. And if he didn't know yet, he soon would.

Unwelcome memories surfaced of my own treatment at his hands. The rage this generated needed to be controlled and channelled.

Due to the loss of drivers, the vehicle configurations needed to be changed. Sierra One remained me, Alain, and Roper; Bravo One now comprised Ryan, Jamie, and Bob; and Sierra Two Mike, Manny, and Izzy.

Driving would be a team effort. It was vital that everyone caught up on rest. Alain, Manny, and Bob all insisted they felt strong and fresh. Their last twenty-four hours had been stressful but not overly taxing. Shortly after midday we rolled through the gate one last time and hit the road for Conakry.

None of the checkpoints demonstrated any hint of unusual suspicion, no signs we might be on any watch list. The regular, bristly interactions were almost comforting. Our paperwork no longer matched our revised manifest, but the explanation of two vehicles staying behind in Siguiri passed muster.

The weapons stayed hidden, yet close at hand. Our self-imposed rules of engagement were to adopt firearms only if we identified a threat to life. A tricky concept when passing through checkpoints, as I knew only too well from my ill-fated skirmish two years before.

As we approached each one, the other two cars dropped back to allow us to gauge the reception. Anyone sleeping was roused and hands lingered close to rifles stowed in car bags or slotted under car seats. Our bountiful supply of official ID card holders had been slashed to one – Alain with his police ID.

His open-minded view of involving the authorities was a welcome contrast to Baldé's natural desire to follow procedure and report to superiors. I didn't forget that Alain's good friend Samuel had been slain the previous day. His motivations for justice and retribution aligned with ours.

A thought plagued me during my stint at the wheel of Sierra One: we couldn't risk returning to the Novotel. We had to assume that our longstanding plan to return to Conakry today had been compromised. If Mamba knew of our imminent arrival in the capital, what would stop him from arranging surveillance, arrest, or even straight kidnap? His dark tendrils would reach into every hotel and lodging. I wrestled to conjure an alternative.

While we stretched our legs in Mamou, I sounded out the others. Roper agreed we needed a safe house.

Manny offered a solution. 'I can arrange somewhere. It's seven-thirty now and we have three hours to Conakry. Enough time.'

When he pulled out his cell phone, I gestured to put it away.

'Here, use this.' I handed him the satellite phone. 'If Mamba's involved, then we have to assume he has access to the phone network. In fact, everyone needs to make sure their mobiles are switched off.'

That prompted two minutes of frantic searching and scrolling once everyone understood the reason. Things had moved fast, but we should have considered that before.

Ten minutes later, after a round of demonstrative phone conversations, Manny handed the sat phone back. 'It's sorted.'

'Well done, mate. A friend's place?'

'Not exactly.'

His cautious smile made me twitchy about what might come next.

'I've arranged for us to stay at the Vatican Embassy. It's still empty.'

Not the answer I expected.

'Where's that? An embassy?' asked Roper, stepping closer.

'It's a former embassy,' I said. 'A good place. Strong contender for an HQ when we set up.' I paused at the unlikeliness of that scenario given recent events. 'Provided it has power and water, then it would make a good refuge.'

'It's all working,' said Manny.

'Can you trust the owner?' I asked. 'Did you tell him who wanted it? Did you mention me or Pinnacle?'

Manny lanced me with an "I'm not a fucking idiot" look. 'Don't worry, I didn't speak to him directly and he doesn't know it's us or Pinnacle. I arranged it through Fauzi, the lawyer.'

'Fozzie?' My mouth curled into a reluctant smile.

'Yep.'

We all breathed easier after navigating the large checkpoint on the approaches to Conakry without any issues. Alain's answers about the vehicle's bulging cargo satisfied the inquisitive commander. He probably wanted to spend an hour unloading and rooting through all our crap about as much as we did.

A determined air gripped the car when we made it through unmolested and closed on the outskirts of the city.

PART IV

DON'T PLAY DEAD WITH VULTURES

CHAPTER 65

2220 HOURS – THURSDAY 29TH JULY

CONAKRY

Manny led the way in Bravo One as our three mud-spattered Land Cruisers stole through the deserted streets in the desirable part of Dixinn. The gates to the old Vatican embassy opened as we arrived, and Manny guided us into the interior of the large compound. The value in his arranging this bolthole couldn't be overestimated.

One other vehicle stood in the dark courtyard. A top of the range Land Cruiser that looked out of place next to our field-worn vehicles. The passenger door opened and Fozzie stepped onto the weed-strewn tarmac. I spotted the moonlit glint from his highly polished shoes before they disappeared under the shin-high carpet as he approached.

'Mister Pierce,' he said, 'in trouble again, I assume.'

'As always. Thank you for arranging this.'

He flicked a dismissive hand. 'Is there something I can do for you…' he looked around at the others, 'and your colleagues? In a legal sense, that is. Better to address a problem before the state brings its weight to bear.'

'Let me introduce you and we can consider the legal side.'

After the introductions, Fozzie, Roper, and I stepped over to the lawyer's car while the rest of the team unloaded the vehicles and explored our new digs. Fozzie sank into the leather passenger seat while Roper and I stood by the open door. His driver, not long returned from gate opening duties, hopped out from behind the wheel and made himself scarce.

Fozzie must have noticed me studying the retreating figure with suspicion. 'Pascal can be trusted. He's been with me a long time and is no friend of the regime.'

'Good. We have a situation, and I don't know whether anyone in authority here is involved. Apart from my old friend General Sylla, that is. He's right in the thick of it.'

Fozzie remained unfazed. He craned his head and made no attempt to disguise his interest in the damage to my face. 'And have there already been clashes?'

'No, but there might be soon.'

His eyebrows lifted at my answer. If he saw through the lie, he didn't call me on it. 'I would strongly counsel against that. The law is strong here. Your position will only be weakened by the perpetration of any violence.'

Roper shot me a warning glance and I chose my next words carefully.

'We don't even know yet if our problem is here in Conakry. Can you help identify a plane and its flight records, and then locate the pilots? Two Russian pilots. Either an office or home address.'

'Russians? You should be careful. There is a heavy Russian influence in Guinea. Mining companies, investments, government links.'

'I understand. These enquiries need to be low key. Well under the radar until we have the full picture. You'll need to be careful yourself.'

The lawyer brushed at a mosquito on his forehead. 'Can I ask the nature of your interest?'

'That's confidential,' said Roper.

After frowning at Roper and studying him for two or three seconds, Fozzie looked down to adjust the cuffs of his suit and then fended off another errant mozzie. 'Very well, I'll see what I can do.'

'Thank you. I need to ask another favour.'

Consternation erupted across the lawyer's face.

'A paid favour, of course. That's just an English expression.'

His taught features softened.

'Can you remain on standby, just in case? I'll need a number where I can reach you, day or night.' I glanced at Roper. 'On a retainer, obviously.'

Once Fozzie had left, we gathered in a large room on the ground floor in the main building. The air conditioners made a racket but all bar one worked. We kept the lights off and sat amidst our gear around a single tilly lamp in the otherwise empty tiled room.

I stood to address the group. 'Listen up.'

Conversations ceased and heads turned my way.

'The reality is that everyone has a tough choice to make. Some of us have flights booked in thirty-six hours' time, others are local and have to live with what happens next. I'm going to give it to you straight. Things could get ugly.'

'You mean uglier,' said Ryan.

'That's right. We've got friends and relatives who have been kidnapped and may face severe mistreatment and mortal danger. Because of the situation in Guinea, we've got to decide if we're going to pursue these bastards or leave it to governments and the law.'

The room was silent, all eyes fixed on me.

'I've made my decision and so have some of you. For others, Bob, Izzy, Alain, even you Manny, you need to think long and hard about staying involved. I can't guarantee this will have a happy ending for the hostages or for all of us here.'

Bob climbed to his feet 'I've told you already, I'm going to stick it to those mongrels along with you guys. I'll be here as long as you're here.' He dropped back to the floor, a muttered profanity sinking to the ground with him.

As Izzy and Alain both stood up, I waved them down again. 'I understand we're all raw and everyone wants to do their bit, but I want to give you time to think about it properly.'

I gestured at the patrol team and Roper. 'For five of us this is our job, and we have a responsibility for what's happened and to fix it. We need to act fast if we're going to act at all. That means tonight.' I reached down for a bottle of water and took a long glug. 'Me, Mike, Ryan, and Jamie are heading out to try and apprehend the two Russian pilots.'

Earlier, it had taken less than thirty seconds for me and the guys to agree that course of action.

'Where from?' asked Manny

'We'll try the club, their usual hangout.'

Manny shook his head. 'You'll need me.'

'And me,' said Alain.

They exchanged glances and smiles.

My misgivings about involving them couldn't suppress a matching grin. 'I take it you're both in, then.'

'What about the rest of us?' said Bob. 'I told you, I'm right in this with you.'

'You three,' I pointed at Bob, Izzy and Roper, 'have been driving most of the day while we rested. We don't know what tonight or tomorrow might bring. While the four of us, with a bit of help from those two, get this done tonight, I need you three to get your heads down and be fresh for the morning.'

Roper had risen to his feet and now turned to Bob and Izzy. 'These guys might have to play rough. I don't want to know the details and neither should you.'

It had taken a bit of convincing to persuade Roper he needed to remain behind. Mike's advice to his old comrade to keep out of the way had swung it.

I nodded. 'This is a stab in the dark. Maybe we'll get lucky, maybe we won't. If not, then we'll all be waiting to hear from Fozzie the lawyer and hoping he can help us.

'Bob, you need to consider what we do with Luke's samples. Preferably get them ready for someone else to submit to SGS after we've flown out. I don't want to be prancing around town tomorrow when we can't quantify the threat.'

Izzy had remained quiet until now. 'I shall be with you until my cousin returns home.'

★

Manny and Alain slipped out through the gate just before 23:00. They were right – we did need them. Both to supply lower profile vehicles for tonight's task and to get eyes inside my favourite local nightspot without attracting undue attention. They returned within forty minutes in Alain's Renault taxi and a Peugeot saloon that had seen better days.

While they waited in the cars, the patrol team huddled for a final pep talk. I kept my voice low. 'Keep in mind these two scumbags are responsible for our friends' abduction and potential torture and murder. They are the key. There's no Geneva Convention for these pricks. We do what has to be done. No judgement.'

The other three nodded. Mike leaned in and said, 'If we get the chance, we go in hard. Otherwise, people are going to get hurt. Dominate the enemy. As John said, do whatever it takes and don't let either of them get away. There's two of them. If one gets fucked up, we still have the other.'

'But let's try to keep this covert,' I added. 'Vittling up downtown Conakry is only going to warn these bastards we're here and get us all arrested or worse. Around the club will probably be too crowded and there might be military around. If so, we house them first then storm straight in. That's if they even turn up.'

Ryan and I jumped in the taxi with Alain, while Mike and Jamie joined Manny in the Peugeot. We each wore one of the six VHF handheld radios equipped with the last of the fresh batteries. For continuity and to avoid confusion, the taxi now took on the mantle of Sierra One, and Manny's banger, Sierra Two – the drivers' regular callsigns. We four passengers maintained our adopted Sierra Alpha, Bravo, Delta, and Echo monikers.

Late night Thursday saw a crowded car park outside the jungle-themed club. We settled into positions left and right of the entrance, both cars having eyes on the main door and down either side of the main building in case our targets attempted to leak out some other way.

The plan was fluid. Manny and Alain, now wearing jazzy disco rig, would head inside to search the club. Alain was armed with a concealed Makarov and carried his badge in case a doorman tried a pat down. Unarmed, Manny had donned a flat cap as a partial disguise. He needed to be careful not to bump into the Russians or get recognised by any of their drinking buddies. If spotted and approached, I advised him to brazen it out, avoid any talk of events up north, and casually withdraw.

Concern flickered on his face and he took a deep breath.

'Just don't fuck it up,' I added.

The creases turned into a grin. 'Let's go,' he said to Alain.

Neither of the guys carried a radio. The noise inside would render them useless and the earpieces would be a giveaway. Twenty minutes later, they reappeared outside the door, Manny instantly recognisable in his flat cap.

'He only needs a cup of Yorkshire tea and a whippet to complete the picture,' said Ryan from the passenger seat. We'd shifted around in case of a fastball. I now sat behind the wheel with Ryan alongside.

Our two friends sauntered over and climbed into the rear of the taxi. 'The Russians are inside,' said Manny. 'No soldiers.'

Energy spiked up from deep inside and my blood surged. 'Delta, this is Alpha, game on.'

'Delta, roger. Standing by.'

CHAPTER 66

An hour later, a steady dribble of clubbers began emerging into the muggy evening. Amongst the locals, the two white-faced, bulky Russian bears would be hard to miss.

That didn't prevent doubt creeping in. Had my decision to keep Manny and Alain outside with us backfired? Losing eyes on the targets had been a risk. A risk only eclipsed by my fear of our guys showing out.

We'd all tried to catch some zeds during the day's long drive, but the recent exertions and sleepless nights were catching up with me. I peered at my watch yet again: 1.20 a.m. The illuminated hands had hardly moved since my last check. I made a mental note to ask Jamie if he carried any pick-me-ups in his med pack.

Upon Alain's return behind the wheel, I had shifted to the front passenger seat and Ryan to the rear. Manny had rejoined Sierra Two.

People hovered in groups around the vehicles in the car park. If the Russians appeared, there was no way we could apprehend them here without broadcasting to an unwanted audience. I clenched my hands together and scanned the bobbing heads of the increasing flow of half-cut revellers. A commotion of boisterous figures turned our way, two familiar, crew-cut-topped white dudes at the centre of the aggressive banter.

'Alpha has visual on the Bears. Bear 1 and Bear 2 in a group outside the door now.'

'*Delta, seen.*'

The group weaved and swayed to three adjacent cars, forty metres past our own. The paltry light thrown from the building had been enough for me to recognise six of the seven men. A rogue's gallery.

The two Russians had been socialising with my old sartorially challenged contacts, Lambert and Sadou. Unless there were two other bat and ball-shaped clowns in town. And I'd seen the sharp features of the long-haired South American beside them less than twenty-four hours earlier with General Sylla. Next to the South American walked a smartly dressed black guy I didn't recognise. He had an arm around an attractive, young black woman, half his size and barely wearing a dress. Then another face hoved into view behind the glamorous couple. Well, well, the silent Lebanese joker, Rami, Ramzi, something like that. He also had a young female draped around him. A fragile waif who clung to him like a leech and stumbled in her high heels.

We watched them roll to the vehicles and split. The South American and the two couples climbed into one SUV, Lambert and Sadou disappeared into a tatty saloon with a faulty rear light, and our Russian targets shouted loud goodbyes before getting into their own Land Cruiser.

'The Bears are in a dark Land Cruiser. We'll lead the follow.'

'Roger.'

Compared to their buddies, Sergei and Peter hadn't appeared too incapacitated. It didn't mean they hadn't consumed a skinful; all the Russians I'd ever met could handle their drink. As if to prove my theory, Sergei – Bear 1 for our purposes – narrowly avoided clipping a car when he reversed. The brakes flashed repeatedly as they jolted their way to the main road.

In common with most drunk drivers, Sergei drove slower than the other light traffic and signalled early for every manoeuvre. I could almost sense the concentration as he led us in the direction of the airport. Alain hung back and didn't need any guidance during the easy follow.

'Which one are we going to take?' asked Ryan. 'Bear 2 is a big lad.'

'We'll take him then. I know how much you like a challenge.'

We turned south off the main N1 highway into an area I didn't know. Within a few hundred metres, the normal city dwellings had been replaced by a higher standard of abode.

'The airport is on our left. Very close,' said Alain.

The roads widened, as did the frontages of the properties. Soon, walls hid the buildings beyond.

'Nice area,' I said.

'The sea is just there,' replied Alain, pointing to the right.

Our target's brake lights flashed in plenty of time before each turn as we drove deeper into the coastal neighbourhood. The empty streets were silent, and I urged Alain to pull even further back.

At my instruction, Manny cruised past and took over. I was taking no chances. If we'd already attracted a second glance, his yellowy Peugeot headlights provided a different signature.

A single turn later, Mike's clear voice announced the Bears were home. *'Bears are stop, stop, stop at a gate on the right, thirty metres past a parked BMW. Continuing forward. Will circle around.'*

'Stop here, lights off,' I ordered Alain, who pulled up sharply behind a small Renault van parked on the right. Then I clicked the pressel switch. 'Roger. Debussing.'

I turned to Ryan. 'Down ramp, out troops.'

He rolled his eyes.

Alain stayed with the taxi as Ryan and I crept forward in the shadows cast by the trees and walls lining the road. Sixty metres ahead, half of an SUV slipped out of sight into a property on the right. A parked BMW halfway between indicated we were on target.

Two hundred metres beyond that, a pair of headlights swung in our direction before being extinguished. The ghostly vehicle approached and stopped fifty metres the other side of the gate.

'Go firm there, Delta. We'll check the gate.'

'Roger.'

Ryan and I used the cover from trees and street furniture to remain shrouded from the moonlight until reaching the gate. There were no obvious cameras, which wasn't a surprise in this low-tech culture. The gate had metal spikes that precluded an easy climb over the top.

'Let's go back to that side wall,' said Ryan.

The perimeter wall jutted out ten feet further than the wall of the adjacent property, creating a pitch-black alcove that Ryan had pointed out when we slunk past.

'Okay Delta, move past the gate and on me.'

'On the way.'

Mike and Jamie strode down the far side of the road rather than pass directly in front of the gate. I waved them across when they reached level with us and we all crouched in the dark recess.

I gestured the guys closer. 'We've got no idea of the layout or who's inside. Maximum aggression. Let's subdue everyone first and work the rest out later. We'll take Bear Two, you take Bear One. If there's anyone else, then improvise. For reference, the Sierra One taxi is parked forty metres down there, behind the van.'

All of us had either jackets or shirts stretched over our slung, folded AKs tucked into the body. I pulled the zip of my jacket down to midway and tested I could reach in and grab the pistol grip of the shortened weapon and deploy it without hindrance. It wasn't ideal, but it would have to do.

'If there's lights or sensors or alarms, then hit them hard however we can. One shot at this, that's all we've got.'

We bumped fists and pulled apart.

Ryan linked his hands by his waist, his back against the wall. 'You first. See you on the flip side.'

With a leg up from Ryan, I rolled across the top of the wall and dropped onto hard ground the other side. The zinc oxide tape applied to hot spots on my toes and heels didn't prevent bolts of pain in both feet during the awkward landing.

I yanked the AK-47 out from its uncomfortable berth inside my jacket and stole forward to a scrawny pair of bushes. A thump behind me signalled Ryan's arrival. He joined me in the minimalist cover.

A metal on concrete scraping sound upped the anxiety levels. On the top of the wall, Mike dragged Jamie over and deposited him on our side before dropping down and joining us with a raised, apologetic hand.

We'd landed in a small, dark courtyard surrounded by neglected outbuildings. A pungent aroma of garbage and worse wafted on the breeze. I led the team through a murky opening concealed under the veil of a large, bushy-topped tree. From the tree's protective shadows, the front of the large two-storey house was visible.

Three lights threw a weak glow outside the main door and across the driveway to the right where a dark SUV stood. The left side of the house remained in darkness. Light shone behind curtains in a downstairs room and a room on the top floor.

'Round the back,' I whispered to Ryan, who passed the message down the line.

We maintained a ten-metre distance from the building as we crossed the driveway. To reduce the risk of activating a security light, we then crept down the side alley in slow time.

At the rear corner, I signalled a halt. Hard rock music thumped from close by.

With my face against the concrete wall, I peeked across the rear of the property and almost laughed out loud. The moonlit private shoreline wasn't a surprise; the fresh salty breeze and whisper of gentle surf had been a growing clue. No, my feral smile sprung from the sight of the two Russians enjoying the same view from their seats at a garden table. Our targets, there for the taking. A clear bottle and a couple of glasses indicated that a scheduled early morning flight was unlikely. It would be downright impossible once we'd finished with them.

I retreated and turned to the others. This close, I stuck to sign language.

Two enemies. We'll take Bear 2.

Fingers raised. Three, Two, One, Go.

I charged across the five metres to the table with Ryan at my shoulder. For a pair of drunks, the Russians reacted fast. Without a sound they both turned at my first step from the shadows.

Sergei pushed himself up from the nearest chair while I focused on Peter, who sprang up from his seat on the other side of the table. He darted towards the house before Ryan and I reached him. Behind us, the crash of glass and metal and a panicked shout were the first sounds of the engagement.

Peter made it through an open door into a low-lit sitting room before Ryan rugby-tackled him and I piled into the pair of them, leading with my piece of Russian-engineered weaponry. I bounced off the big Russian and a kick caught my shoulder. A slash of pain exploded from the clavicle smashed by Mamba two years earlier. As I fell back, Ryan's head jerked as Peter's other foot shot out and found its mark.

Our Bear rose into a stoop and flew across the room past a large widescreen television. I raised the AK up on aim and hammered the safety off.

Ryan beat me to it, shouting, 'Stop or I'll shoot.'

The Russian had reached a low table. He scooped at something and rotated towards us pointing a handgun.

Two gunshots detonated in the enclosed space. The white vest under Peter's open shirt burst with red and he dropped the handgun as he fell to the floor. Ryan stayed put as I scooted forward and grabbed the weapon, briefly registering it was a decent model: a CZ 75 or 85.

The Russian laid on his back unmoving, his white vest now largely red. Two 7.62 rounds to the upper chest didn't leave much room for doubt – one of our targets was now dead. I turned to the motionless Ryan, still poised in a fire position. 'Fuck.'

As I felt for an unlikely pulse at Peter's neck, Mike shouted, 'John, sitrep.'

Ryan answered before I could. 'Bear Two is down. We're ok.'

Mike and Jamie appeared in the doorway dragging a figure between them.

'What happened to fucking covert?' asked Mike.

I looked at the CZ. 'He went for a weapon. It's done now. How's your man?'

'He'll have a sore head in the morning.'

'So will I,' added Jamie. 'Son of a bitch.'

'Bring him here,' I ordered. 'By the sofa.'

They bundled Sergei onto the floor next to his dead friend. The groggy Russian rolled on to his side with his zip-tied hands in front of him, inches from the body. An agonised yell escaped his lips as he realised what lay beside him.

Mike dropped to the ground and wrapped his arm around the prisoner's throat. 'Shout again and I'll cut your fucking balls off.' He kept the choke hold in place to reinforce his point.

I stood up and placed my feet either side of Peter's corpse. 'Listen to me.'

Sergei's head rocked sideways and back as he sought to evade Mike's grip with reverse headbutts. After ten energetic seconds he calmed down and sucked in rasping breaths. Mike had given him an opening to comply.

'Listen to me,' I said again. 'Tell me where you took the three prisoners today. We're not fucking around.'

I swung the rifle behind my back and swapped the CZ into my right hand.

He panted and focused his murderous glare on the weapon pointed at him and then looked into my eyes. 'You haven't got the balls, Englishman.'

I pointed at the coffee table. 'Lift him up. Put his hands out on the table.'

He tried to resist as Mike and Jamie hauled him around Peter's still form. Jamie cracked two punches into the side of his head, both connecting with solid thwacks.

'I'll fucking kill you for this,' he croaked. 'You don't know who you're fucking with.'

I tucked the CZ inside my rear waistband and pulled out my knife. 'Hold his arms down.'

Fear engulfed the Russian's face as his arms were locked against the tabletop and I brought the knife down, spearing through his right palm and into the table. His piercing howl was to be expected.

I leaned over him. 'Listen to me, you prick. Answering my questions is your only chance to live. Did you bring the prisoners to Conakry?'

Through scrunched eyes and pain-wracked moans, he muttered, 'What prisoners?'

'Wrong answer, Ivan.' I wrenched the skewered knife, pulling the blade and its fleshy attachment out of the wood with a vicious twist. When I hammered it back into the table, he slumped forward and appeared to pass out.

'Jesus,' said someone behind me.

'No judgement, remember,' I snarled over my shoulder.

I grabbed Sergei's hair and lifted his head. When his eyes opened, they focused on me with a glassy confusion.

'You brought them here, to Conakry?'

'Water, please.'

I shook him by his hair. 'Did you fly them here? We saw you take off in Siguiri.'

He sagged. 'Da. Yes, we flew them here.'

'Good boy. Where are they now?'

'I don't know.'

'Not good enough.'

I don't know,' he said, louder this time.

'Mike will turn you into a eunuch if you don't answer. Where. Are. They. Now?'

'I don't know. Somewhere by the docks. A warehouse.'

'Conakry docks? Which warehouse?'

'A warehouse. I don't have the address.'

'But you've been there?'

'Yes.'

'Right, you're going to take us there now.' When I tore the knife out of the table and his hand, a groan gargled in his throat. He panted like a dog as blood pissed out of the ugly wound.

'What are we going to do with him?' asked Mike, pointing at the blood-soaked body next to the hunched Sergei.

I regarded the two airmen and took a moment. This was now

officially fucked up. Christ only knew if the police had been called at the sound of shots or the neighbours were on their way round to check things were okay.

'Take a look outside. There must be somewhere we can put him. Jamie, see to that hand. I need to call the drivers.'

When I radioed the drivers to come in through the main gate, I didn't explain the unfolding situation. Alain watched impassively as Jamie and Ryan assisted the cuffed Sergei into the rear of the taxi.

The Russian's facial injuries weren't much worse than mine, so he fitted right in. Red stains had already seeped through the bandage around his right hand. One of Peter's socks had been stuffed in his mouth and was held in place by another bandage wrapped around his lower jaw and neck.

Manny wasn't so sanguine. 'What happened? Where's the other one?'

Without taking my eyes from our prisoner, I replied, 'Dead. You must have heard the shots.'

Manny ran a hand across his scalp. 'I heard two bangs.' He shook his head and pointed at the taxi. 'What are you going to do with him?'

The second time I'd heard that question in the last two minutes. 'I have no idea, mate.' I met his worried gaze. 'But we know where our guys were taken. A warehouse near the docks. We're going to drive straight there, recce the place, improvise a plan, and get them out.'

'Which warehouse?'

'I don't know exactly. Close to a roundabout by the north end of the port. That's why we've got laughing boy with us. He knows the location.'

While still inside, we had discussed moving the dead weight of Peter's bulky corpse. After a test lift revealed what a drama that would entail, we decided the expedient option was to get out of there before anyone showed up to investigate the ruckus.

We cleaned everything that had been touched, acquired another CZ pistol and a wad of US dollars from a drawer identified by our compliant prisoner, and left the big lad where he'd fallen.

There was nothing to tie us to the dead Russian, apart from his mate sat in the taxi next to Ryan. And Ryan's recently fired AK.

CHAPTER 67

Ryan had to give our extra passenger one or two encouraging slaps as we drove through the empty streets. With the windows sealed, all the Russian achieved with his groaning and shouting through Peter's sweaty sock was to piss the rest of us off.

By 03:15 we were parked up with the lights off in a litter strewn side street between two industrial units. Following fifteen minutes of welcome quiet, Sergei had become animated as we'd approached a downtown roundabout at the end of Corniche Nord, close to the port. I'd ordered Alain to pull over.

As Ryan prepared to administer another persuader, I asked the agitated prisoner, 'Are we close?'

He nodded furiously.

I pulled out my knife and held it up. 'We're going to remove the gag. Don't make me hurt you again.'

His head now shook with equal ferocity. Ryan's slid me an approving glance as he leaned over to remove the gag. Unfortunately for Sergei, we were playing bad cop, worse cop.

'Whatever he does to you, I'll do worse,' Ryan whispered as he untied the bandage around the Russian's mouth.

'Which one is it? I asked once the sock had been extracted.

Sergei coughed and retched. 'You passed the turn a hundred metres back. Other side of the road.' His bloodshot eyes found mine. 'You don't need to kill me. I won't talk.'

I ignored the statement. 'How far down to the warehouse after the turn?'

'Fifty metres on the right side. The second warehouse. Can I have water.'

'In a minute. I assume there are armed guards?'

'Yes. I don't know how many. This isn't my business. I am a pilot. I fly.'

'You fly whatever shit these evil fuckers are trafficking. It's your business alright.'

Ryan held up a half full bottle of water with an unspoken question.

'Yeah, give it to him.' I looked at the Russian's tied, red-stained hands. 'Pour it in his mouth.'

We circled the roundabout with Manny holding fifty metres behind and cruised up to the turn described by Sergei. He bobbed his head as we reached it, now on our left.

I spotted a cosy parking area in front of the next group of buildings and signalled it to Alain. 'In there.'

As Alain switched off the lights, Manny rolled the Peugeot to a halt beside us and did the same. Ryan had already reinserted the sock following a brief, one-sided struggle.

I stepped out of the car and leaned in before shutting the door. 'You two stay here and babysit.'

I dropped into the back seat of the adjacent Peugeot. 'It's down that last turning. The second warehouse. Fifty yards or so. I'll point it out and then me and Manny will scout the front. You two take the back. We're expecting armed guards. Don't know how many. It's nearly half three now. Aim to meet back here at zero four hundred. Happy?'

'Let's do it, said Mike.

I had a thought. 'If either pair gets compromised and it goes noisy, then improvise. We'll just have to make it up as we go along. Find the hostages and get them out. Do whatever it takes.'

'Is there any other way in this town?' Mike scoffed.

The folded AK was again zipped into my jacket. This time I also had the CZ and two sixteen round magazines. The 9mm pistol was cocked with the safety catch applied. Mike had acquired the same configuration from our earlier haul, which he carried along with his AKMS. Manny had a Makarov, and Jamie an AK and a daysack full of med kit.

I had a fixed-blade knife and so did Mike. Jamie would have a blade, although more likely designed to aid his medical role. *Carry a knife, save a life* as the saying went.

On our approach to the target, distant clanking and shouting drifted through the otherwise quiet morning. 'Fishing boats,' said Manny. 'Some of the larger ones are berthed not far behind these buildings.'

Cloaked in darkness in the rough ground opposite the nearest warehouse, Mike and I conferred and agreed which building was the target – a basic but crucial detail.

Two bright fluorescent lamps perched on the lip of the roof lit up the thirty-metre width of the facility: a regular-sized door on the right, presumably leading to offices, and a wide, floor-to-roof roller shutter on the left. Compared to the single, feeble light hung outside the larger warehouse next door, it screamed 'high security'. Due to the glare, it was impossible to see if there were any cameras mounted.

'See you back at the cars by four,' I said to Mike, who held something in his hand. 'What's that?'

'Balaclava. We'll put them on once we've circled round to the back. Might take us ten minutes or more.'

'Good idea,' I said, watching the pair of them dissolve into the shadows. I looked at Manny and we both shrugged our shoulders at the same time. 'You could bung your flat cap on.'

We remained static and observed the surroundings while Mike and Jamie moved into position. Apart from a small shack by the road, the two warehouses were the only complete structures in view. Behind us sat a crumbling ruin long past its glory days. There might have been more buildings away to the left where the access road led, but the glare of the fluorescent lights rendered anything beyond a mystery.

The industrious early morning fishermen continued to puncture the calm of the breathless night as they prepared their vessels to sail. In this commercial corner of the city, their rowdy routine disturbed no-one other than nightwatchmen, late workers, and delinquents stalking through the witching hour with virulent purpose, like us.

'Delta in position, eyes on open door. Four tangos, three with longs, over.'

'Alpha, roger. Go firm. We'll check the front door.'

A locksmith friend once told me that almost half his callouts were resolved when he discovered the doors in question were unlocked. He wasn't complaining because he still got paid irrespective of the anguished gripes from the clients. With that in mind, before we dreamed up ingenious options to storm this place, I wanted to make sure they hadn't left the front door open.

Manny and I approached along the front of the adjacent warehouse, hugging close to its exterior wall. I squinted with my disrupted night vision to identify any motion activated security measures or cameras. We'd spotted nothing of concern by the time we crouched either side of the entrance door.

Up close, I doubted the chances of gaining easy entry. A numeric keypad above the handle suggested the presence of a deadlock. I gripped the handle and gave it a go anyway – locked as expected. Pushing the top and bottom of the door revealed no give. That ruled out kicking it down.

I crept further along to the roller shutter. Giving that a hefty yank would achieve the same as ringing a doorbell, but I gave it a cursory check in case a gap at the bottom might provide a glimpse inside. An optimistic thought that was soon quashed.

We retraced our steps and reached the cars at 03:55. Mike and Jamie had remained firm until we'd got clear and the two balaclava-clad ninjas appeared three minutes later. Sergei was silent, eyes closed in the back of the taxi. His facial injuries looked more pronounced than when we'd left.

'He is still alive? I asked Ryan.

'Oh yeah.'

I gathered the kneeling team by the side of the taxi, screened from the road and anyone who might turn into our little nook.

Mike described the walled rear of the compound: an open space shared with its neighbour, which they'd accessed by breaking through a padlocked gate. A locked brick building against the external wall didn't appear to be in use during the night. The yard was empty apart from the occasional appearance of armed guards taking a cigarette break.

They'd identified four men in total. Three carrying Kalashnikovs and one with no obvious weapon. However, Mike couldn't be sure it was always the same three men with the rifles. 'There could be more,' he said. 'I can't be a hundred per cent on the total.'

Regular noise from the fishing fleet still drifted over. I pointed into the air after a loud clang. 'This will give us some cover if it goes noisy. Thoughts?'

'We need the whole team,' said Mike. 'How about a distraction at the front while we make entry with four men at the rear door. Get inside, overpower and neutralise the guards, grab the hostages and go.'

'Simple. I like it,' said Ryan. 'What are we going to do with my new mate though?'

I had an idea about that. 'How about me and you take him to the front door and ring the bell?'

Ryan laughed.

'I'm serious. If there's a spy hole, then they should see a face they recognise. They might even open up. At the very least it will cause confusion while Mike's team assault through the back.'

Mike nodded. 'Yeah. That'll work. Give me the nod when you knock on the door and we'll pile in. Jamie with Alain, me with Manny. Gives us a French speaker in each pair. You've got Ryan if you manage to get in the front.'

He looked into the open rear door of the taxi at the motionless Sergei. 'You'll need to be careful with him. It's not ideal, but I don't think we'll do better.'

I opened my arms. 'Everyone happy with that?'

There were no dissenting voices.

'Once we've grabbed the hostages, we get them straight in the cars and hightail it to the Vatican. The Russian will have to come with us for now. That means there'll only be room for one more, so we'll take Luke. Better to have the fittest guy in case Ivan there kicks off. You take Condé and Hutch. If they can't walk, then the cars will have to roll around there.'

I pointed at Alain and Manny. 'Get ready for that you two and listen in to the net. Once the prisoners are secure, you might need to race back here and bring the cars to the front. Otherwise, we walk them here through the dark, from the back.'

Mike paused as he considered my plan. 'If Luke's still walking, then I suggest you take off. Condé didn't look so good, so we'll follow when we're ready. Less suspicious alone, anyway.'

I checked my watch – 04:15. 'Let's get some water on board, square ourselves away, and move out at four twenty-five. Hit the place as soon as we're all in position. Last thing we need is anyone else turning up and throwing a spanner in the works.'

CHAPTER 68

Moving into position along the front of the adjacent warehouse proved a drama. Sergei was not happy. Whether or not he'd overheard us discussing the plan, he bucked and twisted when he realised our destination.

Ryan swore and punched the Russian with a left hook. I turned and smashed the CZ onto his bound hands, and he fell against the shutter causing a horrendous metallic racket. When no one arrived to investigate, I leaned over him. 'Do that again and I'll fucking kill you. You understand?'

Ryan kicked him hard in the solar plexus. 'Wanker.'

The Russian convulsed and gagged. It made the sock filling his open mouth look like an alien parasite consuming its host.

'Now get the fuck up and keep quiet,' I hissed.

The three of us lurched forward, hampered by the staggering Russian. We slipped into a recess between the two warehouses and behind a pair of stinking dumpsters. I issued a final warning to Sergei. 'Your only chance of getting out of this alive is to do what you're told.'

A vehicle engine breached the silence that followed. Lights flashed across the dumpsters when an SUV drove past and swung to a halt in front of the target building. Footsteps and French voices came within ten feet of us as they walked to the door. I pushed the barrel of the CZ under Sergei's chin as Ryan gripped his upper arms.

Six low beeps indicated the newcomers were using the keypad. A click and rattle before the clank of an opened door, a yelled greeting in

French, and the crash of a door slamming shut. Then peace returned. I wiped the sweat from my brow. 'Alpha, two or more mobile tangos arrived and entered from the front. Weapon status unknown. Ready when you are, over.'

'Delta, roger. In position. Waiting out.'

'Showtime, Ivan. We're going to knock on the door. Is there a camera or a spyhole?'

Sergei nodded.

'A camera?'

He shook his head.

'Okay, a spyhole. We're going to remove the gag. When we do, you're going to be quiet. Otherwise I'm going to terminate our beautiful friendship. Understood?'

I nodded at Ryan to remove the bulging sock. As he extracted it, he whispered, 'That's if I don't kill you first.'

Nice touch. Being an evil bastard had its addictive qualities.

With the coast clear, we crouched either side of the door. Me on the left, and Ryan on the right with his arm around Sergei's neck and his folded AK jammed under the Russian's armpit.

'Alpha, in position, stand by.'

We rose as one. 'A bell?' I asked Sergei.

'Nyet.' *No*

I glared at him. They clearly weren't set up for uninvited callers. I shifted the wedged AK inside my jacket and felt it slip back onto painful welts. CZ in my right-hand, I balled my left fist and smashed it against the door twice, then raised the pistol and pointed it at Sergei's head.

'Start shouting, in English.'

Panic gripped his face.

'Start fucking shouting.'

He got with the programme and began to yell. In amongst all the coughing and spluttering I couldn't tell what language he was using. His breath stank of stale booze and I think he'd pissed himself.

A shout came from inside the door. I crashed my fist against it again. The handle dropped and the door opened two feet.

I whispered into the mic. 'Go, go, go.'

'Que fais-tu ici?' *What are you doing here?* snapped a dark-haired man with Arabic features in the doorway. His eyes widened when he saw my pistol pointed at his face.

Ryan shoved Sergei face first into the door and the bearded receptionist fell back as we breached the building, Ryan in the lead using Sergei as a battering ram and me following right behind.

Loud pops sounded from deeper inside – Mike and his gang introducing themselves. I didn't have time to consider that low profile and covert were out of the window before I spotted a handgun on the floor next to the fallen Arab. His hand reached out for it. I thumbed off the safety and double-tapped into his centre mass. Fuck. Now I acknowledged this thing had gone noisy.

The unmistakeable rattle of a short burst from an AK rang out up ahead. I hoped that was one of ours.

We'd entered a poorly lit corridor with doors along the right side and a wide opening ahead to the left. Forty feet in front, masked figures coming in from the rear turned into the opening. Identifying friend or foe would be a nightmare. Leaving the cavernous storage space to Mike's team, I spotted a narrow stairwell on the right after the first locked door and signalled to Ryan. 'Up the stairs.'

'Alpha taking the first floor.'

Two shots barked from the main warehouse, followed by a third. The sounds echoed into the roof.

'Delta, roger. Four tangos down, no casualties. Clearing the warehouse.'

My attention had been otherwise focused, so it was only now I realised that Sergei hadn't stopped shouting. At the foot of the stairs, Ryan manhandled him onto the first step.

A shattering blast of automatic fire accompanied angry flashes from above. Rounds pinged all around us. Ryan and Sergei slid onto their arses in front of the first step. Even with the Russian lolling on top, Ryan somehow managed to get a couple of shots off.

Forgetting to insert ear pro might have been the least of my worries, but that's the thought that sprang to mind as my head danced.

'You go on,' said Ryan trying to pull himself clear from underneath Sergei. 'He's fucked.'

Both hands gripping the CZ, I aimed at the top of the stairs and wished my torch wasn't wedged into a pouch on my left hip. Bobbing my head, I could see a second flight went up to the left.

Approaching the central landing, I kept tight against the right wall and swung the barrel left. Knowing there was at least one hostile with an automatic weapon, I twitched my head to peek towards the top. A fusillade of hot lead screamed past inches from my face and punched huge gouges into the wall next to me. I wouldn't be trying that again.

I shifted to the left-hand metal bannister, flattening my body against it to ensure the gunman couldn't steal an angled shot around the corner.

Ryan arrived behind me and said, 'Time to switch weapons.'

I stuffed the CZ into my waistband behind the pouch holding the sat phone and dragged out the AK across my complaining torso. Ryan already had his stock extended. I followed suit and locked mine into place.

Another barrage cracked past and thumped into the right-hand wall of the landing. I pressed the safety down one notch. 'Fuck it. Ready.'

'Ready, mate.'

I thrust out the AK at arm's length and held the trigger down with it pointed left up the stairs. The noise and power were exhilarating. Ten rounds, twenty rounds, more. A scream from above suggested at least one had hit home.

Ryan and I both charged around the corner and up the short final flight of stairs. We dropped into kneeling positions on entering a suspended office with long windows overlooking the warehouse floor. The shattered glass heralded an imminent bumper payday for a local glazier.

A prone figure lay on the floor in-between two desks, a Kalashnikov alongside and within arm's reach. After ninety seconds of mayhem, the subsequent silence was unnerving. I checked left; Ryan checked right. 'Clear left' and 'Clear right' rang out in unison.

I scoped the rifle back onto the casualty, who was making a slow-motion attempt to reach his dropped weapon. 'Leave it,' I commanded.

He sagged and became still.

'*Delta has the area secure. No friendlies. Need support? over.*'

Fuck. No prisoners.

That meant our latest prisoner had dipped out. If he didn't know where they'd gone, the imminent interrogation would get messy.

'Roger. Top floor secure, no support required. Lock the front door and prepare to return to the vehicles.'

'*Will do, out.*'

Ryan kept his weapon trained on the fallen gunman as I applied my safety catch, swung the AK onto my back, and dug out the CZ.

Hunched over the man, I recognised him through the tangle of wild hair. Ramzi or whatever the fuck his name was. The silent Lebanese from the bar.

I pulled his right shoulder back to the floor from where he'd tried to reach across to the discarded rifle on his left. It flopped to the side and revealed three bloody stains climbing up his torso from abdomen to upper chest. Lucky shots. Not so lucky for him. His laboured, rattling breaths suggested he was going down.

I knelt close to his head and held the CZ where his staring eyes could see it.

'Where are the prisoners?'

His eyes drifted to meet mine.

'We can save you. There's a medic downstairs. Just tell me where they are.'

A slow smile crept onto his face. 'Fuck you.'

There didn't seem much point in applying pain. He must have realised he didn't have long. It didn't stop me though. I shoved the barrel into the lowest entry wound, causing him to half scream, half groan.

'Where are the fucking hostages?'

I looked across at Ryan for inspiration and noticed the big map on the wall behind him. It showed the tip of Conakry and, a few kilometres across blue water, it featured the familiar shapes of the Îles de Los. The closest island had lines connecting it to Conakry. Lines with scribbled annotations. In fact, the only markings on the six-foot-wide map were on and between Kassa Island and Conakry port.

I turned and leaned over Ramzi's ashen face. 'Kassa Island. They're on Kassa.' Memories, rage, hate – they all surged through me.

He screwed his eyes closed and the smug smile evaporated.

'Should have known,' I said more to myself than anyone else. 'Kassa Island. Well fuck you, Ramzi.' I crashed the butt of the CZ into his temple before stowing it away.

Across the room, Ryan had lowered his weapon. 'We can't leave him here alive.'

We looked at each other in silence. Footsteps bounced up the stairs.

Jamie bustled past, barging me out of the way as he knelt next to the casualty. 'You guys okay?'

'Yeah, we're good,' I replied.

Jamie pulled on a pair of disposable gloves and checked Ramzi's vital signs. 'Well this dude isn't. Scratch another bad guy. That's seven dead including the Russkie.'

'That solves a couple of problems,' said Ryan.

CHAPTER 69

It took less than fifteen minutes to drive through the deserted streets to our coastal hideout. Keeping the vehicles spaced a hundred metres apart, we encountered no checkpoints, heard no sirens, saw no convoys of police or troops rushing to contain a serious incident. The occupants of two static military trucks ignored us while they idled through the predawn city slumber.

Our arrival was hardly slick. The two vehicles stacked up outside the gate for three frustrating minutes until Roper let us in. His bed hair indicated he'd been following the instruction to get his head down. For the six of us just arrived, 5.15 a.m. after another full night awake heralded exhaustion. Drawn faces passed me as the team filed into the makeshift accommodation.

'What happened?' asked Roper.

'Let's go somewhere private.'

I called Mike to grab the lamp and join us.

In the next room we stood facing each other. Roper shivered wearing only a t-shirt paired with his cargo pants. The lamp's subdued light exposed a collection of dark stains on my hands. Another morning with other mens' blood on them.

'The good news is, we know where the guys are being held.'

Mike's head flicked up at my news. We hadn't had time for a debrief during the hurried exit from the warehouse and flight from the scene.

'Where are they?' asked Roper.

'Kassa Island. A few kilometres off the coast of Conakry. Where I was held two years back.'

Roper nodded before glancing at Mike then back to me. 'That's the good news? And the bad news?'

I took a deep breath. 'We had to kill some people to find out.'

Roper didn't interrupt, but he shook his head, stared at the floor, and winced more than once as I ran through the night's events. When I finished, he said, 'For fuck's sake, John.'

'It couldn't be helped,' Mike said to his old special forces comrade. 'Everyone did what was required. We took down two locations, suffered no casualties, and now' – he swung an open palm in my direction – 'we have the location of the hostages. A fucking good night's work.'

'That's all very well, but we're now in a world of trouble. The authorities in Siguiri are going to hear today about the incident and the deaths up there. In the next few hours that warehouse is going to be a major crime scene. You've left a dead Russian there and his partner's corpse is at another property near the airport.' Roper scrunched his eyes shut while pinching the bridge of his nose.

Put like that, things didn't sound great. I looked for the positives. 'It's not ideal, but there's no reason for them to figure we're involved. Not until tomorrow or even next week. No one knows we're in Conakry. We're by the sea. There must be a way we can get to Kassa.'

'Not ideal.' Roper shook his open hands as he spoke. 'It's a fucking disaster. As for getting to Kassa.' He shook his head as he searched for the right words.

I chopped a hand in front of his chest. 'We can't fly out of here tomorrow, that's for sure. We need to get some boats, get to Kassa after dark tonight, rescue the guys, and you need to arrange our extraction from there.'

His eyes blazed. 'You're fucking delusional.'

'Clam down, both of you,' said Mike. 'Tom, it's been a long night. Whatever happens, me, John, and the others need to get some sleep.' He fixed me with a thoughtful gaze. 'But John's got a point about the flights and the island. Let's not rule anything out.' His attention returned to Roper. 'You've got time to speak to your people in London and figure out how this thing ends.'

The door to the adjacent room opened and Ryan peered in. 'Everything okay?'

'Yeah, we're done. Just a debrief, that's all.' I left Roper and Mike and made my way into the larger room.

I swapped my radio battery for a fresh one in the charger, grabbed my bergen, and found a spot in the corner. Competing snores rang out from at least three different parts of the room. Little chance I'd be able to sleep with my mind fizzing and everything up in the air. I visited the heads and cleaned up with a quick dhobi before settling down to try.

★

A brusque shake roused me from oblivion. Roper leaned over me with his hand on my shoulder. 'John, we've got a Brimstone call with London in thirty minutes.'

I struggled with the sleeping bag to free an arm to check my watch. 'What time is it?'

'Twelve. Call is at twelve-thirty.'

Synapses fired and my brain booted up with the situation as at earlier that morning. 'Are they pissed?'

He grunted. 'The initial responses weren't complimentary. Your ears should have been burning. Things have come around though. The boss is working a plan and I think you'll like it.'

I was wide awake now. 'What plan?'

'Get yourself sorted, grab some scoff, and I'll update you before the call. Izzy and Bob have got some fusion brunch on the go in the kitchen.'

I could have done with a few more hours sleep, but after a cold shower and improvised hot food I felt more rested than I had for days. Roper and I stood in the sunshine behind one of the outbuildings and waited for the satellite call from London.

Once Roper had verified himself as Curlew, Chapman launched right in. 'Tom, are you there with Pierce?'

'Yes, we can both hear you.'

'Good. Last night went way beyond what we agreed and jeopardises the entire Brimstone operation. I expressly said you were not to bring war to the streets of Conakry.'

He let the words hang.

'That said, you did achieve the objective and we are now faced with a new situation, a dilemma. Can you hear me, Pierce?'

'Yes, I can hear you.'

'Right, well listen carefully. The delicate political situation precludes us from deploying forces into Guinea or declaring the existence of Brimstone and your presence there to any of our allies. To be clear, the embassy in Conakry knows nothing about you either. That means you're on your own.'

My mouth went dry as I tried to gauge what he would say next. Angry heat bloomed in my core.

'Well not quite on your own. Thanks to Tom and your man from Freetown, we've got a semblance of a plan. Has Tom filled you in?'

'Not exactly. He's told me you and Hope might allow a rescue attempt.'

As far as I was concerned, the people in London could allow or disallow whatever they liked. We'd try and save our friends with or without their help.

'That's correct. I understand you obtained the intelligence that the captives are on Kassa Island. A location you know well.'

'Yes, they're on Kassa.'

'And how confident are you that this information is correct. Bearing in mind you've shot up half the city looking for them already.'

'A hundred per cent.' A lie.

Lie might have been an exaggeration. I was sure that Ramzi's reaction in the warehouse and the marked map pointed to Hutch, Luke, and Condé being held on Kassa Island and facing demons I'd faced myself. Led by a true demon: Mamba.

'A hundred per cent,' I repeated.

'Well in that case, we do appear to have an opportunity. Tom tells me that you and the team are prepared to launch a rescue.'

'If we can reach Kassa.'

'I think we have a solution to that. The experience in your team, and your current location and situation, means you are best placed for any rescue effort. Your people did well last night, if a little profligate with the lives of others.'

'We achieved as much as was possible.'

'Quite,' answered Chapman.

Roper fired a warning scowl.

'In line with what Tom tells me is your own suggestion, we've been considering the options for extracting your team, with or without rescued prisoners, from your current predicament.'

'My own suggestion?' I replied, eyebrows raised towards Roper.

'To land by boat after dark this evening on Kassa Island and conduct a rescue mission.'

'Okay yeah, that's what I think we should do. We've got the manpower and the expertise to punch into the prison block, grab the prisoners, and get out again. It's what happens next that I'm not sure about.'

The noise through the speaker sounded like Chapman had expelled a deep breath. 'Your plan supposes that you can overpower the guard force and that the prisoners are being held in the exact location you suspect. For the moment, let's assume that the rescue goes ahead and is successful. Now, back to your Freetown contact, Manny I believe. Should this operation take place, he and Tom have organised boats for deployment to the island and arranged for a fishing boat, crewed by his own family, to be on station to extract you.'

I blinked at Roper in surprise. He responded with a thin smile.

'Aboard that fishing vessel, with radio communications and a little extra firepower in case of emergencies, will be Staff Sergeant David Morgan. He's Tom's man and already involved in Brimstone.'

'Yes, I know who you mean. He supplied the weapons in Mamou.'

'That's the skeleton. What do you think? It's flimsy, would give the risk management wonks at Vauxhall Cross a heart attack, and will be completely deniable from our end.'

I didn't pause to think about it. 'With the element of surprise, we can do this. We've proved our capabilities over the last week. If you can extract us, then it will work.'

Chapman's laugh rumbled through the connection. 'It's not us extracting you. These are your boats, your people. We're merely trying to help you extricate yourselves from this dire situation. Tom assures me you have the people to carry this off. He has the final say.'

'Thank you,' I said.

Roper might not have been so thankful. It sounded like the ground was being prepared to hang him out to dry if it all went to ratshit.

'Oh, and Pierce. Tom will tell you this and Hope will repeat it, but I also want to make it clear from the outset. The British government will not perform any extra diplomatic acrobatics should you and your people be arrested. Everyone involved needs to understand that. They also need to be informed that an easier option exists, namely forego the rescue mission and rendezvous with the fishing vessel for transport to Freetown.'

I answered for the whole team. 'They are our friends and family. None of us could live with ourselves if we don't at least try.'

A presumptuous statement. Doubt clutched at me as soon as if left my mouth. It wasn't my place to decide for the others or suggest they had already decided.

'Very well. I'll hand you over to Hope.'

CHAPTER 70

Hope, Roper, and I fleshed out the plan. Two motorized canoes would be delivered to the beach behind the Vatican before 1600 hours by Condé's brothers. They had begged to join the adventure without even knowing their brother had been kidnapped. Manny reckoned they were after the extra money to be earned as coxswains on top of the agreed rental fees. We already had one of their family in mortal danger, and Izzy determined to put herself into jeopardy. Any more would be too much to ask.

At 0100 hours, the team would board the boats and launch from the calmest waters alongside the sea wall on the left of the beach. The canoes would blend in with the hundreds of other twenty-metre-plus craft used by artisanal fishermen along the West African coast. Within an hour, the forty horsepower engines would sweep us to our destination – Kassa Island.

Four kilometres southwest of Conakry, Kassa Island was a thin, lumpy cay that stretched for seven kilometres north to south, with a width that varied from a narrow 300 metres near the middle, to almost 1.4 kilometres at its northern, beach club end.

The ten-nautical-mile journey would see us skirt well clear of Conakry port before turning south to hold a course 900 metres east of the Kassa Island coast. At 0200 hours, we'd slip between the rocks to land on a thirty-metre-wide sandy beach. A hundred and twenty metres of jungle separated the beach from the north-south running road connecting the nearby small settlement of Kouromandya with the centre of the island.

The landing point was 750 metres south of the prison where I'd been held and where I knew in my blood the hostages had been taken. The prison sat on the outskirts of the main island hamlet of Cité de Kassa, which sprouted from both sides of a kilometre-long stretch of the road bisecting the narrow island centre. The Brimstone-supplied images showed the small harbour with a jetty protruding 500 metres from the coastline east of the ville. A jetty I vaguely recalled from my one previous visit.

Our supporting asset, Manny's family fishing boat, would have already set sail from Freetown at 2200 hours. Davey Morgan and his hearty crew would aim to arrive eight cables or 0.8 nautical miles southeast of the Kassa jetty by 0400 hours. Quite what an army sniping instructor would think about tossing around on a Sierra Leonean fishing boat in the middle of the night was anyone's guess.

Davey would be equipped with a VHF radio programmed onto our encrypted frequency, plus a satellite phone. He'd also have a sniper rifle with him in case things turned a little fruity come the extraction. I didn't care how good a marksman he might be, I wanted to be well clear if he started winging large calibre rounds down range from a platform bobbing around in the oggin.

Having completed a close target recce and received confirmation 'Captain' Morgan and his shipmates were at the RV, a go/no go decision would be required. Nominally the call was Roper's. However, he'd be at the beach, securing things there. My judgement up at the sharp end with eyes on the prison would dictate what happened next.

If the decision was go, the assault team would enter the prison, rescue the prisoners, return to the beach, and sail off home for tea and medals. The boat would steam south for an hour to place us outside Guinea territorial waters, before turning east for Freetown.

In the event of a no go, the assault team would return to the beach and we'd sail to the RV and onward transport to Freetown. Hope listed 'no go' reasons such as 'failure to locate the prisoners', and 'unexpected and impenetrable enemy strength'. I didn't imagine either of those would prevent our infiltration of the prison.

When it came to code words, Hope proposed *Guinevere* for the go code. A King Arthur-related theme, although I immediately thought of Monty Python.

'In that case, we'll have *Black Knight* for a no go.'

Hope wanted a full range of codes for easy updates to the Brimstone operations room. I imagined everyone in London getting excited over electronic maps and impressive looking symbols for friendly assets. Not quite an accurate representation of our makeshift force in a pair of canoes and a leaky fishing boat with the callsign *Kingfisher*.

On the ground, our team would be sticking with the familiar Sierra callsigns. As far as London was concerned, we were all joined with Roper as *Curlew*. We played the game and settled on the following additional event codes:

Prisoners Secured – *Grail*, to be followed by a number to indicate
   how many
RV with *Kingfisher* complete – *Phoenix*
Emergency – *Quicksand*
Abort Mission – *Bonfire*
Switch to ERV – *Southern Cross*

The grid for the Emergency RV represented the only beach near the southern tip of the island: a fifty-metre-wide stretch of sand on the west side of the rocky southern shores, three kilometres of undulating forest south of our landing beach. An essential planning component that we all hoped would remain unused.

I raised the issue of the two Guinean nationals in the team, Izzy and Alain. If we were successful, might that earn them sanctuary in the UK or at least some sort of protection? Despite Roper's irritation at my question, Hope didn't rule the option out. She didn't rule it in either.

After the call, I summoned Mike, Ryan, Jamie, and Manny for a tactical planning session. We had the broad sketch of the mission – now we needed to fill in the blanks. My reminder they could step away at any time was met with disdain.

Ryan spoke for the group. 'Aye, take our chances with a murder rap and the local bizzies. I'll give this amphibious shite a go, even if the idea of canoeing across the sea in the dark sounds like madness.'

He turned to Manny. 'Are you sure these canoes can handle waves? That wind will be whipping them up.' He shook his head before Manny answered and muttered, 'Second thoughts, don't tell me.'

Manny assured us the canoes were perfectly safe in the shallow coastal waters. The weather bods in London reckoned we'd encounter a south-westerly 12 mph wind that should drop through the night. A gentle breeze that might not feel so gentle while we circled north of Conakry two and a half miles out to sea, and it produced a swell with waves up to four feet high. The forecast for occasional light rain was an added bonus.

'This fishing boat,' said Mike. 'It can carry twelve of us?'

Manny nodded. 'They won't be fishing. The weight isn't a problem. It'll be cramped, but only for six hours.'

Mike shrugged his shoulders. 'If the maritime stuff works, then the rest should be okay. Let's just hope we find the lads this time.'

Jamie slouched with a wide grin. 'I'm all for storming a beach. Semper Fi motherfuckers.'

Once we'd drawn up the plan for the prison recce and infiltration, I took a break to use the sat phone. It showed a missed call from Cal and a follow up message:

Our Friends have been in touch again. Ring me when you can. Shall I arrange airport pickup tomorrow?

I ignored Cal and scrolled to find Fozzie's number. There was no answer either time I rang.

Armed with a fresh coffee, I returned to the planning room. Ryan followed shortly afterwards, leading Bob, Izzy, and Alain. The whole team was assembled.

I was struck by the reduced headcount compared to when I'd given the briefing at the Novotel two weeks earlier. The next hour might see our numbers shrink further.

'While you've been snoozing, some of us have been working,' said

Bob in a combative stance. 'Luke's samples are all sorted and marked ready for collection and transport to SGS.' He turned to the two next to him and dipped his head theatrically as he addressed them. 'Thank you, Izzy and Alain.'

Bob's frustration at being kept out of the loop was understandable. I took control before anyone flashed. This wasn't the time for petty squabbles. 'Well done. That'll keep Pinnacle happy. But we haven't been lazing around. We've got a plan to rescue the prisoners and leave Guinea without risk of being apprehended.'

Bob eyed me with suspicion. 'Apprehended for what? So far, these bastards have murdered and kidnapped our people. They can't hold us for that. Take statements maybe.'

Clearly, not everyone knew what went down overnight.

'You may have heard snatches already. Last night, we had to apply deadly force against the bad guys. Eight people died. All of them connected to what happened up north.'

Izzy stared at the ground and Bob's face froze.

'Was it worth it? said the big Australian. 'Do we know where the boys are? What's this rescue plan?'

I moved everyone over to the maps on the broken, weather-beaten table Ryan had found in an outbuilding and ran through the details.

Once finished, I let the information sink in for a silent ten seconds before continuing. 'Now you know the plan and as much as I do about our situation. Remaining here is a difficult option, if not impossible.' I gestured to Izzy and Alain. 'I'm sorry about that. I know this is your home.

'However, we can deviate the timings and anyone who doesn't want to be involved can be cross-decked to the boat before we hit the island. It won't affect the rest of the plan.'

'Don't give me that bloody nonsense,' said Bob. 'You've already relegated me to a fucking beach sentry. I'm not floating out there like a brown-eyed mullet while you young'uns get all the glory.'

Quiet until now, Izzy pushed forward to stand in front of me. 'Thank you.'

'We'll put you onto the boat. There's a British man will be on board.'

'No, I don't mean thank you for the choice. I mean thank you for finding my cousin. I will be there with you.'

Guilt squirreled through my gut. This entire plan depended on the prisoners being on Kassa. What if I was wrong and they were on the mainland?

No, if Mamba still had them, they'd be in his Kassa Island lair. I could feel it.

Alain remained silent.

'I think you should go back to Siguiri,' I said to him. 'Join up with Baldé and help the investigation when it starts.' My watch showed 15:10. 'If they don't know already, they soon will. If you leave now, no one will know you had any involvement in all this.'

He regarded me for a couple of seconds. 'They killed one of my friends and kidnapped another.'

The room was silent; Alain's words a reminder of what had happened and what we were fighting for. Despite the risks, no one had backed out.

'Everyone should get some rest. It's going to be a long night. We'll assemble here fully kitted up at midnight. We grabbed two more AKs at the warehouse, so now there's enough for everyone that wants one.'

Bob cracked a toothy smile at that news. Izzy pursed her lips and shook her head when our eyes met.

When I walked outside after collecting and folding the maps, the satellite phone rang. A local number I didn't recognise. 'Hello.'

'Hello, monsieur. Don't speak, just listen.'

I recognised the voice. Fozzie – and he didn't sound happy.

'I received a visit from the military an hour ago. They want to know your whereabouts. For reasons I believe you will already be well aware. Likewise, there seems little reason for me to update you with the information you requested.'

The Russian pilots. I wondered if they'd found both bodies.

'You need to be very careful. They recall that I acted for you in the past, and they suspect I am in contact with you. My advice is to hand yourselves in for questioning about the serious incident in the north and any light you might be able to shed about a serious incident in Conakry.'

'Thank you,' I said. 'I can call you on this number in the morning?'

'Yes. On this number only. It is new and unknown to others.'

Fozzie had been vague and after the call I tried to piece together the clues. The authorities in Siguiri clearly knew about the ambush. That we'd expected. The lawyer mentioned 'a serious incident in Conakry'. A singular incident suggested the mayhem we'd left behind at the warehouse. Unless I'd misunderstood. Although an accomplished English speaker, it wasn't Fozzie's first language. Therefore, I couldn't rule out that the authorities had also found Peter's body.

Did it matter though? They were looking for us irrespective of how much they knew. I wondered which arm of the military or police – official, impartial investigating officers, or vicious, corrupt, parasites working with the cartels and al-Qaeda?

Would General Sylla be tying the pieces together? Might he even be expecting us to try something at Kassa. The thought prompted a hot flush of concern. But it was pointless trying to second guess so many unknowns.

I'd have to update the others, but when you boiled it down Fozzie hadn't said anything unexpected. A regular thorn in the government's side, I very much doubted that he'd consider revealing our location. Even if the thought did cross his mind, he'd realise that to do so would risk implicating himself in the process.

My gut feeling after the call – he hoped I'd call tomorrow to tell him we'd do the right thing. Let him take the case and give the state another bloody nose. What he didn't know was that we had alternative plans and intended to be long gone by the morning.

CHAPTER 71

AFTER MIDNIGHT

My pre-mission briefing included the report from Fozzie about the military interest in finding and speaking with us. None of the team dwelled on the news. They all shrugged it off and continued with the final preparations and weapon cleaning.

Everyone applied cam cream. Manny painted dark slashes across Izzy's dulled complexion. Her normal vibrant bloom already pared back by a smeared base layer of the pore-blocking muck.

We'd packed the Land Cruisers with most of our gear and all of Luke's samples. Essentials only to be carried from here on in. We needed to move light and swift to achieve surprise and eat up the hard yards from the prison to the beach once the hostages had been secured. Whether we'd ever be reunited with the kit in the cars was open to doubt.

We filed through the rear gate onto the unlit beach at 00:50, the intermittent moonlight casting eerie shadows. The two long, sturdy canoes were nearby at the back of the beach. Only Manny and Alain had seen and checked them. They had snuck out in shorts and t-shirts during the late afternoon when Condé's brothers made the delivery. What Manny had failed to report was that each canoe had a ten-inch thick 'go faster' yellow stripe painted around the top.

I looked them up and down. 'Nice non-tac paint scheme.'

'It's the Guinea flag colours. Red, yellow, and green.'

It could have been worse. They might have been primarily yellow with a green or red stripe.

I then inspected the boats by hand in the dark to check for any obvious structural problems. Planks fixed sideways across the canoe ran the entire twenty-five metre length of each craft, suggesting a welcome, robust endurance. More thick yellow paint inscribed an eroded and unreadable name on each bow.

'I'm assuming it doesn't say Ride of the Valkyries or Into the Valley of Death.'

Manny peered along the prow. 'No. Olympique Marseille and Gloire du Matin. A football team and Morning Glory.'

We both sniggered like schoolboys.

The mirth was swept away by my sincere follow up. 'Thanks, Manny. You've pulled this together. I'm sorry for how things have turned out.'

He paused before answering, his voice stripped of humour. 'This is Africa. Always there are predators and there is prey. Tonight, we are the predators.'

'Amen to that, mate. I should get you to close up the next briefing. Inspire the troops.'

'We have good men with us and a strong woman. All deserve to see the sunrise. What we do now for our friends is…' He shook his head as he searched for the right words.

I put my hand on his shoulder. 'Come on, mate. Let's get this done.'

We divided into our two prearranged crews. I gripped a firm hold at the front of Olympique Marseille. Spread out holding onto both sides opposite and behind me were Ryan, Bob, Izzy, and our coxswain, Manny.

Four men either side of Gloire du Matin waited for my signal to move – Roper, Jamie, Mike, and Alain.

With both teams ready, I turned to Izzy behind me. 'You okay?'

The whispered 'Yes' was barely audible.

'Shout if you need to. If it gets too deep. You can jump in early.'

She shook her head and smiled. 'No. Thank you.' Her voice firmer.

Like the others in the prison-break team, my weapons and kit were stowed and waterproofed in a half-filled bergen wedged under my alloted seat.

My watch showed 00:58. 'Okay, let's go.'

A false start ensued as the loaded canoes proved heavier than expected. Instead, we ran them down to the water's edge one at a time. The sweat on my forehead and under my jacket felt at odds with the breeze on my face. Surf sizzled across the sand to my feet. The sea standing in our way like a vast living, seething obstacle.

Cold water ran into my boots. 'Let's try that again. Go, go, go.'

Within five metres of hitting the water, we were all clambering to get in the bloody canoes. One moment I was giving Izzy a clumsy push over the side until she rolled and clunked out of view, the next I was neck deep and pulling with all my strength to get purchase with my right elbow. I dug in and got my right foot inside the lip of the boat, before spinning into it with an unceremonious Fosbury Flop-style entrance.

Ryan and Manny heaved a spluttering Bob in from the other side and Olympique Marseille was all set. The passengers in Gloire du Matin didn't answer my initial shouts. Five seconds later, Mike hollered that they were complete. I called to Manny to start the outboard and it burst into life a second after the other boat's engine.

We were only a minute in and already soaked and breathing hard. I delved into the top flap of my bergen and pulled out the waterproof bag containing my GPS, radio, map, NVGs, and red torch.

Our course consisted of four legs. The first took us a mile out to sea; the next ran west, parallel with the Conakry coast to the south, until 1.5 nautical miles past the port extremities; after a near ninety degree turn south, the third leg sliced between the mainland and Kassa Island, keeping us 0.5 nautical miles or 900 metres from the island to our starboard; then a final ninety-degree starboard turn for the run into the beach.

Once we had cleared the protection of the coastline, the canoe was buffeted by modest, consistent waves and rocked from side to side, crashing down on occasion when the swell gave way beneath us. Gloire du Matin kept pace ten metres abreast to our right, bucking and rolling along with us.

A wink of moonlight revealed the sea's energetic dance in a way that my night vision hadn't achieved. Spray slapped my face as we rode the rollercoaster towards our fate on Kassa Island. The lights of Conakry port burned bright as we skimmed most waves and burrowed through others.

Our progress on the map showed that Manny was hitting the intended ten knot pace. Hunkered low while skittering across the surface, it felt faster.

The wind and the swell lessened once we turned ninety degrees into the third leg. The mile-wide lights of downtown Conakry still blazed to our left. On our right, clusters of lights, solitary pinpricks, and linking patches of darkness represented the northern and eastern shores of Kassa Island.

We pressed on, invisible arrows spearing through the night, avoiding the lights of other vessels, large and small. Manny then bringing us back on course using his fisherman's intuition. It might have been a sultry night on land, but I shivered in my soaking clothes.

Images of an exercise from over twenty years earlier sprung from nowhere. Recruit Pierce bouncing across the coastal waters of the English Channel in a rigid raider, cap comforter on my head signalling the commando phase of Royal Marines training, the lights of South Devon to starboard.

The image dissolved to be replaced by Claire's smile and those of my ever cheerful three daughters. Like most families, their routine days rolled by while unsung dramas of life and death played out in hidden corners all over the world. Claire and the girls were my bedrock, my focus, and yet here I was, putting my head in the lion's mouth again and risking their innocent happiness.

Those thoughts prompted a detached sadness. I'd evolved into a perpetual wanderer. A curiosity at the school gate and a transitory brother-in-arms on short-term projects, flitting between two lives and never belonging in either.

I caught a mouthful of salt water and coughed out an ironic laugh at an unwelcome realisation: I had to survive tonight because there was no way insurers would pay out if I died assaulting a government facility in Africa – no matter how just the cause and how despicable the enemy.

We drew level with the elongated glow of lights from Cité de Kassa spread across the narrow centre of the island. The engine tone dropped as Manny reduced speed. Without charts, he'd told me he needed to be cautious of shipwrecks and rocks. Gloire du Matin had tucked in behind us when we turned south for the third leg.

Through the NVGs I could see past our crew to the two figures tucked low at the prow on either side of the following boat – Roper and Jamie. An ex-Hereford spook and a squid who had muscled his way into the crack units of the USMC.

It crossed my mind that this would be my first ever operational amphibious landing.

I looked to where the illumination dwindled south of the town. In that vicinity lay our target. One-and-a-half kilometres to the south, another batch of lights tilted on the side of an unseen hill.

I checked the map. Nine hundred metres until we turned right for the run into the beach – five cables until the starboard turn if I wanted to get all nautical about it.

Six minutes later I yelled back to Manny, 'Turn ninety to starboard and into the beach.'

The canoe lurched to the right and pointed into the darkness between the two settlements I'd been observing. Manny maintained the slower speed. A fifty-metre-wide channel led to the beach, and rocks on either side presented a danger. We didn't know how far they protruded from the shore. It might not derail our insertion but wrecking one or both canoes would seriously hamper our exfiltration plans.

The crinkle of waves massaging the shore rose above the rhythmic ticking of the outboard as we drew closer to the beach. Eighty metres out and white surf flashed left and right, suggesting Manny had judged our approach to perfection.

Now carrying the AK and wearing my bergen, I concentrated ahead through the NVGs, straining for any sign of danger on the surface. As we reached the final twenty metres, the canoe caught a wave and surged forward in a final uncontrolled rush towards the shore.

I spotted large boulders looming out of the sea immediately in front of us. 'Right, right, right.'

Manny's efforts to turn couldn't prevent us glancing off a dark, chunky mass with a painful crunch before the bottom of the canoe grounded noiselessly on an even surface.

I dropped over the side into eighteen inches of water and waved the others forward. 'Okay, let's go. Get the boat on the beach. Ryan, on me.'

I scanned left and right through the NVGs. The low level of ambient light was enough to see the small beach was empty – no fishing canoes or signs of other stores. It was a reason we'd selected a remote spot. Even though we hoped to be making our escape within three hours, night fishermen stumbling across our boats and the beach team would present a problem.

To the right of our damaged boat, Gloire du Matin glided into the shallows like a fairground ride. Ryan and I had moved twenty metres forward to check along the rear of the beach. All quiet. No sign of life or usage. A thick wall of jungle sloped up from the back edge and cloaked our arrival. Ryan adopted lookout duties while I returned to the boats.

I grabbed Manny and then Mike, giving each of them the same message. 'We'll drag the boats into the trees. It's only twenty metres.'

We pulled them across the sand one at a time. Manny got us to roll Olympique Marseille to check for damage. Water we'd taken on board gushed out – an added bonus.

'What do you think? I asked him.

'We wouldn't get a deposit back,' he said, running his hands over the hull, 'but it's nothing critical.'

With the boats nestled against the treeline and the team spread into a defensive arc facing into the undergrowth, I knelt next to Roper. 'Two oh-five. On schedule, near enough.'

I glanced at the thick trees and the gradient of the slope. 'Terrain is going to be shit for comms. Both of us will probably be able to reach Kingfisher though. Might need him to relay messages. Otherwise, it will be sat phone only.'

Roper disentangled his earpiece and fixed it ready to make a call. 'I'll try him now for a sitrep.'

The sat phone keypad lit up as he rang our ride home. If things had gone to plan, they'd be ten to fifteen nautical miles away and closing.

'Kingfisher this is Curlew, good to hear your voice.'

I couldn't hear the reply.

'And you. We are feet dry and complete. Is your ETA still as planned?'

Roper's face contorted. 'Shit. How long?'

His head shook as he listened. 'Call me as soon as you're underway again. There are no issues our end. However, we anticipate comms may be difficult. You might need to relay messages. Recap of callsigns. I'm also Sierra Charlie and my 2IC is Digger.'

Roper chuckled at the unheard response.

'The other team is Sierra Alpha, Bravo, Delta, and Echo. Alpha leads.'

'Okay, good. Just checking you didn't get a duff steer from London. Give me that call when the engine is fixed, and we'll radio check when you get to the RV.'

Roper faced me when he'd hung up, 'You got the gist of that?'

'Yep. They've broken down.'

'Manny's brothers say they can fix it. They're on it now.'

'I fucking hope so. I wouldn't fancy those canoes all the way to Sierra Leone.'

'We haven't got the fuel for that. Kingfisher is already halfway and should be on station by five if they get moving soon. Plenty of time for us to slip away before dawn.'

I chose not to dwell on alternative outcomes. 'At least Dave's aware of the comms situ.'

'That's right. And he'll come in close if we need it.'

'Hopefully, we won't. Just slink off and get the fuck out of here. Talking of which, we'll be on our way. I'll try a radio check from the crest. After that, it'll be the go/no go using whatever method works.'

'Roger that. Good luck, John. Don't be afraid to say no.'

I could hardly make out his features in the darkness. 'Thanks for your support, mate. Career breaking stuff for you.'

Roper let out a low, mirthless laugh. 'If it goes wrong, my career will be the least of our problems. And I told you before, I've always been on your side.'

We slapped our hands together in a brief, gripped handshake.

I gathered my patrol team, checked the compass bearing, and set off into the dense foliage. Six of the group would move forward to the prison and split into two teams of three: Ryan and Manny in my team; Jamie and Alain in Mike's team.

Remaining at the beach were Roper, Bob, and Izzy. Bob's disappointment at being left behind had been tempered by the issue of a VHF radio and the award of his own call sign – Digger. It meant each three-man team possessed two radios and a satellite phone. Roper held the fourth sat phone in reserve.

After twenty-five metres of cloying, claustrophobic forest, which snagged on faces, weapons and rucksacks, we emerged into clearer terrain. Not a moment too soon for me – I could have sworn something ran across my shoulder as I shimmied out of the grasp of the last elastic branch. Judging by the shaking limbs and wild hand movements of the others, I wasn't the only one who'd encountered the local wildlife.

The wider gaps between the trees and bushes didn't make as much difference to the oppressive night as I'd hoped. The wind had dropped just when a fresh breeze would have been welcome.

After 200 metres we'd climbed about sixty feet. A car rumbled past on the main road fifty metres to our left, known to us as *Regent Street*. We only heard the engine noise and detected a vague shimmer above the treetops. I relied on the map to fill in the blanks.

Five kilometres to our right, across the water, the business end of the Conakry peninsular glowed: 2.25 a.m. on a Saturday morning and the bars would be rocking. Sales of Vodka might be down though, now the Russian ex-pat contingent had shrunk by two.

I signalled a halt and reviewed the map. The gradient had flattened, and I needed to adjust the bearing slightly right to handrail *Regent Street* for 150 metres to the next waypoint near a track junction.

At that waypoint, christened *Piccadilly*, we would adjust right again to stay this side of the closest of two forked tracks. For simplicity, we marked our fork as a continuation of *Regent Street*. Following it for a further 200 metres would bring us to another track junction – *Oxford Circus*. There we'd have to cross a track that drifted down the slope to a sizeable building near a rocky cove.

In the shallow 150-metre slope between our route and the shore, London had noted the 'cove' building, but couldn't identify if it was privately owned or linked to the camp. We'd keep well clear, just in case.

Heading north from *Oxford Circus*, the map suggested we'd encounter 120 metres of thick jungle before reaching the southern camp perimeter. From there, the prison building, tagged as *The Ritz*, ought to be visible on the other side of the fence.

After a concealed approach, we'd split into the three-man teams and perform our close target recces. I hoped my memory of the layout proved accurate and the reality on the ground didn't present any nasty surprises.

Along *Regent Street,* past *Piccadilly*, through *Oxford Circus*, and on to *The Ritz*. It wasn't quite an accurate representation of central London, but it was close enough.

CHAPTER 72

Setting off to handrail Regent Street to the first junction, my confidence was sky-high despite the news about Kingfisher's engine trouble. In single file behind me were five good men: Ryan, Manny, Alain, Jamie, and Mike covering the rear as always. Some of the best guys I'd ever worked with. If I was inside that cell, we were the team I'd want coming to the rescue.

One hundred and thirty metres later we reached the crest and I stopped to give Roper a radio check. As anticipated, the signal with the beach team was already breaking up. However, it was stable enough to hear that Kingfisher hadn't called yet.

The island was only 500 metres wide along our route. Regent Street, the single main road, ran along the 100-foot-high central spine with the jungle sloping away evenly left and right to the sea on both sides. It meant we couldn't see anything of the west side of the island to our left. According to the map, it should consist of similar jungle-covered terrain and little else.

We'd debated approaching along the left of Regent Street instead of the right but decided to use the insertion leg as a route recce for the return journey. A return journey for which we expected to have three additional personnel with unknown levels of mobility.

The last we'd seen of them, Luke appeared fit and well, Hutch walked while wearing a sling on one arm, and Condé had been on a stretcher. I knew from experience how quickly a man could deteriorate after twenty-four hours in their current hell hole. If all three of them were unable to move unaided, our 750-metre exfil could turn into a serious test of endurance. Especially if chasing troops were snapping at our heels.

Despite this, the bubble of confidence remained. It would work out okay – these things always did. The boat engine would be fixed; the guys would be fit enough, or we'd carry them out; and my remaining team would get through this unscathed.

'Piccadilly,' I whispered to Ryan behind me, chopping a hand in the direction of the junction forty metres through the trees to our left.

He passed the message down the line. A slap on the back thirty seconds later indicated the message had been received by the whole team. I turned onto a new bearing and we began the 200-metre downhill leg to the waypoint just shy of Oxford Circus.

Despite occasional gaps in the trees, we hadn't yet caught a glimpse of the camp or Cité de Kassa. The only evidence of the town was the hazy orange flavour to the night sky. Due to the curvature of the ground, we wouldn't see either until we were almost on top of the target.

Thirty metres south of the Oxford Circus junction, we hit the next waypoint and crossed the track that led down the hill to the cove.

The surrounding night was silent apart from the usual soundtrack of nocturnal jungle critters. The crunch of our careful footsteps and the swish of disturbed vegetation provoked irrational fears of immediate compromise. Fears that needed to be suppressed as we closed on our target.

A subdued glow appeared above the trees ahead. It had to be generated by the camp. The concealment offered by the dense bush meant I still hadn't seen the target, even though it should be less than 100 metres away.

We wriggled forward through the undergrowth. I signalled to Ryan to close up. We needed to stay within touching distance to avoid losing anyone. Stumbling around trying to find each other in this pitch black, sweltering salad bowl would be amateur hour.

Doubts crept in: *Where the fuck was the fence? Don't let me have veered off and somehow missed a huge fuck-off prison camp.*

I swept a branch out of my path and slammed my right eye shut to save some night vision. There it was – a barbed-wire-topped fence stretching across our front ten metres away.

The cleared space between fence and treeline contained ragged grass filled with tree stumps and sporadic, pulverized bushes attempting a return to former glory. Parts of the fence were illuminated by floodlights, other parts consumed by darkness. I let the leafy branch fall back into place and brought the others in close.

'We've come out in the right place. The Ritz is fifty metres ahead, close to the left fence line. There's a covered approach up to the area behind it, but it looks like it opens out beyond that.'

I picked out Mike among the spectre-like forms in the shadows. 'We'll take the left. You recce down the right side, past those two buildings and level with the far end of the target. Seen?'

Mike followed the line of my extended right arm. 'Seen.'

I swung the arm twenty degrees left. 'There's an admin building and the main gate down the far end. Let's avoid tangling with anyone down there.'

In truth, I couldn't make out much beyond vague angular shapes in the shadows. The images of the admin building and its medical centre had materialized from my memory.

'Two fifty-seven. Let's meet in the treeline by the left corner in one hour. Zero four hundred.'

I decided openness was the best policy. 'Kingfisher is delayed. Maybe an hour or more. I'm waiting for an update. If we need additional recce time, then we've got it. Once it arrives at the RV, I'll confirm the go/no go and we can get this shit done.'

Whatever their feelings about the delay, the team all kept their thoughts to themselves. Kingfisher hadn't been due at the RV for another hour, so it wasn't mission critical, yet.

'We need to check for alternative routes out,' murmured Mike. 'It would be hell to get the guys through that bloody jungle. Especially if one or more need to be carried. Take too long.'

It was a good point. 'We'll get eyes on the road and tracks on our side. Nothing obvious showing on the map for your side. Could be a path connecting to the building by the cove. That might contain trouble though.'

'If there's time, we'll have a look.' He put a hand on my arm. 'Before we go, actions on?'

'Actions on compromise, both teams cut into the fence at the nearest point and roll into an assault on The Ritz. Use speed, aggression, and hand-to-hand where possible to try and avoid waking up the entire island. We clear inside and extract the prisoners, you hold outside. Improvise from there.'

'Roger that,' he replied. A sentiment that was echoed by other murmurs from around us.

Through my NVGs, I watched Mike's team patrol away down the slope on our right, tucked tight against the edge of the forest. We'd emerged near the southern left corner of the rectangular compound. The sixty-metre fence line to our front was one of the two shorter sides of the perimeter. The longer east and west sides ran for 200 metres, and the main gate was positioned at the far end, in the centre of the northern fence.

All our interest was focused on the nearby prison building and its surroundings. We intended to avoid whoever might be in the rest of the camp.

When Mike's team had been swallowed by the night, I led my team around our corner and pushed forward, my left shoulder brushing the branches and bushes of the thinning cover. The treeline stopped suddenly twenty metres before the target building. Open ground dominated the area outside the camp on this side.

Ten metres away, a track curved past and ran uphill behind us to the left. The map indicated that it met Regent Street forty metres later. An unbroken dark mass in that direction suggested the jungle bordered the far side of the road.

Mike's point about the route out was foremost in my thinking. Instead of trying to force our way through the jungle, we could dash up the track, along Regent Street, left at Oxford Circus junction onto the track to the cove, before cutting right towards the beach through the bush.

Two hundred metres of road and track to reach cover.

Even with rescued prisoners hoisted into a fireman's carry and run out on our backs, we should make that in two minutes. That compared to the excruciating time it would take to drag them back through the thick jungle. With the alarm likely raised by our attack, speed would be critical.

But on the road and tracks we'd be exposed.

Two minutes. Could we do it and get away before the defenders could react?

While I settled with Manny to watch for guards and patrol patterns, I sent Ryan left to check the short route to Regent Street. It might have been less than fifty metres away, but it was out of my line of sight and I wanted to be sure the ground matched the map.

By 04:00, Mike's team had rejoined us in the muggy jungle at the designated corner. They'd seen two guards at the double door to the target building, one of whom circled around for a wander every fifteen minutes.

In the limited time available, they hadn't seen any other patrols. That matched with our observations: no patrols and no sign of CCTV or technical security measures. And no sign that the previous night's attack on the warehouse had raised alert levels. It was quiet. Was it too quiet?

For the exfiltration route, a narrow path had led away from their side, parallel with the coastline. But Mike didn't hold out much hope for it. 'We'd need to spend another hour following it back to see where it comes out. Longer if we wanted to check any buildings that might be along the way. The sea's only fifty metres further down. It might just turn left somewhere and end at a beach.'

I told him about the track and road option to the left. With time still in hand, the two of us then went forward and reviewed the ground together. Mike agreed with me – this was the way out.

The satellite phone had no signal back by the corner. When I checked in the thinner foliage near the tracks, it picked up enough satellites to whisper a call to Roper.

'John, can you hear me?'

'Yes, mate. All good for Guinevere. What's the latest with Kingfisher?'

'The boat is underway, problem resolved. ETA at the RV, zero five-thirty.'

I checked my watch: 04:25. 'Cutting it fine. We'll launch at zero five hundred. By the time we reach you and get afloat, Kingfisher will be at the RV.'

'Okay. I'll call you if anything changes. Did you hear my radio checks or get my SMS?'

I peered at the handset. 'Just seen a message has arrived while we've been talking. Nothing on VHF. I'll call you by this means in thirty mikes for final confirmation.'

'Roger that. Good luck.'

Ten minutes later we returned to the dank corner where our four comrades and hundreds of mosquitos were waiting. After two long, lukewarm slugs from the Camelback, I outlined the plan. Once I'd finished, there were no questions. 'Right guys, it's zero four forty-five. Square yourselves away. Move out in ten.'

CHAPTER 73

The success of the mission depended on the element of surprise. It also relied on avoiding entanglement with the prison guard force and getting away sharply to the boats. That meant we needed to hit the target with speed and aggression and have lady luck on our side.

Ridiculous, but I cursed my missing lucky charm. That plastic eyeball had always been in a pouch or pocket before, although maybe it didn't work so well in Africa. After all, my last visit to this island hadn't been memorable for the right reasons.

Taking out the two guards in front of the prison required stealth and agility. Four of us carried half-filled bergens. The uncertainty of how events would evolve meant dumping them now might mean losing them for good.

Manny and Alain didn't carry packs and volunteered for the task of leading the attack. It needed to be clinical to avoid the alarm being raised. With one friend dead and another inside the building, they were up for it. It helped that both were locals and spoke natural French if challenged.

Based on experience, I expected the guards' Kalashnikovs to be loaded and not made ready. That would give us vital moments to stop either of them taking off the safety, cocking the weapon, and firing shots that would signal a disastrous compromise.

At 04:55 clouds wandered in front of the Moon and the light levels dropped. The areas outside the floodlit pools reverted to darkness. A good omen.

The six of us moved forward to the edge of the thinning treeline on the left. The satellite bars locked into place and I called Roper. 'Status on Kingfisher?'

'ETA unchanged. He'll reach the RV at five-thirty.'

'Roger. We're set. Go for Guinevere.'

Instead of a confirmatory reply, the earpiece wailed as the signal bounced thousands of miles into space and back to a position less than a kilometre away. I pulled the handset out of the vest to check if the call had dropped.

'You sure?'

'I'm sure. Guinevere. It's on.'

'Okay. Good luck. See you when you get here.'

We listened and observed for the next four minutes, straining for any sign we were walking into a trap.

At exactly 05:00, Mike and Jamie crept forward through the long grass and thigh-high bushes to the unlit compound perimeter. Through NVGs, I watched the two ghostly green figures use secateurs to cut the chain link fence. The snaps rang out in the hushed night.

Two nerve-wracking minutes later, Mike waved us over and we filed through the breach. Once the team were all inside, Mike fixed the removed section back into place. It wouldn't stand up to close inspection, but it shouldn't need to. We'd be kicking it through and running down the main drag in ten minutes.

Ryan and I moved in the darkness to the southeast corner of The Ritz and went firm. I scanned the southern end of the compound with my NVGs one last time before getting Ryan to stow them in my backpack. Our end was clear.

We waited for Mike, Jamie, Manny, and Alain to skirt around the back of the building. Manny and Alain would go firm thirty metres away on the northeast corner. Mike and Jamie would provide cover to the north.

Sixty seconds later, Mike whispered, *'Delta in position. All set, no issues. Two tangos at the door, over.'*

'Alpha, roger. Send them when ready.'

'Stop, stop, stop.'

Fuck. The temptation to peek around the corner was overwhelming. Something must be happening.

'One tango mobile and moving your way, over.'

'Count him down to the corner.'

'Roger. We'll launch from this end with you.'

Manny and Alain had borrowed Mike and Jamie's knives. Ryan and I still had ours. I signed to Ryan that an enemy was coming our way and that I'd deal with him. He shook his head and prodded his own chest. We both stood and adopted a ready stance.

I held three fingers in the air at shoulder height and waited for Mike's countdown.

'Corner in three, two, one.'

When my last finger dropped a figure materialized within touching distance. The sight of a living, breathing man so close was a shock, even though I knew he was coming.

Ryan lunged forward and a sickening squelch suggested his blade had found exposed flesh. The embracing couple fell to the ground this side of the corner with only a gurgled moan from the guard. I landed on top of him and smashed the butt of my CZ into his temple. Ryan slammed a shape into his mouth to make sure he kept quiet.

'Oumar, que faites-vous?' called out a sharp male voice. *Oumar, what are you doing?*

Running footsteps and a panicked 'Quoi..?' preceded the tell-tale sounds of a scuffle. After a loud groan, the noises stopped.

'Stay there,' I said to Ryan and charged around the corner. The front of The Ritz was bathed in dim yellow light, exposing a small gathering. In front of the double doors, Manny and Alain were placing plasticuffs on their face-down, unmoving prisoner.

'Go to the other one.' I muttered to Alain, pointing to the corner where Ryan waited.

I hit the pressel switch. 'Alpha at the door. Echo, on me.'

'Roger'

A nearby radio burst into life. 'Lancine, Oumar, quell est tout ce bruit ?' *Lancine, Oumar, what is all that noise?*

Manny plucked it from the prostrate prisoner's waistband and gave me a questioning look. I thrust a flat hand downwards in his direction to indicate not to fuck around on the radio net. Ryan arrived and slapped me on the shoulder. 'Ready.'

'I'll take left, you take right.' I gripped the handles and threw them open, darting left and out of the doorway immediately on entry. I crouched and swung the CZ at the desk set against the far wall twenty feet away, just like the last time I checked in.

The startled man sat behind it with a radio in his right hand stared back.

'Put it down,' I shouted.

He looked at it before clamping it to the side of his head.

The pistol bucked in my hand as the shot blasted through the silent night and through our plans to keep the operation covert. The 9mm round hit the man in his upper chest and punched him backwards. He toppled over and disappeared behind the desk, taking the chair with him. His radio clattered as it hit the stone floor.

I crabbed left, keeping my arms extended and the CZ pointing towards the target. Judging by the blood and shit spattered on the wall and the big red patch on his shirt front, it was a fair bet 'desk man' wouldn't be getting up again. A cursory check of his breathing and pulse confirmed the prognosis.

'Your turn to fuck things up,' said Ryan, scoping the room and staircase with his AK-47.

Not the ideal start. I ignored the jibe. 'Secure the top floor. I'll do the ground.'

I dumped my bergen before setting off to clear the ground floor. At 5.00 a.m. we expected the building to be quiet. With the red filter removed and the torch adjusted to maximum brightness, I pushed open the door under the stairs. My head, torch, and weapon roved in unison as I advanced: soft elbows, outstretched arms crossed at the wrist, pistol in the top hand, torch in the bottom.

Two offices in the rear of the building contained stacked files and paperwork on the desks. They had the token tidiness of a day's end.

Grimy, blank computer monitors, empty ashtrays, and the enduring funk of stale cigarette smoke. No steaming drinks, blinking screens, open files, or other evidence of a keen early riser.

The toilets were in a grim state and the kitchen not much better. Four heavily stained mugs sat on the draining board.

Before I could transmit a warning, the earpiece squawked into life. *'Echo has one more for the collection.'*

By the sound of it, Ryan had made the acquaintance of the owner of the fourth mug.

'Alpha, you require assistance?'

'Negative. Coming down, top floor clear.'

With the bottom floor also clear, I sent Mike an update. 'Building under control. Bring the prisoners inside. Keep one man on the door. We'll be as quick as we can, over.'

'Delta, roger.'

When I returned to the reception hall, Ryan had a dazed soldier by the scruff of the neck as he walked behind with his AK pressed into the guy's back. The ugly swelling around the prisoner's eye and the blood dripping from his mouth indicated how the introductions had gone.

Ryan gave his new friend's collar a rough shake. 'Sleeping beauty here was alone upstairs. His weapon is still up there. I've taken the mag.'

The man's good eye was glued with manic intensity to the gruesome sight behind the desk.

'Tie him up and get him on the floor next to the other one.'

Manny and Alain had already dragged in a motionless, bound prisoner and laid him by the wall. They returned twenty seconds later with a second man whose neck and torso were covered in blood. That would be the wandering guard Ryan and I bumped into; now either dead or close to it. I didn't have time for feelings of guilt.

Alain went back outside to his post while Manny stepped over the body sprawled behind the desk and inspected a key board on the wall.

'Heard anything on the radio?' I asked.

'A question for Kemoko.' He glanced at the corpse. 'They asked twice if everything was okay and then nothing.'

'Shit. Might not have long. We're looking for the key to that door and the cells behind it.' I was pointing at the grilled door to the left that I'd passed through two years earlier. Memories of the cell and the torture flooded back and filled me with foreboding for what we might find.

Manny selected a large ring of keys. 'These are for the cells, but the key for the access door is missing.'

I walked towards the door. 'We'll have to break through.' Then I spotted something that raised a smile. 'Forget it. The key's in the lock.'

'That'll do nicely,' said Ryan.

I turned the key and yanked the heavy door open. The gloomy, stinking corridor from my nightmares stopped me in my tracks.

'This it?' asked Ryan.

While my attention was gripped by the three cell doors and grim memories, he pulled out a torch and red light danced over the minging, damp walls. 'What a shithole.'

'Yeah, this is it.' I said. 'Try that one.' I pointed at the left-hand door, my old cell. Manny moved forward with the keys. The mechanism clunked open at his second attempt.

Ryan peered through the viewing hatch of the middle door. 'Hutch, Luke, you there?'

I didn't hear the mumbled answer clearly. By this time, I'd pulled open the door of the left cell, and squirted a bright beam from my own torch into the left corner at the bed. A head lifted and rasped, 'You took your fucking time.' Hutch.

'Manny, open this one up. Luke's in there,' said Ryan from the corridor.

'How are you mate?' I said to Hutch as the neighbouring cell clanked open and excited voices implied Luke had also been found in a lucid state.

'I've been better,' said Hutch. 'Are we free?'

'Sort of. It's a rescue. Can you walk?'

'Once you get these fucking chains off.'

I'd forgotten about the chains. 'Manny, we need the keys to the leg irons.'

'He's already gone for them,' Ryan answered. 'How's Hutch?'

'He'll live. What about Luke?'

'I'm okay,' the Canadian called out.

I turned back to Hutch. 'How about you, can you walk?'

'I can walk, but my arm's fucked.' He looked at the limb slung across his stomach. 'Took a round in the shoulder.'

He fixed me with a chilling stare. 'He's here.'

'Who? Where?'

'The general. He's here and he knows you.' Hutch's bruised face knotted into a grimace. 'He's evil. Enjoys the torture. Enjoys the pain. They'll kill us.'

'No, mate. We've got you now. We're going home.'

Mamba was here. Maybe in this camp right now. Even though I'd seen him in the flesh less than twenty-four hours earlier, I shivered at the prospect.

The stench of human waste registered for the first time. A flashback to my own incarceration in this same cell. The torment in Hutch's eyes spurred deep sorrow for what he'd been through. Regret at bringing him here.

He dropped his gaze and shook his head. 'They drowned him, and I couldn't stop them. Again and again. I didn't know the answers. He wanted to know why you were back. I told him about you watching the border. I'm sorry.'

'Forget it. That op is well blown, mate. Drowned who?' I touched his shoulder. 'Hutch, who did they drown?'

Keys jangled and a muted clunk indicated the third cell had been opened.

'Manny, how's Condé?' I shouted.

I didn't hear a reply.

Ryan appeared in the doorway and came into the cell with a keyring in his hand. 'Luke's free. Alright, Hutch. Give me two seconds.'

I left them to it and went into the corridor. Luke had bent down to rub his ankle and I tapped his back as I passed. 'Glad you're okay.'

It dawned on me that both men wore orange jumpsuits and had bare feet. We needed to find them footwear asap.

I shone my torch into the right-hand cell. Manny was bent over a figure on the bed who I assumed was Condé. 'How is he?'

Pain was etched on my friend's face as he blinked into the light. 'I think he's dead.'

I grabbed the radio. 'Echo swap with Bravo. We have a casualty requires immediate attention, over.'

'Echo, roger,' I heard through the radio and from the corridor behind as Ryan rushed past.

'Bravo, roger. On way.'

I led Hutch and Luke into the reception hall where they both squinted despite the meagre light. They took in the sight of the three handcuffed prisoners and the bloody mess by the desk without comment.

Jamie burst in though the main door. He smiled and raised a hand to the two men alongside me. 'Where's the casualty?'

I pointed to the open door behind me. 'Through there, first on the right.'

'Alpha this is Delta, movement to the north. We need to get moving, over.'

'Alpha, roger. Wait out.'

I glanced at the two pairs of bare feet next to me and over at our prisoners. 'Don't just stand there, take their boots.'

Hutch and Luke both nodded unconvincingly. The shock at their change in fortune was probably still sinking in. After a moment, Luke dropped to the ground and started undoing the nearest prisoner's laces. Hutch surprised me by snapping out of his torpor and scurrying over to the desk.

'Ha, this is the bastard who took my Altbergs.' He knelt at the dead man's feet to recover his expensive jungle boots.

Manny appeared from the cell block shaking his head. He held up the radio. 'They're calling again.'

The radio squawked into life. 'Kemoko, si vous m'entendez, j'envoie des gars avec des piles.'

'What was that?' I asked.

'Says he's sent guys with batteries.'

'And Condé?'

Manny shrugged his shoulders and looked away.

'Delta, four tangos closing. It's going noisy in the next thirty seconds.'

I strode back to the cells and looked in on Jamie from the doorway.

'Any chance?'

'No,' said Jamie. 'He's gone.'

'Fuck.'

'I'll carry him,' said Manny from over my shoulder. 'I won't leave him here.'

'We've got to go now,' I replied. 'You might have to leave him.'

'No.' Manny pushed past me into the cell. Jamie helped him lift Condé's body. I returned to the reception hall where Hutch and Luke waited. Both now wore camouflage smocks over their jumpsuits.

'Alpha, We're coming out in…'

A volley of high velocity shots erupted from close by. I hoped it was outgoing.

'Here, take this.' I handed Hutch the CZ and a spare magazine. 'One arm should be enough. You're a gash shot anyway.'

'Delta, contact. Four tangos, range thirty metres. Two down, over.'

A long burst of automatic fire answered from further away and a series of thumps hit the wall.

'Come on guys, let's go,' I called out.

Jamie pushed the cell block door open and held it as Manny squeezed through sideways with Condé's limp form draped across his shoulders. I couldn't help thinking it might be more respectful to leave him here rather than drag him through the jungle.

The firefight outside continued with nearby deliberate fire answered by distant automatic bursts. With two men just released from leg irons and a dead comrade needing to be carried, it was imperative we got a head start before the local garrison could mobilise.

CHAPTER 74

With the team assembled by the door, I got on the radio. 'Alpha ready. Are we clear to peel right?'

'Delta, you're clear to move. We'll lay down covering fire.'

Next to me by the door stood Jamie, Manny with Condé hoisted in a fireman's carry, and our two haggard comrades, one of whom had a sling on his left arm. The sight caused my earlier sky-high confidence to dial down a notch or two.

The three incapacitated guards hadn't moved, and their level of consciousness wasn't clear. In an ideal world, I'd have dragged them into the cells, shut the doors, and thrown away the keys. Right now, a fast getaway took priority.

The volume of deliberate shots increased to rapid fire. Hopefully, that was Mike, Ryan, and Alain increasing the tempo to cover our exit.

'I'll lead, you three follow,' I said, sweeping a finger at Manny, Hutch, and Luke. 'Jamie, you bring up the rear.'

'Oorah,' the American replied, patting his AK.

I pulled my own rifle into the shoulder and fingered the safety catch.

'Out the door, immediately right, and right again at the corner. That should give us cover from enemy fire. Go firm there against the building. Me and Jamie will open the fence and call you over. I'll lead you to the trees ten metres to the left. All good?'

With a noisy backdrop of sustained rifle fire, the response was a mixture of nods, elevated thumbs, and murmured approval.

'Delta, vehicle lights to the north. You need to move now.'

'Understood. Moving.'

The firefight had been loud from inside the building. When I threw open the doors and hurtled out to the right, it was deafening. Alain lay in a prone position two metres away, launching rounds down range with abandon. More firing barked from the left, where Mike and Ryan prowled.

I bolted for the corner. 'Follow me. This way.'

Once around it and into the cover of darkness, I raised my weapon into the shoulder and peered back the way I'd come. Manny lumbered towards me, Condé's body toppling to the ground when he stumbled into the turn. Hutch and Luke were on his tail and moved past to nestle against the building wall. As Jamie reached me, I signalled left. 'Go to the fence.'

He ran to the cut section and began removing it.

'Alpha is clear. Going through the fence to the treeline.'

'Delta, roger that. Watch out for vehicles on the left flank.'

'Will do. I'll signal when firm.'

With the team sheltered against the wall, I joined Jamie unhooking the wire strands. How the hell did it get this snarled up so quick?

In the darkness we used brute force to rip the cut section away, slicing my hand in the process. In the half-light, a stinging black line led from the top of my thumb to my watch strap. Another minor wound to add to the collection.

'Come on, let's go,' Jamie shouted to the others, while I slipped through the hole, dashed to trees, and scanned for the vehicles Mike had warned about. Distant lights danced through the branches of a copse 100 metres to the front. It seemed reasonable to assume the perimeter track swung to the right behind the copse and followed the fence to the front end of the camp. That would place those lights not more than 200 metres away.

The road fifty metres to the left, which joined with the perimeter track somewhere behind us, remained empty. It led to the Oxford Circus junction and was our intended route out. How long would it take the enemy to flood the area with men and vehicles? *Come on lads. Hurry up.*

A wretched scene played out at the fence as Manny tried to crouch-walk through the gap with a dead body on his back. The figures merged into one as he encountered trouble fitting through and Jamie tried to help.

After thirty seconds, a shape slumped to the left of the gap, bounced against the fence, and flopped to the deck with an awful finality.

Manny emerged from the hole and scurried towards me, rifle in both hands.

'I had to leave him. God forgive me.'

Tears glistened on his cheeks.

'He'd understand.' A meaningless reply, but I had to keep Manny focused. The headlights filtering through the trees were getting closer.

'Kingfisher, I have you loud and clear, over.'

My watch showed 05:36. Didn't time fly when you were having a clusterfuck. The message from the boat was the standard British military reply to a radio check. That suggested Roper had good comms with Dave on the Kingfisher.

'Kingfisher, this is Sierra Alpha, message, over.'

'Kingfisher, send, over.'

'Alpha, relay to Charlie that we are in contact. Status Grail Two. Shortly inbound to his location. ETA figures two zero, repeat back to me, over.'

'Kingfisher, relaying to Sierra Charlie that Alpha is in contact. Status Grail Two. En route to Charlie location. ETA two zero mikes, over.'

'Alpha, your message all correct. Will notify when approaching Charlie, out.'

'Sierra Charlie this is Kingfisher. Alpha will report when approaching your position. I will relay if comms still difficult, over.'

That brief interlude from mayhem straightened my disordered thoughts like a trainer slapping his boxer's face. Cover the road, call Mike's team in, hoof it down the main drag, blast through the jungle to the beach, get to the RV.

Jamie and the other two had reached the trees and dropped behind me. Hutch's pronounced limp was a worry. The approaching vehicle lights an even bigger worry.

'Delta, this is Alpha, we're firm at the treeline. Be advised we have vehicles closing along the main drag from the north. Pull back to our location, over.'

'Delta, roger. Breaking contact, out.'

I turned to the four faces behind me. Two pale and two cammed out. Manny was looking across to the fence where Condé's body lay.

'Manny, we need to stop those vehicles, okay.'

He looked at me and nodded.

'Shall I take these two along the road?' asked Jamie, indicating Hutch and Luke.

'No, we'll wait for Mike. We can't be sure the route's clear.'

I put my hand on Manny's shoulder. 'You and me take the lead vehicle. Jamie, you hit the rear one and anything else behind that. Don't worry about spotting individual targets. We just need to stop them.'

I pushed down the safety one notch and brought the rifle up on aim. 'Automatic for this.'

Both men shuffled into kneeling positions in my peripheral vision and there were metallic clicks on my left and right.

Vehicle engines rumbled closer. The lights swung right then left into our faces as the front SUV cleared the copse with a second vehicle close behind.

'Rapid fire,' I ordered before letting go with a controlled burst of five rounds.

A wall of noise exploded around me as Manny and Jamie joined in. My opening shots knocked out the right headlight of the lead vehicle, which turned away and accelerated towards the road on the left. I smashed a second burst into the side of the target before a line of trees forty metres ahead obscured my view.

Lights behind the copse were extinguished. 'Is that car two behind those trees?' I asked.

'Yeah, I got rounds into the cockpit. Shithead still managed to reverse into cover. Didn't see a third car,' said Jamie.

With the lights of both vehicles doused, the only illumination of the battleground came from the weak floodlights on the camp perimeter.

The chain link fence rattled as, one after another, three shadows forced themselves through the jagged grasp of the escape hole. Mike led Ryan and Alain straight to our position, all three of them breathing hard. He landed next to me and said, 'There's two vehicles moving up inside, plus guys on the ground. They'll need to clear the prison, so that should buy us time.' He loaded a fresh magazine from his vest as he spoke.

'Two vehicles to our front,' I said, deploying a knife hand for emphasis. 'One behind the trees forty metres to the left, the other behind that copse a hundred metres on the right. We've put rounds into them, but they are still mobile.'

'Get your team down the road through the junction and go firm,' he replied. 'How are the lads?'

'Condé didn't make it. He's in the grass over there. You must have missed him.'

'Shit. How about Hutch and Luke.'

'I'm okay,' said a soft Canadian voice from behind us.

'Hutch is suffering, but he'll make it,' I added. 'We'll be slower than I hoped.'

A lengthy salvo of automatic fire erupted from the left-hand treeline forty metres away. Spaced out, deadly flashes spat furious swarms of lead into our sanctuary. Bullets zipped through the foliage around us and a red-hot zing flashed across my cheek and snicked my ear. A cry of pain sounded from close behind. I clutched at my face and the fingers came away covered with dark liquid. My ear blazed with pain, but it was still attached.

Our own enhanced arsenal responded with a withering barrage. After ten seconds, the rate of outgoing fire dropped. Mike and Ryan conferred about arcs and allocated one to Alain.

'Luke's hit,' said Jamie as he bustled past my back.

'Can he move?' asked Mike. 'You need to get going.'

'It's my wrist,' said Luke.

'Two hundred metres and then Jamie can deal with it,' I told him. 'Hutch, are you okay?'

'I'm not hit,' he replied.

With Mike's three-man team putting deliberate, single shots into the enemy position on the left and answering sporadic bursts from the copse on the right, I raised into a crouch. 'My team, with me. I'll lead. Hutch and Luke you follow. Manny, keep with Jamie and help these other two if they need it.'

I didn't wait for answers. 'Let's go.'

My emergence from cover was greeted with an incoming salvo that slapped into the foliage like a sudden hailstorm. Any complaining muscles went unnoticed as I ran left along the track to follow the route Ryan had checked out earlier. People shooting 7.62 mm in my direction has always motivated personal best sprint times.

Against every instinct, I slowed after thirty metres to check behind. The two recently rescued prisoners might not be so light on their feet.

Ten metres back, Hutch loped in a rolling gait with the CZ swinging wildly in his right hand. The white sling on his left arm and his bright orange legs were unwelcome aiming marks. Behind him, Luke ran with a hand clamped to his forearm, teeth bared and head leaning away as though trying to escape the pain.

Bringing up the rear, Jamie knelt and pumped three rounds back towards the nearest enemy position. He'd changed to single shot. Manny squatted a few metres to his left and let rip a satisfying rattle on automatic.

A flash in the treeline showed the enemy were still engaging. Not at me though. I dropped onto my knee and blasted two automatic bursts into the shooter's vicinity.

'Good effort, keep going,' I said to the two stricken men as they reached me.

Having switched my own selector to single shot, I raced ahead and led them left onto the main road – in reality a hard-packed dirt track.

Sunrise at 06:45 was still over an hour away, but the black of night was already being lost to the oncoming dawn. Shit – we needed more time. Not that the internal screams of a 21st century King Canute wannabe were going to hold back nature's rhythms.

Faraway cracks turned into nearby thumps as our adversaries took advantage of my team fleeing down the road. The firefight continued to pop and snap in the distance as I slowed after fifty metres of hard targeting.

The Oxford Circus junction was thankfully clear.

Straight ahead the narrow track led off left down to the cove. The main track veered right where it met the Piccadilly junction 250 metres further on. If troops poured down that route from Piccadilly, Mike's team still holding the position near The Ritz would be cut off.

I moved to the bushes at the side of the track and looked back. After cursing under my breath at their slow progress, I shouted encouragement to Hutch and Luke.

Manny was alongside Hutch pushing him forward. Luke had now pulled ahead and still ran with one arm across his chest. Jamie was tucked low, facing backwards. The gunfire had merged into one and I assumed some of it was his.

'Less than a hundred metres and we'll go firm,' I called out, pointing Luke down the narrow track.

I leapt to my feet, although creaked might have been a more accurate description, took a final look down the main track leading right to Piccadilly, and spurted forward to edge ahead of Luke on the narrower track. If the enemy had already mobilised a blocking force in this area, then we'd be in trouble. Only 150 metres further down this track, the building near the cove also worried me.

Twenty seconds later, I hadn't recognised any markers from our inbound march. Panting hard, I pulled up and raised my left hand. 'On me. Luke. Go firm here.'

After steering him under the trees, I faced the direction we'd run from. The others weren't in sight. Had I seen them follow us through the junction? If they'd gone up the main track it was job fucked. We'd never get back together before follow-up troops arrived.

Clumping boots and low voices approached. Manny had an arm round Hutch's back. Jamie hovered behind them.

I stepped out from the deep shadows as they reached me. 'In here.'

Hutch collapsed next to Luke, and Manny staggered before sinking to the floor.

'Get some water down your neck lads. You too Luke.' I peered under the canopy to see he already had a bottle to his lips. 'Good man.'

'Let me see that arm,' Jamie said to Luke. He caught his breath before saying to me, 'Couldn't see anyone following.'

'Sierra Delta, this is Alpha, gone firm as agreed. Withdraw to me, over.'

There was an ominous silence. Five seconds later I repeated the message.

'Sierra Delta, roger. On way.' Mike's gulped breaths suggested he had heard my first message and was already breaking contact. Not a surprise if he'd taken care of other business before responding.

Gunfire still crackled in the distance. The enemy were 200 metres from our current position and out of sight around a bend and over a rise in the road. That wouldn't last long. They'd soon be chasing us now Mike's team were pulling back. And how many other troops were right now converging on the prison and our last known sighting?

'Arrgh. Arrgh.'

'Sorry, I need to get this shit out of the wound and clean it up,' said Jamie.

Luke continued to whimper as the medic got stuck in.

'You okay?' I asked Hutch.

He nodded an unconvincing reply.

'We'll make it. There's less than 500 metres to the boats.'

His second nod carried less enthusiasm than the first.

'How about you?' I asked Manny.

'I can't believe it,' he said, raising a hand to his forehead.

I squeezed his shoulder. 'I know, mate. Let's make sure we get everyone else home.'

Running footsteps approached from the direction of the junction. I knelt in a firing position in case unfriendly faces showed up. When Mike, Ryan, and Alain dashed around the bend, I threw out an arm to signal our position.

They'd arrived just two minutes after my team. The time was now 05:47.

'How long do you need?' Mike asked.

'A couple more minutes. It's just a graze,' answered Jamie.

'I'll cover at the bend,' said Ryan, and he trotted off twenty metres up the track.

'Anything from down there,' asked Mike, flicking his head downhill towards the cove and its uncharted building.

I shook my head. 'Nothing.'

'Two more bounds?' he asked.

'Yep. Let me get the map.' I pulled it out of my vest, checked my torch was on red filter, brushed stones and a dead branch out of the way, and rotated the map to the ground.

'If we pull back to here,' – I used a twig to indicate a point midway between our current position and the beach – 'it's two hundred and fifty metres. Leaves us two hundred plus for the final leg. It's a hundred metres east of Regent Street and before the slope becomes a problem. What do you reckon?'

He studied the map in the pool of red light.

'Yeah. We'll trail fifty metres behind you, give or take. Be on your tail at first. There's not enough cover here and they'd bump us straight away if we hang around. You need to keep the pace going up front. Who knows what they're sending out?'

'If they come from the road, the bush will slow them down. With luck they might think we've gone for the cove.' I traced the twig along the coast. 'Shit. After that, our beach is the next one that isn't covered in rocks.'

'Best we get a fucking move on then,' said Mike with a painted smile.

'Yeah, best we had.'

CHAPTER 75

Jamie finished patching up Luke and issued both him and Hutch with pills he promised would take the edge off. He spotted my new action-man facial decoration and made a half-hearted offer to take a closer look. He'd already turned away before I declined.

I took point as we set off through the uneven forest terrain. Even in the open ground between clumps of trees we couldn't run like on the tracks – the risk of a twisted ankle or worse was too high. And I had to balance the tactical situation. We needed to move at a decent clip but also stay alert in case the enemy outflanked us.

Now 05:50, the morning had turned a noticeable shade or two lighter. I hoped that was due more to my improving night vision than an oncoming early sunrise. It was twenty minutes since the opening contact outside the prison.

My imagination pictured troops being hauled out of bed, packed into vehicles, and ordered to hunt us down.

Five hundred metres to the beach. Regular jungle patrolling could take half an hour. Way too long. I wanted to be at the beach in less than fifteen minutes.

I lengthened my stride. 'Come on guys, let's drive forward.'

'Negative, nothing heard. I'll try them now. Hello, Sierra Alpha this is Kingfisher, Charlie is requesting sitrep, over.'

The message from the boat was a morale boost, a reminder that we weren't alone. I scanned the dark canvas to my left where Dave and the Kingfisher would be waiting. No lights. They'd be running dark routine.

'Kingfisher, Sierra Alpha, At Charlie's location in figures one five, over.'

'Kingfisher, relaying to Charlie your ETA figures one five. Out to you. Sierra Charlie, did you get that?'

Any more of the communications were lost in a blizzard of scratching foliage and cursing as I fought my way through thick bush. Once clear of the suffocating undergrowth, I nuzzled the water bladder mouthpiece like a baby and sucked greedily. Open terrain meant quicker movement through less cover. That was a balance I was happy to accept.

We swerved between dark clumps of thick cover as we climbed a gentle slope to its crest. Vehicles and voices carried through the air, the loudest behind and to our right in the direction of Piccadilly. The enemy could be only 100 metres away if they'd slapped a roadblock at that junction. Fortunately, that 100 metres comprised dense jungle, in a straight line at least. There were bound to be tracks and routes through or around it.

The four men behind me stayed with the pace. They were arranged in two cosy pairs: Manny pushing and dragging Hutch; Jamie guiding and encouraging Luke. Mike and his gang were somewhere in the murkiness to our rear.

From the crest, the south-eastern coastline emerged like a map. Our beach was only a couple of hundred metres away, although that short distance included some tough going. The 300-foot-high hill in the south of the island loomed directly ahead like a huge shadow. Lights twinkled in the town at its eastern base, beyond our beach. Other lights, moving lights, were a concern. Vehicles heading north from the town – in our direction.

With the jungle thickening around us, I signalled a halt and checked the GPS. Close enough. 'Delta, this is Alpha, firm at waypoint, over.'

'Roger, we're right behind you.'

Jamie checked Luke's bandage while Hutch slumped against a tree trunk. Manny fiddled with something on his hip. He pulled out the guard force radio he'd taken at The Ritz. 'They're talking. I couldn't hear while we marched but now it sounds like English.'

I crunched down into an uncomfortable kneeling position sat back on my foot. The other four guys were either busy or crimped, so I was force protection. I kept the butt of the AK in my shoulder and lowered the stock to rest across my thigh. 'Turn it up.'

Manny adjusted the volume.

'…*no escape.*'

We frowned at each other. Before I could say anything, the radio crackled to life again.

'*Redcoat, I know you're out there. I'm coming for you and there's no escape.*'

Mamba was here. And he knew I was on the island. Or at least he thought I was on the island. On balance, there weren't many other candidates to lead a prison break of his latest guests. I wasn't going to disappoint him.

I let go of the rifle stock with my left hand and grabbed the radio from Manny. 'Listen Mamba. You're lucky I didn't kill you yesterday when I had you in my sights.'

'*Redcoat. Come now. You don't want to upset me when soon you will be returning to my care.*'

'General, stand your men down. There's no need for any more of them to die. We won't initiate contact.'

'*John Pierce, I knew you were a spy when I first met you. I let you go once, but this time you need to give yourself up.*'

I handed the radio back to Manny. 'Turn it off, mate. He's obviously got rebro stations on the island and I've got no idea if you can trace these things. Throw it back there towards the road.'

Manny pushed himself to his feet, stepped out from cover, and hurled the radio into the distance. As he sat down, three recognisable silhouettes jogged into view.

'What the fuck was that?' hissed Ryan. 'Go through all this shit and something nearly took my frigging head off.'

I couldn't help but laugh. 'It was a radio. I didn't like the programme they were broadcasting.'

Ryan halted in front of me and examined my face. 'What you mithering about? You haven't given him morphine have you, doc?'

'Mate, I could do with some. All good?'

'Yeah. Fucking hairy but no harm done. Not to us anyway.'

Mike settled beside us. 'There's vehicles and troops on the road. The chasing pack aren't far behind us. We need to get moving before they land on top.'

I looked at Jamie, who had finished checking Luke's arm wound. He gave me a thumbs up.

'Right, let's move. Power through this shit to the boats. I'll try a radio check with–' a broken transmission erupted in my ear and I held my hand up for quiet.

'…off the beach.'

'You…carry on…'

'Yes, push through…too many of them.'

Roper and Bob. Something had gone badly wrong on the beach. Tucked into thick cover, we had no way of seeing anything down there.

I didn't want to interrupt critical messages, so waited fifteen seconds before trying comms. 'Sierra Charlie, this is Alpha, message over.'

No reply on the radio. No sounds of shooting from the beach either.

'Sierra Charlie, this is Sierra Alpha, message over.'

'Alpha, this is Digger. We had to run. Bastards came down a hidden track on the right. Where are you?'

'We're two hundred metres northeast. How many hostiles?'

After a worrying pause, Roper's voice came over the net. 'Alpha this is Charlie, my radio is u/s. We had to bug out. Eight to ten soldiers hit the beach. Vehicles on the road and tracks. We're unseen, over.'

'Alpha, understood. We're two hundred metres to your eleven o'clock. Contour the slope and I'll guide you in.'

When I stopped talking, the rest of the team were staring at me. Mike, Ryan, and Jamie had already heard the exchange over their radios. I brought the others up to speed. 'They've been bumped. Troops all over. We need to spread out to catch them when they get here.'

'Fuck's sake,' said Ryan.

Mike let out a weary sigh. 'I guess we need another plan then.'

CHAPTER 76

The implication of Roper's message began to sink in. The blisters on my feet pulsed fire, the shredded skin under the rucksack straps cried for attention, and each movement in my sweat and saltwater-stained rig aggravated inflamed hotspots. Everyone's posture had slumped. Heads had dropped, including mine. I fought the grasping sense of failure. 'Mike's right, we need another plan. If we can stay undetected for ten minutes, until Tom and the beach team arrive, then we're still in with a shout.'

'It's a long swim,' said Ryan.

'Not so far if the boat comes in closer.' I replied, although without any conviction.

My eyes were drawn to Hutch and Luke's bandaged limbs and sunken demeanour. Swimming was a non-starter. 'Okay, that won't work, but we've got to do something. We can't surrender to this guy. I can't do it.'

I glanced around the team. Jamie had moved into a defensive fire position and directed Alain to cover the other flank. The two escapees sat curled into their own thoughts. Manny's blank gaze went through me.

'What do you think, Manny? Any contacts on the island? Any ideas?'

He looked at the AK-47 laid in his lap. 'I think you don't play dead with vultures.' He lifted his eyes back to me. 'We have to fight.'

My earpiece sparked up. *'Sierra Alpha, Sierra Charlie, this is Kingfisher, message over.'*

When Roper didn't answer, I did. 'Sierra Alpha, send, over.'

'*Alpha this is Kingfisher, can you reach Southern Cross, over?*'

Mike and Ryan both watched me as they listened to their own earpieces. Southern Cross was the emergency RV at the southern tip of the island. Mike shook his head.

'Alpha, negative. The route is blocked, and our boats are believed compromised, over.'

'*Can you reach the jetty at Kassa, over?*'

Ryan offered a doubtful expression. Mike looked thoughtful before waggling his hand from side to side. Maybe.

I tried to picture what lay between us and the jetty. Dozens of hostile troops and the scene of the prison raid for a start. But if we could reach it, was Dave Morgan really suggesting Kingfisher would dive in to rescue us?

'Sierra Alpha, that's unknown at present. Are you suggesting a change of RV?'

'*Kingfisher, affirmative. Give me a time and I'll be there.*'

The three of us all looked at our watches in unison – 05:57. Mike held up three fingers and then made a zero with finger and thumb.

'Kingfisher, Sierra Alpha, suggest jetty RV at zero six-thirty. If we can't make it, will send abort code, over.'

'*We'll be there. Good luck gents, out.*'

With a new plan now in place, I met the wry smiles on Mike and Ryan's camouflaged faces. 'How the fuck are we going to do this?'

'There's only one way I see this working,' said Mike. 'We need a diversion while the main body slips north and evades the hunters.'

'Like blowing some shit up?' asked Ryan.

'Not quite. Although if we had some frags or claymores then I'd be well up for that.' Mike turned his head to me. 'We'll engage the enemy. Shoot and scoot and keep them focused away from you. You take your team and Tom's, hug the coastline and squirt out to the jetty.'

'What about you? You think the three of you can make it out? If not, then we should stay together.'

'We'll be okay. Ryan?'

'Yeah, those gadgies back there might have a problem though.'

Mike grunted approval. 'Three of us will haunt them like wraiths.' He swept an arm towards the rest of the team. 'If we all stick together in a big cluster, we've got no chance. We haven't got time to fuck around and this can work.'

Mike was right about having no time. Shouts were now audible behind us and in the direction of the road. And the light was lifting way too fast. Within six feet, faces and details were clear. Even thirty feet away, I could see Alain's outline against a backdrop of dark brush.

I peered into the nearest undergrowth. 'If Tom doesn't get here soon, it'll be all over anyway.'

At 06:05, Roper, Bob, and Izzy broke out from an adjacent grove one after the other, sweating, covered in jungle detritus, and panting hard. Bob helped Izzy extract herself from a lunging twine, before blowing out a long breath. 'Jeez, the bush doesn't get any easier.'

'Did you hear the comms with Kingfisher?' I asked Roper.

He shook his head as he snatched something out of his hair. 'Very broken. Clambering through that shit.'

'We're going to RV with Kingfisher at the Kassa jetty at six-thirty.'

Roper looked at me and then Mike. 'Is that realistic?'

'We're bang out of options. Mike's team is going to run interference and get in their faces. Provide a diversion while we run for the RV.'

Roper's face screwed up in obvious concern. 'That's a big risk, Mike.'

'Don't worry, George. We've got it covered.'

'Stand to, stand to, hostiles twenty metres.'

Mike, Ryan, Roper, and I all heard Jamie's message at the same time and crouched while bringing our weapons into the shoulder.

'We'll relieve Jamie,' whispered Mike. 'Send Alain to us and tell him to stay low. You try and break out down towards the shore. Don't hang about. Call it in when you reach the jetty.'

'Okay. We'll hold the land-end till you get there. See you at six-thirty.'

I bumped fists with Mike.

'Laters,' said Ryan as he passed me and followed Mike towards Jamie's position.

'Good luck, mate. Keep your head down and don't be late.'

I told Manny to send Alain to Mike. Then I got Roper to take the team down the hill and into a murky patch of cover at the extreme of my view. Fifteen seconds later, Jamie jogged towards me as Alain passed him going the other way.

'You and Manny bring up the rear. Me and Tom will protect point. Bob can stay with Izzy and the guys. We must keep closed up. I'm aiming to skirt the edge of the jungle strip that borders the coastline.'

'Sure,' said Jamie, 'I'll keep an eye on Hutch and Luke as well. They're not doing too good.'

'*Delta, contact imminent.*'

Jamie and I both looked left on hearing Mike's message. His team were the other side of dense brush and out of sight. We scuttled down to join our guys, where I conveyed the order of march while Jamie grabbed Manny to cover north-facing arcs.

With the team in the prescribed order, I led them in-between and past Jamie and Manny, heading northeast towards the sea's expanse. Ahead of us, the open sloping ground was dotted with shadowy scrub and knots of trees. Great for fast movement, not so good for remaining concealed in the dawn twilight.

On our right side, the thick edge of the jungle curved down the hill. I wanted to take advantage of the natural cover without fighting through it. We'd be here all day trying to wade through that shite.

Although I was expecting it, the outbreak of rifle fire from less than thirty metres up the hill made me jump. Mike's team were in contact.

Screams rang out over to our left. Low voices called out to each other in French from very close in front. If I'd been hearing them through stereo headphones it couldn't have sounded closer. I couldn't see fuck all.

From behind a mass of brambles, a human form loomed in front of me. So close I could almost touch it. I double-tapped two rounds into the figure, which collapsed at my feet. I snapped right at rapid movement and an accompanying savage war cry.

As Roper blasted three shots that took out my charging would-be attacker, a round cracked past my left ear. I couldn't see a new target but splashed un-aimed rounds into the bush ahead. A flash amongst the foliage was followed by a jolt on my right side. That pulled the aim of my next two shots right on target, judging by the ugly scream that rang out.

I felt the area above my right hip although there was no pain. That could be a bad sign. My hand caught a flap of jagged material. He'd missed me and hit the bergen. Another one of my nine lives gone.

The shock of sudden, deafening violence was replaced by a lull over this anonymous woodland patch now transformed into a killing ground. A fierce exchange continued out of sight. French cries and British shouts mingled as Mike's team continued the fight. Every instinct screamed to help them, but that wasn't my job. I had to get this group to safety.

I'm no doctor, but it was safe to say the guy at my feet was dead. Even so, I unloaded his AK and flung it deep into the bush. Roper did the same with the war cry dude. I assumed his three bullets had prompted endex for that guy as well.

For some reason, shooting a man at point blank range felt dishonourable. Fuck it – all's fair in love and war. Better him than me.

'Alpha, clear my side,' I murmured into the radio. The shooting to our left had ceased and been replaced by the plaintive cries of a wounded French speaker.

'*Charlie, clear this side.*'

'*Bravo, clear.*'

'Alpha, moving out.'

Then came a message that lifted me like no other I could remember. '*Delta, see you in two zero mikes. Don't leave without us.*'

Mike and his team had dealt with their opposition. Now we needed to keep a careful watch for anyone hiding in the shadows while we hustled our way to the jetty.

We patrolled forward ten metres before I stooped to check the figure sprawled in the bushes.

'Is there anything I can do?' Izzy called out from over my shoulder.

The man's staring eyes blinked at me. I snatched the rifle from his loose grip and unloaded it. 'No, we need to keep moving.'

I deep-sixed the AK into the bracken and turned to find Izzy glaring at me from ten feet away. 'Is he alive?' she asked.

'Yeah, for now. The sooner we get out of here, the sooner someone might find him.'

She jutted out her chin and pulled her shoulders back.

I cut her off before she spoke. 'We stop, we die. Let's go.'

We cleared the contact point and made good speed hugging the fringe of the jungle. I guessed everyone had been invigorated by the adrenaline rush from the firefight. We couldn't afford to waste the opportunity to ride the back of that. It wouldn't take long before the inevitable slump in energy levels. I hoped we could make the jetty before that happened.

Within two minutes we'd dropped to only thirty metres from the unseen shore. The sea lapped against the rocks in a comforting rhythm totally at odds with our precarious circumstances.

The thick wedge of jungle expanded again as we contoured the slope north for another five minutes before a track came into view through the trees ahead. We'd bunched up like a conga line and I heard jangling kit and laboured breathing when I knelt and signalled a halt.

I opened the map, orientated it to the ground, and beckoned Roper alongside. The lifting twilight made a torch redundant.

'This is the track leading from Oxford Circus to the cove building. The Ritz is at ten o'clock, a hundred and fifty metres through thick forest. That's the ground we know, but it's likely full of hostiles.'

'What about this way, to the cove?' He pointed down the track to the right, which led on the map to a large square structure.

'I don't know. Mike saw a track between the camp and the shore pointing that way. Maybe it links to the one at the cove, maybe it doesn't.'

Roper looked up from the map and into my face. 'I haven't seen the ground. What do you think?'

'There could be a path. Otherwise we'll have to make our own.' I looked left at the track leading towards the scene of the earlier contacts. 'I can't see us making it through that way.'

Roper clasped me on the shoulder. 'Okay, decision made.'

Muted shots rang out up the hill away to our left. The mixed terrain made it difficult to judge the distance. The first snaps soon quickened like microwave popcorn. There was no point dwelling on Mike and the guys. We had to concentrate on getting our people to the RV.

It was 06:20 and we were 500 metres from the jetty. If we found a path and remained unmolested, we'd be late for the RV. If there wasn't a path, we'd be very late.

'Kingfisher, this is Sierra Alpha, message, over.'

'Kingfisher, send, over.'

'Alpha, new RV time zero six forty-five, please acknowledge, over.'

'Kingfisher, acknowledging RV is delayed one five mikes, over.'

'Alpha, roger, out.'

The pops to the west had diminished. I regretted agreeing to the diversion plan. We should have stayed together. I whispered into the radio. 'Stay alert. We don't know what's down here. Be prepared for a fast withdrawal.'

Two pairs of double clicks answered.

When I crept onto the track, I caught my first sight of the cove building. From the small section I could see through the trees, it appeared to be an impressive colonial residence. Good that it wasn't a barracks or obvious military facility, not so good that it looked well maintained. Even if the residents weren't early risers, I couldn't imagine anyone would ignore a stream of rolling firefights rumbling past their gaff. A phone call to the security forces would complicate our morning. Maybe it would be better to brazen it out and act like we belonged.

I clicked the pressel switch again. 'If we bump into anyone, speak French.'

The two-storey villa was set in a pleasant glade. As we hugged the edge of the treeline and went past the front door, the bonnet of a parked SUV with darkened windows came into view around the left corner. A gap between the trees on the other side of the thirty-metre-wide clearing revealed an ocean view. Nice place. Two more SUVs were parked next to the first in a neat row.

With my rifle in the shoulder and feeling exposed, I willed any occupants to stay out of our way. The trees curled left and I caught a glimpse of a scenic tunnel leading north through the forest. Elation ripped through me.

A loud double-snick from the house was followed by a bellow in French. 'Où allez-vous?' *Where are you going?*

Then, realisation must have dawned. 'Arrêtez là.' *Stop there*

Before any of the team could answer, a French shout chilled my blood. 'Général, les terroristes sont la.' *General, the terrorists are here*

General.

How many generals could there be on this small island?

After a hushed pause, a burst of automatic fire erupted from an upstairs window, causing the line behind me to dissolve.

Luke was knocked off his feet and crashed to the ground with a howl.

Bob bent into a crouch and lifted his AK-47 to send a salvo smashing through the windows above. In that moment I saw a younger Bob – the digger in 'Nam.

Two men poured out of the front door, but my attention was caught by movement down the left side of the house. Two more men with AK-47s. I got three shots off while the front guy fiddled with the safety. He flew backwards and the rifle jumped out of his hands. The soldier behind ducked out of sight.

A volley of fire erupted to my right. In my peripheral vision, Roper engaged a target towards the front of the house from a classic kneeling position.

While I was distracted by the two enemy figures now crumpling by the door, a soldier on my side popped up closer then disappeared again. 'Enemy left,' I shouted, looking across to see Hutch letting rip with the CZ at the upper windows.

Izzy knelt beside Luke, her hands already pulling at his smock and jumpsuit.

They were out all out in the open and exposed should more gunmen joined the fray. So was I.

A head and shoulders behind a rifle popped up above the bonnet of the nearest SUV. I pulled the trigger three times. By the third shot I was already falling. A vicious punch had smashed into my chest. I landed flat on my back, the sounds of gunfire and shouting cascaded over me like angry waves.

The AK remained in my hands and I was still breathing. My chest hurt like hell but there was no wet rattle, no fluids in my throat or smothering my body.

What the fuck?

I was hyperventilating and expected the onrush of drowning death at any moment.

High velocity gunshots and smashing glass resonated as Roper's face looked down at me. 'Where are you hit?'

I gulped one more beautiful, greedy breath before answering. 'Chest.'

He turned his head and shouted, 'Medic. Jamie.'

Then he looked down into my chest and said, 'He's on his way. Hold tight.'

The shooting had stopped although the shouting continued. All of it in English, indicating we had control of the situation.

I ran my left hand over my chest. No sucking chest wound. I rolled onto my right side before sitting up.

'Whoa, cowboy,' said Jamie as he knelt beside me. 'Let's see what we've got here before you go jumping around.'

'I think I'm okay. I don't know how.' I looked down and saw a messy hole in my vest. The dented black metal of an AK-47 magazine showed through. 'Fucking hell. It hit the mag.'

His eyes searched the area and his hands felt for wounds. 'Are you sure?'

I nodded and a laugh escaped. 'Yeah.'

'You lucky fucker.'

I pressed a hand on my chest. 'Still fucking hurts though.'

Jamie's attention was elsewhere. Guarded by Hutch, Izzy was on her knees attending to Luke, although all I could see of the Canadian were his motionless, orange-clad legs.

'Go deal with Luke. I'm fine.'

Jamie helped me to my feet, and I rolled my shoulders and twisted my neck and hips to check for undetected damage. Nothing. Yet another of those nine lives scratched off.

My chest throbbed, but I doubted the strike had even cracked a rib. It wasn't much sorer than everywhere else.

I glanced at the team's dispositions. Aside from the three grouped next to Luke, Roper weaved by the vehicles and Bob and Manny were knelt in fire positions, scoping their weapons across the front of the house.

'Is that guy down?' I called out to Roper.

'Yeah, you got him. Looks like he came off worse like his mate here. No sign of any others.'

Although Jamie was within shouting distance, I chose to ask the next question via the radio in case it elicited a bleak answer. 'How does he look, Bravo?'

Jamie raised his left hand in a thumbs up. *'He'll live. He won't be walking anywhere though. Caught one in the thigh and another in his calf.'*

The answer to that conundrum stared me in the face. I ran across to the corner of the house where Roper was loading a fresh AK magazine. 'We need to get keys to one or two of these vehicles. If you search the bodies, I'll clear inside.'

Roper shook his head. 'Leave it. Get a car and we can go now, before reinforcements arrive. You don't need to deal with the general.'

I shook off my bergen and propped it against the wall. 'Oh yes I do.'

CHAPTER 77

I tapped the top of my head with an open palm. 'Manny, on me.' He dashed over to join me up against the front wall of the house.

'You okay for ammo?'

'Yes. I'll change now.' He tore off his magazine and replaced it with a fresh clip. 'Ready.'

I pointed at the large, adjacent window and made a running motion with my fingers. Then I darted past and stopped against the wall. Once Manny had copied my move, we repeated the manoeuvre past the second window and reached the two mangled bodies by the open front door. A gory scene. Both men had taken a lot of hits. At least death would have been quick.

One of the men had been armed with a Makarov that now lay ten feet away. I ignored that and instead grabbed the much closer AK-47 dropped by the other guy. I unloaded the mag and handed it to Manny, before chucking the weapon in Roper's direction.

'Any idea how many inside?' I whispered.

'No. At least one on the top floor.'

'Okay. Go firm when we make entry. I'll go left, you go right. After that, we'll deal with the closest rooms. Then you can cover the stairs while I clear the rest of the ground floor. Got it?'

'Got it.'

'Three, two, one, go.'

We hurled ourselves through the doorway and into opposite corners at the front of a spacious entrance hall. The air was still. Not the stillness of an empty building but an ominous silence where danger lay in wait. We didn't have time to dick around. Whichever general sheltered inside would have called for backup.

A door on our left was open, the one on our right closed.

'Cover that door and through there.' I pointed at the closed door and down the hall to the bottom of a sweeping white staircase.

I took a deep breath that made my bruised chest ache as it pressed against the kit in my vest. Weapon in the shoulder, soft finger inside the trigger guard, I crashed in through the door slamming it to the right, jinked left out of the doorway, scoped right, left, right again. Room clear.

I used the sweat rag on my left wrist to wipe my forehead. One down, the rest of the house to go. And somewhere inside, that Mamba bastard might be waiting in ambush.

My whistle-stop tour of the ground floor passed without incident. It was a beautiful pad. Not a family home, not a woman's touch, not even a bachelor pad. It felt like a show home – a showing off home. Posh décor to impress visitors rather than for relaxation and comfort.

I joined Manny near the bottom of the wide, curved staircase. He pointed up and mouthed, 'Voices.'

'How many?'

He shrugged his shoulders. 'Two? Three?'

We'd both been careful to remain out of sight from anyone stationed at the top of the stairs.

'I'll run across the bottom into that alcove. If anyone starts shooting, mallet them.'

He frowned.

'Shoot them. On automatic.' I adjust my own weapon to the same. Tough shit to whoever got in the way.

'Alpha, this is Charlie, we've moved the casualty next to the vehicles. No keys found on the bodies, over.'

I whispered my reply into the mike. 'Alpha, roger, wait out.'

Manny and I nodded at each other before I sprinted across the hallway and past the bottom of the stairs. Automatic fire spewed down from the sneaky fucker who had been lurking at the top. Bullets skittered into the masonry as though someone had thrown a handful of frozen peas.

The thunder of rapid fire was joined by Manny leaning out and spraying rounds up at our unseen foe. The previously pristine floorboards, bannisters, and ceilings were ripped open as a deluge of lead danced across every surface.

I'd landed in a snotty heap and slammed into the wall of a small alcove, smacking my head and aggravating my latest chest injury. After righting myself without registering any new traumatic damage, I joined Manny in unleashing hell up the staircase, firing the first shots as I leaned out left from behind cover before even seeing a target.

Unluckily for our mystery assailant, he'd chosen that moment to lean out himself to try to get a bead on Manny. My long burst swept onto the target and peppered the uniformed figure, following him as he spun to the right and toppled down the stairs.

'Go, Go, Go.' I yelled as I took off up the stairs, swerving around the fallen defender and firing in short bursts to keep any other jokers' heads down. The sound of smashing glass and pottery hung in the air even after I'd reached the empty top floor landing. That would pass, unlike the heavy, enduring roar from assault weapons. Either my wild suppressive fire had been unnecessary, or it had scared the shit out of anyone who'd been up here and now they were hiding. Manny joined me on the empty landing.

I loaded a fresh thirty-round magazine. There were some range days where I hadn't fired this much ammunition. It was a 'targets will fall when hit' kind of day. Flesh and blood targets. I switched back to the moment – the personal moral inquest about killing soldiers who might be uninvolved had to wait. Manny copied me and clicked a full mag into place.

My ears sang as though tiny manic bellringers had taken residence. The acrid smell of cordite hung heavy and out of place in these domestic surroundings.

I scanned the landing and the four closed doors leading from it: pockmarked walls, smashed windows and ceramics, an obliterated painting clinging to one hook, a blood spatter on the parquet floor, and danger skulking behind at least one of the doors. The aroma of war and death now owned this place.

'John, are you there?' Bob's Aussie accent rang out from below. 'John! Manny!'

I held my finger to my lips and then pointed at my chest. I chopped a knife hand at the door on my left and signalled for Manny to watch the others.

My earpiece buzzed into life.

'Alpha this is Charlie. Nothing heard. If you can hear me, Delta is in contact with multiple vehicles near Piccadilly. We haven't got long, out.'

In all the fun and games, I must have missed an earlier message. Mike was still roaming the island causing mischief. The crackle of distant gunfire attested to the accuracy of Roper's report.

I reached for the door handle, gave it a rapid twist, and pushed it open, before jerking back into cover. Two shots blasted through the opening, followed by two more. They ricocheted off the far wall above an untouched, tall wooden cabinet that I noticed for the first time.

Rather than go all *Antiques Roadshow*, I chose to turkey peek around the door frame while snap shooting a generous spread of 7.62mm as a dissuader. The brief glance revealed an open room. I'd been concerned there might have been a deadly small corridor or other restrictive setup. Because my attention had been grabbed by a bulky uniformed figure diving behind a large oak desk, the rest of the room and anyone hiding in it remained a mystery.

Three shots answered my contribution and shattering glass indicated the wooden cabinet had just seen a reduction in value.

Stalemate.

Parking warfare's equivalent of the Queensbury rules for a moment, I flapped a hand at Manny. He'd understand shortly.

'Manny, I'm hit. I'm hit,' I cried out in my best theatrical impression.

Given how many bits of my body hurt like fuck, it didn't take much imagination. 'Go and get the medic. Now.'

I counted to five and then repeated the turkey peek.

Ah ha, sucker.

A slim soldier approached the door with a handgun held in front. My four rounds struck him on the midline from his breast plate to his forehead.

There was no time to feel sickened by the explosion of red mist because a familiar face peered from behind the desk at the far end of the room.

A shot whistled past. Bloody close. If I'd had wavy blond locks it would have parted them.

That familiar face – Mamba.

'Give it up, General.' I called out. 'Your men are dead and you'll be next. Call off your troops and I'll spare you.'

Laughter boomed from inside. 'Redcoat, you English have a way with drama. I hope you're not too badly injured.'

'I'll get over it.'

'It is not me that should surrender, it is you and your criminal spies who must lay down your arms. Reinforcements will be here any minute.'

'I don't think so. That sound you can hear is the rest of my platoon teaching your reinforcements a military lesson.'

I tried a rapid peek and a shot whizzed past. So that's how we were playing things.

'A platoon.' General Sylla let out a derisive snort. 'You think you can fool me. You have a handful of spies who will soon be facing the harshest sentences for the murder of Guinean soldiers.'

'That right? It didn't take much to trick your batman did it. Radio your troops to stand down and give me the keys to your cars. On my word, I'll let you live.'

I hadn't decided anything of the sort, and my conscience would allow me to lie to this scumbag all day long.

'I knew you were a spy the moment I met you. I knew it.'

'And I knew you were an evil bastard the moment I met you. The name Mamba suits you. But I'm not a spy and never have been. Not then, not now.'

Another economical use of the truth if you counted Project Brimstone.

'Only you know why you ordered an attack against an innocent mining company. Your people killed good men for no reason.'

I heard movement inside the room, not that I was going to try another peek unless it was behind a wall of lead.

'Not my men,' he shouted. 'I knew nothing about it. Nothing about you. Not until our friends told me of a suspicious British group right next to their interests.'

There was a soft laugh.

'I thought of you, immediately. Redcoat. The British spy who got away. I'm sure you laid awake on many nights and remembered our time together.'

'Alpha this is Charlie, Delta has broken contact. Enemy forces could arrive at any moment, over.'

'Alpha, roger. I'll be two minutes, out.'

'I'd love to stay and chat,' I said, 'but I've got places to be. Give the order and throw me the keys or you won't be overseeing the renovations of your mansion.'

His reply was filled with sickly intensity. 'When they told me they'd attacked a convoy and captured prisoners, I longed for it to be you. To savour your screams again. To hear you begging for your mother. Imagine my disappointment to find you had got away. Your spineless friends gave you up in minutes. I hoped you'd come.'

A laugh slipped out. 'And how's that working out for you? All this death and destruction and you didn't order it.' My next laugh was loud and ironic. 'I get the chance to kill you thanks to al-Qaeda. Cheers, Osama.'

'Never,' he roared, and two more shots zipped past.

A giveaway click spurred me into action. Either a magazine change or some other adjustment. I rushed into the room behind multiple short bursts. He rose with a large handgun in his outstretched, meaty hand.

It registered that I'd seriously miscalculated. He had a Glock, not a low-capacity Makarov, and he hadn't been changing mags.

The reservations dissipated as my rounds splashed into his torso. But he absorbed them without being thrown backwards. It triggered a stab of fear that he'd brushed those hits off.

I pumped more instinctive shots at the target.

A tight grouping in his upper left chest caused his hands to lift skywards and the pistol to fall out of sight past his shoulder. He toppled like a felled tree after it, his head crashing against the side of the polished desk on the way down.

I spun right to check the rest of the room. Just my luck if some other joker had been hiding in a corner.

I changed magazines and called Manny into the room. 'Grab that radio and transmit a message in French. Say, "The general is safe and leaving his residence. Keep out of the way".'

Manny transmitted the message while I checked on the general. A vulture with his wings well and truly clipped. He'd landed on his back with the Glock by his side. A fresh cut in his hairline was the least of his problems. The thick, sausage fingers of both hands clutched at his punctured chest in a futile effort to hold on to life. Bright red blood oozed between them, flowed over his left shoulder, and pooled onto the floor by his ear.

'I'll add that to my collection.' I scooped up the Glock and wedged it into a bulging pocket on my vest.

Malevolent eyes tracked my movements. For a dying man, he wasn't letting this go easily.

'I'd offer you medical attention in return for safe passage, but I wouldn't trust a word you say. Now where are those car keys?'

When I turned to search the crap on his desk, I half expected a hand to reach out and grab my ankle. But the lights were going out on Mamba's journey. His glare lost more of its menacing intensity each time I glanced down.

I'd never studied a man as he died. Even with a vicious bastard like General Sylla, it felt like an uncomfortable intrusion into a man's soul. I'd leave that to the Big Man up top.

'Come on, where are they? I opened the top drawer on the right. 'Ah ha, thank you very much.'

I glanced down at the general to see the spark hadn't completely left him. He didn't focus on me; he stared to my left. I followed his gaze and leaned down to open the door to a desk cupboard under the drawer. It revealed a grey metal desk safe with a digital keypad next to a thick silver handle.

'Ill-gotten gains, eh? I don't suppose you want to give me the code.'

His eyes burned into mine. Pure hatred depleting the last of his life force.

'No, I didn't think so.'

'We go?' asked Manny.

'Yeah, just let me try…' I gripped the silver handle and gave it a twist. The safe clicked open.

'Fucking hell.'

Neat bundles of US dollars were stacked on the bottom shelf. The visible notes all Benjamins. But it was the top shelf that took my breath away. Five huge, glittering, marble-sized stones. My memory beamed back to a hotel room two years earlier.

I pulled out the tray with the diamonds and turned to Mamba with a broad smile and a knowing nod. His very essence shrivelled at the sight of me holding the treasure. The now vacant eyes closed and his head lolled to the side.

Manny and I stuffed as much cash as we could fit into our pockets. We divvied up the stones – three for me and two for him. Manny didn't say anything, but I felt the need to justify the theft. 'The insurance will be fucked, so this is compensation for the dead guys. And something for us.'

His face conveyed only sadness.

I grabbed the Makarov dropped by the general's lackey, applied the safety catch, and passed it to Manny. 'Let's get the fuck out of here.'

CHAPTER 78

We found a jittery Bob hovering inside the front door. His shoulders relaxed when he caught sight of us. He opened his mouth to speak just as the radio blared in my ear.

'All stations, Kingfisher beginning the run in. See you in ten, out.'

Once out the door, the front of the house was deserted, which took me by surprise. Then I remembered that Roper had gathered the team round the side by the vehicles. The odd shot popped in the distance – in the direction we'd be driving. Although nothing sustained to indicate Mike's team were in serious contact.

A ripple of apprehension stirred. I'd been too busy with General Sylla to concentrate on the inbound radio messages buzzing in my ear. My unease worsened at the long faces around the team. Was Luke more seriously injured than we'd thought?

First things first. I waved the keys in my left hand. 'I've got two sets.'

The first blipped open the black Land Cruiser with the darkened windows. The general's car I assumed. Roper caught the other set when I threw them over.

'What's wrong? Is Luke okay?'

'It's not Luke, it's Mike's team. Alain. He's been hit.'

'Bad?'

'He's dead. They had to leave him. Mike and Ryan are somewhere in the jungle near the prison.'

The cam cream on Izzy's face was eroded by vertical tear tracks.

By the shudder of her shoulders, it was clear she was still crying. Her cousin was dead and now so was his friend.

Sadness and anger welled up from the futility of this entire episode. Good people were dead and for what? I wanted to holler 'endex' – have everyone go non-tac, shake hands, and piss off home to our real lives.

'John?' Roper stared at me.

'Sorry, mate. I didn't catch that. Shall we take two cars?'

'Yeah, that's what I said. We need the room for Luke. And we've got to get a move on.'

Manny and I dealt with business first. We shovelled the cash and diamonds into my bergen. Roper watched me with a questioning look.

'Compensation from the general,' I said, zipping the rucksack shut and hoisting it onto my shoulder. 'For the families and for us.'

'In return for what?'

I shook my head. 'No. He's dead. He didn't feel like negotiating. We're going to need your help to get this lot home with the paperwork it needs.'

'I see.'

I opened the passenger door to the general's motor and a thought struck me. 'I might have bought us some time. Sowed a little confusion at least.'

Roper looked at me across the roof of the car. 'We need all the help we can get. Kingfisher's on the way to the RV.'

I assigned Manny to drive our car and he led off up the track. Hutch and Izzy sat in the rear seats. Izzy was keeping busy checking Hutch's wounds. After spying her examining a nasty cigarette burn on his bicep, I turned to concentrate on the road ahead.

'Stay close, Charlie, and don't stop. If it goes noisy, we drive through.'

'*Roger.*'

I tried reaching Mike. 'Delta, this is Alpha, we'll be busting through Oxford Circus in one mike. Signal if you need a lift, over.'

There was no reply. I repeated the message. Still nothing.

'Alpha, nothing heard. We'll watch for you, out.'

I unfurled the map and checked the route.

The distance by road to the jetty was only 750 metres and it would be difficult to get lost. Up the winding track 200 metres to Oxford Circus; past the prison until we reached a dustbowl; across that and onto the island's main north-south artery towards Kassa town; a hard right at a blurry junction before the town centre; then burn rubber 350 metres to the jetty entrance.

The map appeared to show we could carry straight on and drive along the 250-metre man-made spit of land to the pontoon that I assumed Kingfisher was heading for. A long concrete section lay at an oblique angle beyond the pontoon, but the Google Earth image showed the two parts of the jetty were unconnected. I imagined the twenty-metre gap had resulted from erosion and shoddy workmanship.

Some might have considered it optimistic to be worrying about the RV when we had yet to pass through untold numbers of hostile troops. I got on the radio anyway. 'Kingfisher, Sierra Alpha, we need you at the pontoon on the north side. The concrete section is not connected, over.'

'Alpha this is Kingfisher, understood. Will you be on time, over?'

Oxford Circus had come into view and it was filled with soldiers. 'Hit the horn and don't stop,' I said to Manny. He didn't need telling twice and his left hand pummelled the wheel.

With the horn blaring and men scattering, I scanned the undergrowth as I answered Dave on the boat. 'We'll be there, but we might need to wait for Delta and Echo.'

Manny kept his foot on the gas as we bumped past the camp on our right side. Across the clearing where the first firefight of the morning had taken place, I watched the prison building slide past and thought of Condé, forsaken by the fence.

So much for never leaving anyone behind.

I dismissed the option of following the warrior code by stopping to collect his body. Too high risk. It didn't stop bitter self-loathing from surfacing.

Mike and Ryan were nowhere to be seen. We kicked up a cloud of dirt as Manny navigated the dustbowl. 'Do you know where you're going?' I asked him.

'No.'

I grabbed at the map and zoomed in on the route. 'Right turn in a hundred and forty metres. Immediately past the first building on the right. Don't miss it or we'll be visiting the town square.'

He shot me a look without answering. I hoped the ground hadn't changed since the Google Earth image was taken.

'Okay, there it is.'

A building in the right place on the end of a line of trees.

I spoke into the mic. 'After the building, right, right, right.'

'There's no road,' Manny said with more than a hint of panic.

'Just take it.'

The rear of the Land Cruiser slid left as Manny made a tight turn into the front yard of a smallholding. Chickens bomb-burst in all directions and one flapped into the windscreen with a fleshy thump.

'Keep going, keep going.'

No wonder the junction had been unclear on the map – there was no junction. As we bounced over the uneven ground and narrowly avoided a collection of tools and buckets stacked against a water well, the bottom of the car grounded on a large rock with a hell of a bang.

'Left. Down the side.'

'Fuck,' was Manny's considered opinion.

Another wide, single-storey dwelling loomed ahead. Time to meet the next-door neighbours. According to the image in my hand, on the other side we'd have a clear run down a wide track to a four-way junction. Cross that, and we'd be on the approach to the jetty.

The space between the left of the house and the adjacent trees was narrow, very narrow.

I jabbed a finger towards the pedals. 'Foot on the gas.'

The bodywork screamed as we juddered against the stone building on our right and scraped the trees on our left. Once clear of the building, the driveway opened into the wide track as anticipated. I checked the wing mirror and saw Roper's white Land Cruiser crash through in similar fashion.

We were nearly there. Against the odds we'd almost made it. But where were Mike and Ryan?

CHAPTER 79

We flew down the hill through a shallow right bend. A collection of wrinkly tin hooches garnished a rubbish-strewn patch of open land on our immediate left. None of the residents were up and about and there was no police or security forces presence.

Two hundred metres away, the channel between the island and the mainland rippled under a clear morning sky. Dawn had well and truly broken. Sunrise was seven minutes away according to the schedule from the Brimstone Met guys. Not that it would make any difference – it couldn't get much brighter.

We skipped left around an outcrop of trees that had been blocking the view of the jetty and beyond. The four-way junction I'd identified was more of a bend in a main track that a few minor tracks had latched onto. A hotchpotch of warehouses and shacks lined the larger track, which led off to the left past a nubbin of a quay surrounded by a smattering of fishing boats.

As we crossed through the heart of the junction, the view of important terrain on our right hit me all at once. Everything was so close.

At our three o'clock, 150 metres to the right, the tops of buildings were visible in the camp. The main gate was out of sight due to a group of low buildings on an intervening rise, but we could assume there would be officers and troops swarming that area.

Two hundred and fifty metres directly ahead was the jetty, dressing slightly to the right. The man-made harbour was further enhanced by an angled protrusion at the far end. At a guess, that was the unconnected concrete extension.

If my energy level fizzed at the sight of the jetty, it exploded at a blue and white fishing boat heading in from the right.

I hit the pressel switch. 'Kingfisher one thousand metres at two o'clock.'

'Charlie, seen. He'll be there bang on time.'

'I've heard nothing from Delta. Stop by the buildings at the jetty entrance.'

'Roger.'

'This is Kingfisher, told you I'd be here.'

'You're a sight for sore eyes. Sierra Alpha, out.'

We passed more canoes and nets and other fishing paraphernalia on both sides. Hunched figures glanced up and quickly turned away. No surprise given who normally rode in this distinctive, sinister car.

I put my hand on the dashboard and told Manny to stop at the large building.

We skidded to a halt at the jetty entrance. Three buildings stood on our right, with the largest in the centre boasting a crest and a load of official text. The 250-metre-long jetty comprised a raised, ten-metre-wide concrete roadway bracketed by rubble running down to the water. At the far end of the jetty, the empty berthing pontoon floated on the left-hand side. Thankfully, there was no sign of a hostile reception committee.

Five more minutes and we would be out of here. Bruised, saddened by losses, but free and running for international waters and then Freetown. However, that depended on Mike and Ryan evading the hornets' nest they had been poking for the last half hour.

'Sierra Delta, this is Alpha, send sitrep, over.'

It felt so long since I'd heard from Mike or Ryan, that I hadn't expected the immediate answer that followed.

'Alpha this is Delta, I am in difficult terrain east of The Ritz. I have one friendly KIA, no longer with me. ETA at RV, one zero mikes, roger so far over.'

'Alpha, sitrep well received so far, over.'

'*I have hostile forces heavy on top. Estimate less than five zero metres distance, over.*'

'Understood. We are at the RV approach and will hold until your arrival. Currently no hostile activity. We are mobile if you reach open terrain, over.'

An automatic weapon rattled a few hundred metres to the south. Due to the buildings, I couldn't see the jungle Mike was battling through.

We needed to get organised and move an advance group forward to the pontoon. When I exited the car to issue instructions, a man in a plain grey uniform with bars on his epaulettes strolled out of the large building a few metres to my right. My attention was drawn to the big, floppy holster on his belt.

We stared at each other. His expression one of surprise, which I'm sure matched my own. I pointed the AK at his chest and clicked the safety catch off. 'Anyone else inside?'

He remained rooted to the spot; eyes fixed on the rifle barrel.

'Les autres dans la…dans la…fuck I don't know. La maison?' My French might have been shit but he understood.

'Oui, oui.'

'Les autres ici, now.' Aiming the muzzle at his face did a better job at prompting a shout into the open doorway.

'Fucking hell, Manny. Give me a hand here.'

'Hang on. We might have a problem.'

Two slovenly minions with open shirts bimbled out of the office, looked at me, looked at the AK pointed at their boss, surveyed the two vehicles and the team, shrugged their shoulders, and sat down. Neither displayed weapons so I didn't subject them to any excruciating commands in French.

Over my left shoulder, I said, 'What's the problem?'

'On the radio. They've found the general. Now they're all looking for his car. This car.'

I turned to look at him. 'What radio?'

'The one I took from the general's office. I turned the volume up and heard the messages.'

'Shit. Keep listening.' I glanced at Roper as he approached while inspecting my latest set of prisoners. 'Tom, did you catch that?'

'I heard,' said Roper. 'Not good news.'

I considered our situation and options. Hutch appeared calm if a little woozy. His recent traumas and the drama of the escape were catching up with him. Jamie stood by the Land Cruiser, reaching over the rear seats.

'Jamie, how's Luke?'

'He's stabilised and I've given him morphine. The Quickclot kicked ass to stop the bleeding.'

'Could Izzy take care of him for a few minutes?'

He looked past me and smiled. 'Yes, she's more than capable.'

When I checked left, Izzy's indignant expression was aimed in my direction. I raised a hand in apology. 'Sorry, Izzy. I meant the drugs and dressings. Of course you're capable.'

'Yes, I am,' she replied, eyes narrowed.

'Tom, take your car with Izzy, Luke, and Hutch to the pontoon. I'll stay here with the others until Mike and Ryan make it out.'

Roper looked out to sea as he considered my proposal. Kingfisher wasn't far off now – a matter of minutes. 'Okay. If you need me, I can come back down once the guys are on the boat.'

I unhooked my bergen and prepared to throw it in the back of his car. 'I hope it won't come to that.' I patted the rucksack. 'Make sure you don't leave this behind.'

He took it and handed me two of his spare AK-47 magazines before climbing behind the wheel.

Izzy assisted Hutch to the rear car and sat him in the front passenger seat, replacing Bob. She then received a patient handover from Jamie before wedging her slight frame into the rear footwell by Luke's head.

Roper dipped his head as he set off onto the narrow causeway.

Dust from the car swirled around Bob and Jamie's feet. The Aussie wore his black hat and a contented smile. 'Sun will be in our eyes any minute.'

I gestured at Jamie. 'You and Bob, me and Manny. You two tie these prisoners up while we hide the car.'

'Too late,' said Manny from inside the black SUV. 'They've spotted us.'

I peered towards the camp and saw a convoy of five vehicles 150 metres away, snaking through the trees in our direction. 'Delta, this is Alpha, mobile tangos approaching my position from the west. Your ETA, over?'

'We're east of the compound next to the camp. Moving faster on easier ground. Two hundred metres from your location.'

'Roger. We'll cover you in.'

I handed two full AK magazines to Manny. 'That should keep you going.'

The other pair had already taken charge of the three prisoners. While Jamie fixed plasticuffs on the boss, Bob had nestled in between the two seated, disinterested soldiers and encouraged them to lie on their faces by way of a hearty shove in the back. 'Easy tiger,' he said to one who didn't take kindly to the hands-on directions.

'Jamie, once you're done, you take the right flank, we'll take the left.'

'Wilco.'

Seventy-two minutes since the first contact outside The Ritz and the defending forces had mobilised an increasing number of troops. It didn't help that over an hour later we were sat on exposed ground only 350 metres from the scene of the raid.

Apart from the SUVs making their slow approach from the camp at our ten o'clock, another collection of camouflaged and police vehicles had appeared at the four-way junction directly ahead. The black SUV would be hidden from the left group, but the police and military stopped at the junction had easy line of sight.

The buildings provided some cover but staying there meant we couldn't cover Mike and Ryan's approach. Facing back at the island, the immediate ground was a seventy-five-metre square wedge of land contained light scrub, a ramshackle single-storey building, and a few withered trees.

A small cove on the right hosted a dozen or more fishing canoes, both floating in the water and laid on the beach. Three men were crouched among them minding their own business. They were in for a shock.

Directly ahead, past the wedge of land, were the unpaved roads, tracks, and undeveloped open ground we'd crossed on our mad dash from the general's place. As I jogged out from the cover of the official buildings with Manny behind me, the view to the left flank in the direction of Mike's approach opened up.

A crescent-shaped sandy bay ended in the forest where Mike and Ryan were running for their lives. The beach would have been a lovely place to take the family, if it wasn't for the small, half-eaten trawler in the middle of the sand, stranded like a fish out of water at low tide.

I veered left and upped the pace. 'This way. To the boat.'

The fifty metres across the energy-sapping sand felt a lot further. When we reached the stern, gunfire had broken out again to the south – where the lads were coming from.

I swung an arm in the general direction of the assembled enemy on the higher ground. 'Cover me, while I climb up.'

Bullets pinged off the boat's hull as I clambered through the twisted metal and reached a ladder leading up top. Like the start of a rainstorm, the initial few plinks accelerated to a hail of lead hosing down our prominent piece of cover. Maybe this hadn't been a good idea.

The whole world was letting rip as I peeked from behind the wheelhouse towards the far end of the beach. Mike and Ryan were a hundred metres away, bent low as they ran along the shoreline.

From my elevated position, I could see standing soldiers creeping down the hill to cut them off. The convex slope above the beach seemed to be providing our men temporary cover.

'All stations, Delta and Echo coming in from the south. Alpha is providing cover from a beached trawler. Bravo, you need to keep the route to the jetty open, over.'

'Bravo, roger. Me and Digger are in rough cover on the right of the track. Vehicle and troops approaching from our ten o'clock and twelve o'clock. Engaging, out.'

'Alpha and Bravo…Blue Red Blue on Kingfisher…engaging targets… front…luck gents, out.'

The second message had been drowned out by my own automatic fire as I engaged the troops advancing down the slope. Mike and Ryan were also shooting at them while they ran. Loud volleys from below me must have been outgoing fire from Manny. Either that or we were in real trouble.

The Blue Red Blue callsign would be Dave Morgan. It was the calling card of the Guards Division.

I glanced over to where Jamie and Bob were holding the jetty entrance route open. I couldn't see either of them, but they were making plenty of noise. Rounds smashed into the remaining glass in the wheelhouse and caused me to retreat behind sturdier cover.

We were massively outgunned. I'd seen at least three of the enemy fall but there must have been thirty or more weapons pointed our way. That number would only grow as troops who had been sweeping the island arrived as reinforcements.

'Stoppage,' screamed Manny.

Good drills but not what I wanted to hear. Unlike the decent AK-47s supplied by Dave, Manny and Bob had trophies we'd captured over the last day or so. I prayed Manny could clear the stoppage fast.

I came up on aim from a new firing point and dropped two targets in quick succession, this time with the selector on single shot. They had been leading a pack chasing Mike and Ryan along the shoreline. Their oppos dived for cover.

There were so many targets, I was worried about our ammo state. I'd already fired umpteen rounds on automatic and lost count of my magazine changes.

Outbound fire resumed from below. Single shot like mine. A good idea if the feed on Manny's AK was iffy.

A heavy rattle of automatic fire erupted from over by the camp. It sounded like a belt-fed weapon. A PKM at a guess. Fuck.

'Blue Red Blue engaging machine gun position.'

A loud crack boomed out from behind and the machine gun stopped firing. Sniper Dave was in the fight and he'd brought along some firepower. The blast reverberated over the battlefield noise as though the rest of us were firing pop guns.

The battleground had settled into a static engagement, apart from Mike and Ryan hard targeting towards the boat. Winning the firefight was a vital part of section and troop battle drills. Regrettably, this was a shootout we couldn't win.

Sand kicked up at Ryan's feet and he faltered but kept going behind Mike into the shadow of the stern.

'Keep going,' I yelled down at them. 'Push on fifty yards to the shack and cover us back.'

Getting into an elevated position to cover the team's approach had seemed like a good idea. Having to faff around getting off the bloody boat as hordes of enemy closed-in didn't strike me as quite so smart.

Another loud crack boomed above the clattering exchanges of the AK-47s on both sides. Get in! I wouldn't fancy opposing a British army master sniper instructor with a big-ass weapon in his hands.

The rucksack-clad backs of Mike and Ryan retreated to our rear, one of the men with an encouraging arm round the other's back. If Ryan had been hit, he was still running, so it couldn't be too serious.

Vehicles were on the move above the slope and at the junction. Our enemy must have realised we were getting away.

I looked across to the pontoon at the far end of the jetty where Kingfisher bobbed alongside. The white SUV was parked nearby. Once Manny and I had pulled back to the others, the six of us had to cross the 250-metre narrow, open causeway to reach safety. I'd consider that problem once we made it to the buildings.

At the top of the ladder, I looked past the Kingfisher to Conakry in the background. Best Guinea didn't have any kind of naval forces on standby.

'I'm coming down,' I shouted to Manny. 'Get ready to leg it.'

'Delta in position.'

Mike's message arrived as I climbed through the trawler's carcass. They were ready to cover our withdrawal.

When I stepped out onto the sand and looked left, Manny was tucked firmly against the stern and behind a protruding piece of the hull.

'Fucking hell, you've burrowed in there, mate. Time to go.'

Manny blinked and offered a strained smile. At a guess, he'd attracted his fair share of incoming.

'You alright?'

'Yeah, I'm ready.'

Crouched against the side of the vessel, we were out of sight from enemy forces. That was until two vehicles darted into view as they charged down the main track towards the jetty. A hail of gunfire homed in on the lead car, shattering the windscreen.

The chatter of exotic birds broke into my consciousness, as though a sound engineer had dialled back the cacophony of men trying to kill each other. It was so explicit it scared the shit out of me. Like a supernatural portent that the bullet with my name on it might be close by.

We were running out of time.

I keyed the mic. 'Alpha moving.'

CHAPTER 80

As we bolted across the sand, I recalled the beach scene from *Chariots of Fire*. Not that the serene image had much in common with our desperate dash for safety as we hard targeted to avoid incoming rounds I could no longer hear. Blood pumped in my ears as I jinked left and right, eyes focused on a selected piece of cover.

Ryan's arm waved towards the water. He must have needed line of sight on targets behind us. I braced for a devastating impact that never arrived. We collapsed into the rough dunes behind Mike and Ryan's fire positions.

The sweat swilled onto my face as fast as I could wipe it off. There was no time for respite. I led Manny to the right edge of the shack, which sported numerous 7.62mm ventilation holes. Jamie and Bob were twenty metres ahead on the other side of the ten-metre wide track.

The volume of automatic fire had diminished. We wouldn't be the only ones concerned about ammunition levels. Our six-man team were all firing single aimed shots, augmented by a regular discharge to our rear courtesy of call sign Blue Red Blue and his hand cannon.

With my breathing under a semblance of control, I got on the net. 'Prepare to withdraw to the jetty. First bound to the black car, over.'

'Bravo standing by.'

'Delta standing by.'

'Delta, you move first, over.'

'Roger, moving.'

When Mike and Ryan ran past, Ryan's face was etched with pain and he had an obvious limp. I took up a position covering their previous arcs on the left of the ventilated shack. 'I'll shout when it's time to go,' I called over to Manny.

In front of me, the soldiers and police were advancing behind their vehicles. I could see six SUVs and a tipper truck with heads bobbing behind them. Twenty-five or thirty men. That was just my restricted view of the left flank. More vehicles would be advancing from the 4-way junction. There was also rough ground with natural tree cover in front of Jamie and Bob's position on the right flank. We needed them out of there before the local commanders got cute.

'Bravo, you're next,'

'Moving now.'

An intense barrage sparked up over to the right – worryingly close. I could hear shouting. It sounded like Manny had another stoppage.

'This is Bravo, Digger's down.'

Bob. Dread clamped my chest.

I left my position and ran behind the shack where Manny was swearing furiously as he sought to clear his weapon yet again.

Ahead of us, Jamie dragged Bob by his shoulders in our direction. Mike appeared to my right and raced past in the middle of the track, firing on the move. Ryan followed close behind him.

'Get back to the car,' I said to Manny.

He looked at me, stood up, and charged in the opposite direction to join Mike and Ryan going to aid Jamie and Bob.

Enemy troops had appeared on the right at the edge of the rough ground, on top of Jamie and Bob's former position. Just what I'd feared and tried too late to avoid. Mike assisted Jamie to drag Bob towards me. Ryan knelt in the open on the track smashing out covering fire.

I leaned around and fired dangerously close to Mike's left shoulder. A soldier dropped when the first round hit him. My second shot hit his buddy who staggered backwards and fell.

When Manny got hold of Bob, Mike let go and dropped to one knee. Incoming fire had dwindled and the wave that had threatened to overrun Jamie and Bob had been repelled.

As Manny and Jamie swung the big Aussie to safety behind the shack, Jamie let out a yell and buckled. He landed heavily under his medical rucksack. I darted out and hauled him behind cover.

'Pull back,' I yelled at Mike and Ryan, both still out in the open. 'Jamie's hit.'

'Fucking piece of shit weapon.' Bob's voice faltered as he spoke, but it was a relief he felt well enough to moan. 'Bloody thing seized up just as they appeared.'

I eased off Jamie's rucksack and chest webbing and scanned his body for wounds. Blood soaked through his shirt above his right hip. When I pulled the material clear, I could see it was bad.

I pulled out a sachet of Quickclot from my vest and a large dressing. After tipping the granules onto the wound and using my free hand to stop them pouring to the deck, I covered it with the pad and pressed down hard.

'Are you hit anywhere else?'

He nodded without replying. Keeping the pressure applied with my right hand, I pulled up his shirt and looked inside. Another entry wound under the armpit. No obvious exit wounds.

Mike and Ryan were now close by – one examining Bob and the other firing from the corner of the shack.

'This is serious,' I called to Mike as he applied a field dressing to Bob's midriff, 'Chest wound.'

'We've got to move them, or we'll be overrun,' he replied. 'Reinforcements have arrived up top.'

Jamie won't survive that, I thought but didn't say out loud. 'How's Bob?'

'Not great, but you'll be alright won't you, big man?'

Like Jamie, Bob had lapsed into semi-consciousness and didn't reply.

'I'll take Bob,' said Mike.

'And I'll carry Jamie,' I added.

'No, I'll take him,' said Manny.

I thrust a bandage under Jamie's back and wrapped it tight around his body to hold the dressing over the Quickclot-infused hip wound. Not my greatest work but it would have to do.

'Get in his rucksack, rip the plastic off a dressing and tape it over that hole,' I said to Manny, pointing at the sucking chest wound. 'You see it?'

'Yeah, I see it.'

'Shout when you're done. Then we'll bug out.'

I surveyed our tactical position: situation normal, all fucked-up.

Mike nodded when our eyes met. 'Let's take control of this party.'

I moved out to cover an arc on the left of the shack while Mike and Ryan dealt with the centre and right flanks. A strike from one of Blue Red Blue's sniper rounds destroyed the windscreen of an advancing vehicle and caused the enemy in my view to stop and take cover.

After an age that was probably less than two minutes, Mike spoke on the net. *'All stations, this is Delta, casualties ready for extraction.'*

I hotfooted it behind the shack to where Mike and Manny were lifting Bob and Jamie onto their respective backs for a fireman's carry. The two carriers' rucksacks made it tricky, but both waved away my offer to take them off their hands.

'You run them back to the car. Me and Ryan will cover.'

'Roger that,' said Ryan, firing another shot down range. A crack and thump from behind indicated Blue Red Blue continued to wreak havoc with his large calibre weapon.

The radio sparked into life. *'Alpha this is Charlie, do you need me at your location, over?'*

Two men seriously injured, two others carrying them, and only two shooters. We needed all the help we could get. 'Affirmative, Charlie. Stop your car behind the black SUV and get ready for exfil.'

'On my way.'

Ryan had made himself at home at the corner of the shack and I didn't want to disturb the target selection for his rapid fire.

I shouted, 'Far side,' and sprinted across the track to land heavily in a sandy depression behind some scrawny bushes. While making the leap, I spotted the three fishermen still tying nets on the beach with their backs to the life and death drama playing out metres away. I wanted some of whatever they were on.

Movement and a snatched view of berets and faces fifty metres away confirmed that another wave had succeeded in reaching the cover in front of Jamie and Bob's old position. Judging by the extent of the activity, we were at risk of being rushed. These troops were more cautious and methodical. Accurate fire forced me to keep my head down; rounds thudding into the sandy dirt all around me. Ryan had also gone quiet. The deliberate sniper fire from the jetty wouldn't hold the enemy back on its own.

'*Alpha, Echo, this is Delta.*' Mike paused with a gulp. Heavy breaths panted into my ear before he said, '*Move when ready.*'

With my head still down, I looked across at Ryan. He'd been forced to dress back from the shack behind his own lifesaving divot. His grimace and thumbs up were at odds with each other.

'Alpha moving.'

My attempt to spring up and launch myself towards the car fifty metres away felt like slow motion. As I passed Ryan, he took a final shot and staggered to his feet to join me 'advancing in the opposite direction'. As a para, he'd never have called it retreating.

I weaved left and right, more from exhaustion and trying to stay upright that some nimble effort to defeat the enemy's aim through agility. Dust kicked off the dirt track and strikes hammered into the general's executive ride. Bullets zinged past causing glass to shatter and bodywork to buckle as I ate up the ground.

On reaching the car I ducked behind it. Ryan slid in from the other side to join me on the deck. A ricochet pinged between us and slapped into Roper's white Land Cruiser parked behind.

I shook my head. 'Fuck this for a game of soldiers.'

The rattle of rounds hitting the black car was snowballing. The thing was a fucking bullet magnet.

Mike returned fire from a position next to the harbour office, while Roper was engaging from behind a big slab of rock on the right. Manny laid one of the casualties on the back seat of the white car. I tried to make myself small behind a rear wheel of the general's car and began slinging rounds back the way we'd come.

A door slammed and Manny shouted, 'That's it. We can go now.'

Roper leapt from behind his rock and raced for the driver's side. He said, 'Mike's been hit,' as he passed behind me.

Manny crouched by the front passenger door with a baffled expression and his hands outspread.

When I looked across at him, Mike flicked his eyes towards the enemy and went back on aim.

I turned back to Manny. 'Take them. Get the casualties on the boat. Tell Izzy about the Quickclot and the plastic. Open it if Jamie's face turns blue. We'll hold them here and bring this car.'

The vibration of the bullets pinging the metal chassis above my head didn't augur well for its roadworthiness. A good job we only needed to drive 250 metres.

The improvised casevac vehicle spun away, its engine screaming as Roper hurled it down the causeway to Kingfisher.

A distinctive blast from behind showed Blue Red Blue hadn't run out of ammunition. I didn't see any close targets fall. Either Dave had missed, or he was focusing on suppressing the forces gathered at longer range. I hoped it was the latter.

'Magazine,' Ryan shouted on my left. He too had snurgled behind a wheel – at the other end of the car.

As soon as he resumed firing, I called out the same and snapped a fresh clip into place. I wasn't sure if I had any full mags left after that. I'd soon be down to the ones that only contained the remnants from earlier skirmishes.

The narrow terrain had begun to play to our advantage now that the advancing enemy had little room to manoeuvre. We were at the entrance of the jetty causeway, which only stretched twenty metres across, and ten metres of that was comprised of the rocks either side of the roadway. Sure, we were outnumbered, but the enemy couldn't bring a huge weight of fire to bear; not without risk of hitting their own people. However, one big problem remained: even if we could hold them without anyone else getting hit, at some point we needed to stop fighting and start running for the boat.

Roper's message about Mike taking a bullet concerned me. 'Delta, Alpha, are you hit, over?'

'*A scratch. I'm still in the game.*'

At a guess, we were now in a close quarter fight with two groups of around ten men each, spread either side of the track in the dunes and by the shack. I winged a man thirty metres away sprinting forward on the right, and a soldier lying in poor cover opposite him on the left screamed in pain and clutched his face as a shot from either Mike or Ryan must have hit home. A loud crack from the Kingfisher sounded a split second after an officer behind them bounced into the air like a rag doll and disappeared, a radio spinning out of his hand.

The engine block of the black car must have taken damage along with every other part. My trust in climbing into the car and getting it started – without being shot – was low. Make that miniscule.

I spoke into the radio. 'Gentlemen, let's run it.'

Ryan answered first, yelling from the other end of the car. 'Like the fucking Mogadishu Mile? I've got a bullet in my arse, but I'll thrash you, cabbage head.'

'*If we've gotta go…*' Mike panted '*…we'd better go hard and go now.*'

Instead of replying via radio, I shouted, 'Five seconds.'

The three of us snapped out several quickfire shots that were joined by two thundering booms from behind.

'Now.'

My legs were jelly as I pushed off again into another mad dash for safety. We had to hope the enemy wouldn't realise what was happening until too late.

Having only suffered superficial injuries and that thump to the chest, I easily outpaced my two oppos, both of whom had fresh gunshot wounds and still carried bergens.

'Come on, come on.' I yelled over my shoulder.

Ryan was a few metres back, Mike a few metres further behind.

'Come on Para Reg, let's fucking move.' I knew their para pride would hate to see a bootneck urging them on like this, even with their current disadvantages.

Blue Red Blue's sniper rifle barked rapid fire as we closed on the boat. Halfway. One hundred and twenty-five metres to go.

Fifty metres.

'Fucking run. Nearly there. Come on.'

The pain on both my friends' faces was agonizing to see, but they ran through it. They kept going.

Then we were on top of the white Land Cruiser, Roper and Manny firing past us to targets I imagined on our heels. In a prone position behind a long, black-barrelled beast of a weapon lay a khaki-clad figure wearing a bush hat.

Mike collapsed and landed hard close to the edge by the pontoon. I removed his bergen and slung it onto my back.

'Manny, help me.'

He ran to grab Mike's other arm and we stood him up and walked him onto the wooden pontoon and over to the bobbing Kingfisher.

The deck of the boat was strewn with the wounded bodies of my friends. Izzy knelt over Jamie, Bob was slumped alongside them, and Luke lay beyond him. Hutch sat hunched against the starboard side, his slung arm protected by his knees and a pistol hanging loose in his other hand.

Two strapping men took Mike from us and carefully laid him down. Manny's brothers bore a close resemblance to their sibling in both stature and their intelligent, friendly features.

'I don't know where Mike's been hit.' My shout to Izzy competed with the roar of another sniper shot.

'Help him on,' I said to Manny, indicating Ryan. I ran back across the pontoon to the two-man fireteam pinning the enemy down at the far end of the jetty.

Bullets buzzed through the air like wasps and the car was attracting a hit every half a second.

'Time to go, gents,' I said. My attention was drawn to the large sniper rifle and the man rising from behind it. 'Dave Morgan, I assume. Nice rifle.'

'Aye, in the flesh wi' me Denel. Let's leave the intros for later if you don't mind.' He hefted the South African weapon into his arms and beetled off back to the boat.

'You got my bergen?' I asked Roper as he shimmied past.

'It's onboard.'

A bullet smacked into a wooden post between us, encouraging me to drop to a crouch and scramble onto the pontoon behind him. A check along the jetty pinged a horde of men 150 metres away and closing fast.

'Fucking hurry up, we've cast off,' yelled Ryan.

The Kingfisher's prow had already swung out. Roper hopped onto the stern over a three-foot gap. When I reached the pontoon's edge at a sprint, the distance had grown to six feet. I pushed off with my right foot and sailed through the air, landing among thick, stiff fishing nets with a bruising lack of grace.

Raps on the wooden hull from bullet strikes showed the danger hadn't passed. Ryan, Roper, and Manny were all jammed against the port side, returning fire against our foiled pursuers.

'In your own fucking time, Royal,' shouted Ryan as I untangled my AK from the reeking nets and prepared to join them.

Dave's cannon blasted two more 20 mm rounds in quick succession. It would take braver men than me to keep advancing with those six-inch monsters inbound.

Within thirty seconds we'd put more than a hundred metres between us and the pontoon.

The Kingfisher circled to the right in a lazy arc to maintain distance, until we headed southeast. The jetty and the island were on our starboard side more than 200 metres away. The plink of bullets hitting the boat had ceased and we stopped returning fire. Instead, we began scanning for seaborne threats.

I dug the binos out of my bergen and focused on the jetty. The troops had given up the chase and only a handful continued walking towards the perforated white Land Cruiser, weapons dangling by their sides.

Behind me, Roper spoke into the satellite phone. 'Dawson this is Curlew. Our situation is Grail Two, both British nationals on board, and the Phoenix RV with Kingfisher is complete. If possible, we need helo medevac asap for two serious casualties.'

Izzy waved her hands at him from where she was working on Mike's back. 'Three, three. Mister Mike has a very bad injury.'

Roper conveyed the update. 'Did you hear that? We have three VSI needing urgent medical attention. Shall I send a nine-liner?'

He listened to the answer and replied, 'I'll revert with that info shortly.' Then he pulled the phone away from his ear and settled it on an upturned crate. 'Meanwhile, you're on loudspeaker and the team can hear you.'

While Roper dug out his notebook and began to compose a nine-liner medical evacuation request, a familiar voice addressed us – Sandy Chapman. 'Well done, everyone. Fantastic job. We'll do everything we can to get you medical help as quickly as possible.'

After that short but sweet contribution, a female voice replaced his on the line. 'John, it's Hope. Can you hear me okay?'

'Yes, I'm here.'

'We don't believe the authorities in Guinea will be interested in pursuing Kingfisher. We've reached out to certain "friends" and explained why that would not be a good idea for anyone involved or for either presidential candidate. There is a British warship in the region, and we'll try to organise helicopters from there or Freetown. I can't promise anything, but we will try our best.'

As I watched Izzy and Ryan working on Mike, and Manny crouched between Jamie and Bob with a hand on both men, my answer caught in my throat. Finally, I said, 'Thank you. Whatever you can do.'

It was 7.00 a.m. on a glorious summer morning. The savage battle raging for the previous ninety minutes had evaporated as though carried away on the light wind that rippled the calm sea. At any other time, I might have appreciated the spectacular views in the company of friends. Instead, Kingfisher's thumping engines competed with urgent shouts from the drama playing out on its deck. Izzy directed us as we fought desperately to save the lives of our wounded comrades.

CHAPTER 81

16 DAYS LATER, ST JOHN'S CHURCH, A TOWN IN WEST ENGLAND

The funeral took place at an ancient stone church tucked away in a picturesque part of the English countryside. The kind of place that features as a background in celebrity wedding snaps.

Most funerals these days seemed to be held at crematoriums. I'd told Claire I wanted an old school burial with wailing women throwing themselves after my coffin when I went. That and mysterious, glamorous mourners and a right good piss-up afterwards.

It seemed as though Mike had issued similar instructions. When his coffin was lowered into the ground, a slim, blonde woman in a figure-hugging black dress sobbed while a teenage girl clung to her arm, tears streaming down her young face. The light-heartedness of my jovial request had been forever punctured by this harsh reality.

Guilt was the overriding emotion. For Mike. For the others that died: Condé, Alain, Demba, Samuel, and Yaya. And the 'enemy' dead. Not the militants – they'd made their choice – but the guards and soldiers doing their duty.

Guilt at the serious injuries suffered by my team. And guilt that I didn't feel more sorrow, more sadness. That in practical terms, none of the deaths would impact my own life. A numb sense of survivor's guilt. But not just a survivor. This had been my operation. It was down to me that these men were involved.

I shouldn't have been able to compartmentalise all this guilt and smile and laugh and love and enjoy. But I could. And I had.

There were plenty of mysterious attendees. I counted our group, standing on the opposite side to the family, in that number.

Not so many glamorous interlopers, although Hope Crosby could have taken that slot. Stood next to Hope, both Claire and Ryan's wife, Amy, also looked elegant in black outfits with matching veiled hats.

Claire insisted on accompanying me, relieved that evidence of my recent facial injuries had disappeared to all but the most careful observer. That also meant a shadow no longer crossed her face every time our eyes met. Other scars and their resulting shadows would take longer to fade. She had only met Amy a handful of times, but they latched onto each other in this alien environment.

Hutch came alone, complete with sling. His wife, Liz, had declared she wouldn't be able to restrain herself from kicking off if she encountered my ugly mug. Unable to drive due his injuries, Ryan and Amy had taken a detour to pick him up. I'd offered, but a scene outside his house was too big a risk.

A huge, vibrant bouquet of flowers caught my eye. Ordering them on Izzy's behalf, I'd had to repeat the request before the florist accepted that I understood they were an unusually cheerful arrangement for a funeral. The exuberant African contribution stood out among the dozens of traditional, beautiful yet sombre arrangements.

Against all advice, Izzy returned to Guinea the day after we reached Freetown. The British government and Fozzie the lawyer had moved fast to obtain promises of immunity from prosecution for everyone involved.

Post 9/11, no leaders wanted to be regarded as siding with terrorists, drug cartels, and organised criminal groups. Although a lot of soldiers had died performing their loyal duty to the state, it was deemed that they were victims of the crimes of their commanders rather than imperialist mercenary dogs.

It helped that a ministry official, Yaya, was killed during the initial ambush – helped us that is. It clearly wasn't a good outcome for him. That enabled the whole saga to be wrapped in a narrative that a deplorable conspiracy had targeted the Guinea government and an international mining company. And been foiled.

It all sounded a bit flimsy to me. Any of us hopping on a flight to Conakry wouldn't expect to be received with open arms.

Claire had demanded that I settle down and stop putting her and the girls through the constant worry and anguish, neither of which apparently ceased when I repeatedly returned home damaged. I'd avoided a definitive answer.

Although Mike's catastrophic blood loss from the bullet wound in his lower back meant Izzy had been unable to save him, she had worked miracles to keep Jamie alive. He remained in hospital in the US and his flowers stood alongside those from Izzy and a wreath from Luke.

Luke was deeply apologetic that he couldn't attend. I'd told him on the phone not to worry. It was far more important that he followed his doctor's advice and stayed in Paris to continue the intensive treatment for his wounds.

When the vicar had finished the graveside eulogy, Bob leaned back in his wheelchair and whispered something to Manny, who then wheeled the Aussie forward. He bowed his head, held out his battered Akubra hat, and flicked it into the grave where it nestled on top of the coffin.

Over 100 mourners turned out to remember Mike. Many of them had squeezed bulky frames into little-worn suits and tugged at shirt collars to loosen the unfamiliar encumbrance of neck ties.

With the service completed, the mourners began to drift away from the graveside. Some walked to the edge and dipped their heads in remembrance. Private words were shared and earth scattered.

The woman and the teenage girl looked in my direction, before walking around the grave, still clinging to each other, and towards our little group.

They stopped in front of me. 'I'm Sarah, Mike's ex-wife. You're John Pierce?'

From the acidic tone of the question, I braced for a slap or a dressing down at the very least. I couldn't remember if the divorce had been amicable – not that it mattered anymore. 'I'm so sorry for your loss. Mike was a good friend.'

'Was my dad brave?' the girl asked. Tilly. I remembered Mike talking about her once. I didn't usually raise the topic of children with him. Not after hearing his son had been killed in an IED blast in Helmand.

Before I could answer, Bob broke in. 'He was the bravest man I've ever met. He died saving my life. I know it won't help, but you should be so proud of your dad.' Bob squeezed his eyes shut as tears ran free.

'Thank you,' said Sarah, giving me a final stare before leading her crying daughter away.

On the other side of Hope, Claire, and Amy stood another small group. Sandy Chapman, Tom Roper, Cal Simmons, and Sir Jeremy.

To give them their due, Pinnacle had picked up the tab for the funeral and the wake. They had also paid out the equivalent of the insurance policy money to all those affected by the fallout from Brimstone – without any certainty that the insurers would pay out in turn. Unsurprisingly, eager loss adjusters were flexing into the wriggle room provided by the unconventional circumstances of the deaths and injuries.

'If you and Amy go back to the cars, we'll follow on shortly,' I said to Claire. She glanced at Hope and the four-man group beyond and pursed her lips. After whispering with Amy, the two of them set off towards the car park.

Roper pulled Ryan to one side, while Hope and Chapman separated from the others and steered me to a secluded section of the graveyard.

'Occasions like this are very sad,' said Chapman. 'A reminder of the risks that are taken at the coal face. We did everything we could to save him.'

If the bullet hadn't nicked an artery, Mike would have survived for sure. The two US Navy helicopters that arrived ninety minutes after we left Kassa Island had rushed him and Jamie to operating theatres on board a US warship, but it proved too late for the ex-SAS man.

While Mike's deterioration proved sadly irreversible despite all our efforts, Izzy's medical acumen and dogged determination helped Jamie cling to life until the naval surgeons could work their own magic and ensure his survival.

I don't know if the Americans were pissed at being kept in the dark about the Brits running around shooting up the neighbourhood, but they acted fast and pulled out all the stops once they were informed.

I had been summoned to the house in Mayfair for a debriefing the day after returning from Africa. Although our part of Brimstone had finished, the office was a hive of activity to coordinate action against the camp we'd found in southern Mali.

Their comments were guarded, but I got the impression from Roper and Hope that the events in Guinea had helped Chapman to rally support for a renewed focus on the emerging threats in West Africa.

Attending the debriefing suited me. I wanted to make sure no one forgot about the liberated cash and diamonds or siphoned the proceeds off to a black ops slush fund. Chapman laughed at that suggestion and my naïve 'James Bond' ideas of how the intelligence world worked. He'd supported Roper's recommendation for returning the funds to me for distribution to the team, tax free.

But $1.2 million didn't go far between so many families and individuals. When Pinnacle offered to make good the insurance monies, we'd all breathed a sigh of relief. They didn't know about Mamba's additional contribution, and I certainly wasn't going to tell them.

'We've got an update since our last meeting,' said Chapman. 'I thought it only fair to inform you of certain outcomes. And given that you're already bound tightly by the Official Secrets Act, I wanted you to know.'

'To know what?'

Hope took over. 'The camp you discovered was raided by British, French, and Malian special forces shortly after you visited us in London. Unfortunately, it had been abandoned. But in their haste, the departing groups made mistakes that led to the capture of two high value targets. It's not much, and I'm sure it pales into insignificance against the loss of your friend's life, but it shows there was legitimate justification for Brimstone.'

'Thank you. Although I'm not quite sure why you're telling me this.'

Chapman assumed a friendly voice that took me by surprise. 'John, you and your team did well. We want to stay in touch.'

I snorted a laugh. 'If my wife has her way, I won't be going anywhere more interesting than family holidays to the Med. I don't think we'll be crossing paths again.'

There was a twinkle in the old man's eye. 'Never say never.'

After Chapman and Hope had left, I returned to the last pair of suits standing near Mike's final resting place. They watched as flowers were moved and gravediggers prepared to complete the burial. The melancholic business of death playing out.

Sir Jeremy reached out a hand when he saw me approaching. 'We're not going to stay for a drink, so I'll say farewell now. Pass on my regards to those of your team who couldn't be here. And if you change your mind, there's a position waiting for you once the new president is in power.'

When I'd met Sinjun and Cal at the club the previous week, I turned down their offer to run the operation in Guinea. Turned it down flat.

Cal had phoned twice since then trying to convince me to accept. It sounded as though they finally realised it was a firm 'no' and not a negotiating tactic for more money. I'd suggested they approach Ryan, but he also turned them down.

'There's nothing wrong with your offer, but I can't go back. I've promised Claire.'

After shaking hands with Sir Jeremy, I did the same with Cal. 'I'll call you,' he said. A man not used to accepting no for an answer.

The wake was a boisterous affair at a local pub. It was a welcome relief from the sadness at the graveside to hear people laughing and joking about Mike and his escapades over the years. Even Claire and Amy now engaged in animated conversation helped by a few glasses of wine.

Bob remained subdued despite Manny's efforts to liven him up. I didn't ask whether he would return to the Siguiri project once he handed his wheelchair back. He probably didn't know yet himself. Getting up and about again was his focus, and I was happy to leave it there.

Despite his limp, Ryan waved away offers of help and delivered a tray of unspilled drinks to the table. When he finished handing them out, I cleared my throat and raised a fresh glass. 'To Mike and other absent friends.'

As the others repeated the toast and sipped their drinks, Roper pulled the pint from his lips and said, 'Chapman really likes you two, you know. I'm sure something else will surface from our side before long.'

He hadn't included Hutch. The threat from Liz to anyone luring her husband away probably outdid any peril Britain's enemies might pose.

'My Ryan is getting a local job,' said Amy, louder than necessary. 'He's giving up contracting and putting me and the kids first.' She turned her head to Claire. 'What about John? Is he the same?'

Claire's response was an icy glance in my direction.

When I looked over Amy's shoulder and lifted my eyebrows in Ryan's direction, he winked at me and tried to hide a smirk from both his wife and mine. Claire hadn't missed it though. A wistful expression flowed over her face.

Claire and Amy were both right: for people in our game, there came a point when life told you it was time to stop. The question was – were me and Ryan ready to listen?

ACKNOWLEDGEMENTS

My sincere thanks to a couple of subject-matter experts whose advice I sought to try and avoid an avalanche of piss-taking jibes from those that know:

Thanks to the real Dave M. for a master sniper's input about weapon characteristics for the Denel NTW-20 14.5 Anti-Materiel rifle. I owe you a beer, mate.

And thank you to veteran pilot Dave Wilton from Canada for his calculations and technical detail regarding the Antonov AN-28 'Cash'. Standby for more questions about STOL bush planes for the next book, Dave. Beers are on me when we get a chance to meet in London or Winnipeg.

ABOUT THE AUTHOR

Jack Leavers is a former Royal Marine with over thirty-years' experience spread across the military, private security, corporate investigations, maritime counter-piracy, and risk management. His varied career has included numerous deployments to conflict zones around the world such as Northern Ireland, Bosnia, Iraq, Afghanistan, trouble spots in Africa, and the Somali pirate-infested waters of the Indian Ocean.

He continues to work in challenging environments and has now begun to pen novels inspired by some of the more enterprising projects that got the green light, and other audacious plans that didn't.

Jack is normally based in London but finds he's at his most productive writing-wise when deployed overseas. New projects in Iraq and Africa beckon, which should be good news for the third book.

For more information visit jackleavers.com